Pentose Phosphate Metabolism

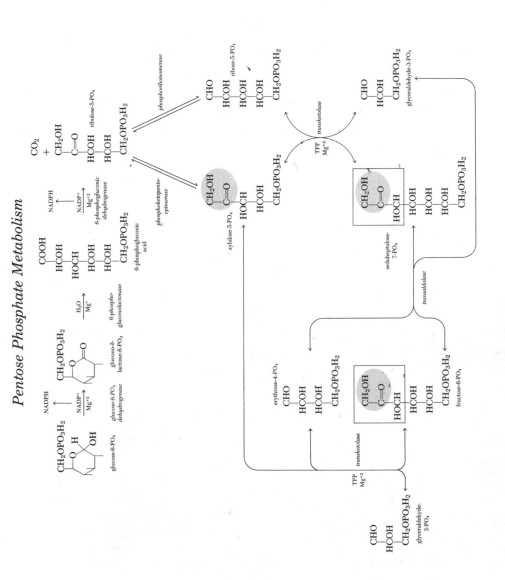

Outlines of Biochemistry

Outlines of

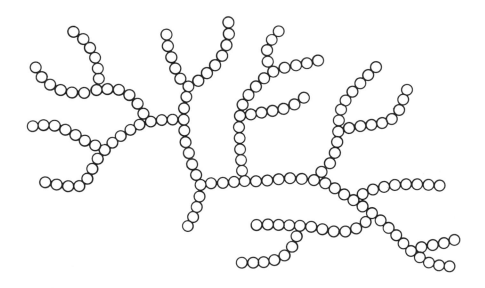

Biochemistry

Eric E. Conn and P. K. Stumpf

Both of the Department of Biochemistry and Biophysics

University of California at Davis

John Wiley and Sons, Inc.

New York · London · Sydney

Library of Congress Catalog Card Number: 63-8054
Printed in the United States of America

Preface

This book is the outgrowth of experience gained from teaching a one-semester course in general biochemistry on both the Berkeley and the Davis campuses of the University of California.

It is our opinion that the subject of biochemistry can be introduced to upper-division undergraduates and first-year graduate students, majors and nonmajors, in one semester. In writing our book we have attempted to acquaint the students with a skeleton—a rather substantial skeleton to be sure—of intermediary metabolism. This has required a brief review of the chemical properties of compounds of biological interest; it appears in Part I. Part II opens with a plunge into energetics and enzymology to prepare the student for the backbone of the course. This is found in the chapters which describe the metabolism of carbohydrates, lipids, amino acids, and proteins. Not even an introductory course in biochemistry is complete without an attempt to integrate this knowledge of the metabolism of the major cell constituents through a consideration of the interrelations among the carbon, nitrogen, and energy cycles. This attempt is made in Part III.

Since every student in a biological science feels compelled to take an introductory biochemistry course, the instructors of that course are obliged to present some of the important areas of modern biochemistry. The problem is one of careful selection of topics and limited discussion of experimental data. This procedure requires generalization, but the student learns when he is made aware of the significant exceptions.

The appendix is employed to review pH and buffer problems, common weaknesses of most students entering biochemistry. This is followed by a brief discussion of some of the concepts of modern organic chemistry that can be applied to biochemical reactions. Finally, a description of methods commonly employed in biochemical research is included to familiarize the student with the terms employed. The student is advised to make use of the appendix as he proceeds through the book.   Key references are given at the end of each chapter for the student to explore the area under discussion further.   From these references he can be easily guided into the much larger literature of the particular area.

Although the theme of our book is intermediary metabolism, we do not claim to have covered all areas of metabolism.   In addition, some of our readers may consider the chemical treatment of the major cellular components too brief.   Finally, those accustomed to the discussion of the classical subjects usually found only in medical biochemistry texts will find these topics either missing or drastically abbreviated.   We ask that our colleagues again consider the audience of upper-division and graduate students, majors and nonmajors, for whom this book was written.

E.E.C.

P.K.S.

Davis, California
January, 1963

Contents

Part I

Chemistry of

Biological Compounds

One

pH and Buffers

Introduction

The term pH and its use in biochemistry must be thoroughly understood by students of this subject. This term, soon to be defined, is a
convenient expression of the amount of hydrogen ion (H^+) in an
aqueous medium. Since almost all biochemical reactions occur in
aqueous systems under conditions where the concentration of H^+ ion
changes only slightly, it is important to understand the mechanism by
which the H^+ concentration is controlled. To make it clear we review
the Law of Mass Action.

The Law of Mass Action

Consider the reaction

$$A + B \rightleftharpoons C + D \tag{1-1}$$

where two reactants A and B interact to form two products C and D.
The rate of the reaction from left to right (R_1) will be proportional to
the concentration of both A and B. That is,

$$R_1 \propto C_A \times C_B$$

We can represent this function as a constant k_1:

$$R_1 = k_1 \cdot C_A \cdot C_B$$

Similarly the rate of the reverse reaction in which A and B are
formed from C and D can then be represented as

$$R_2 = k_2 \cdot C_C \cdot C_D$$

At equilibrium the concentrations of the four substances are no longer
changing; that is, the rate of the forward reaction must be equal to the
back reaction:

$$R_1 = R_2$$

Therefore $\qquad\qquad k_1 \cdot C_A \cdot C_B = k_2 \cdot C_C \cdot C_D$

Combining the constants we have

$$\frac{C_C \cdot C_D}{C_A \cdot C_B} = \frac{k_1}{k_2} = K_{eq} \qquad\qquad (1\text{-}2)$$

where a new constant K_{eq} is substituted for k_1/k_2. This is an expression of the *Law of Mass Action* as first formulated by Guldberg and Waage in 1867. *At equilibrium the product of the concentrations of the substances formed in a chemical reaction divided by the product of the concentrations of the reactants in that reaction is a constant known as the equilibrium constant, K_{eq}.* This constant is fixed for any given temperature. If the concentration of any single component of this reaction is varied, it follows that the ratio of the concentration of the other components must change also in order to meet the conditions of the equilibrium as defined by K_{eq}.

As an example for reaction 1-2, consider that the concentrations of A, B, C, and D at equilibrium are 0.1, 0.01, 0.05, and 0.06M respectively. The K_{eq} may be calculated from these data by substituting in equation 1-2:

$$\begin{aligned} K_{eq} &= \frac{C_C \times C_D}{C_A \times C_B} \\ &= \frac{(0.05)(0.06)}{(0.1)(0.01)} \\ &= 3 \end{aligned}$$

If the concentration of A were to double and become 0.2M, the concentration of B would have to become 0.005M or the concentration of C or D would have to double in order to attain equilibrium.

To be precise we should distinguish between the concentration of the reactants and products in this reaction and the *activity* or *effective concentration* of these reactants. It was early recognized that the concentration of a substance did not always accurately describe its reactivity in a chemical reaction. Moreover, these discrepancies in behavior were appreciable when the concentration of reactant was large. Under these conditions the individual particles of the reactant may exert a mutual attraction on each other or exhibit interactions with the solvent in which the reaction occurs. On the other hand, in dilute solution or low concentration, the interactions are considerably less if not negligible. In order to correct for the difference between concentration and effective concentration, the activity coefficient γ was introduced. Thus

$$a_A = C_A \times \gamma \qquad\qquad (1\text{-}3)$$

where a refers to the activity and C_A to the concentration of the substance. The activity coefficient is not a fixed quantity but varies in value depending on the situation under consideration. In very dilute concentrations the activity coefficient approaches unity, because there is little if any solvent-solute interaction. At infinite dilution the activity and the concentration are the same. For the purpose of this book, we do not usually distinguish between activities and concentrations; rather, we use the latter term. This is not a serious deviation from accuracy since the reactants in many biochemical reactions are quite low in concentration. In addition, the H^+ concentration in most biological tissues is approximately 10^{-7} mole/l, at which concentration the activity coefficient would be unity.

Dissociation of Water

Let us apply the Law of Mass Action to the dissociation of H_2O, a weak electrolyte which dissociates only slightly to form H^+ and OH^- ions.

$$H_2O \rightleftharpoons H^+ + OH^-$$

The equilibrium constant for this reaction has been accurately measured and at 25° has the value of 1.8×10^{-16}. That is,

$$K_{eq} = \frac{C_{H^+}C_{OH^-}}{C_{H_2O}} = 1.8 \times 10^{-16}$$

The concentration of H_2O (C_{H_2O}) in pure water may be calculated to be $1000/18$ or 55.5 moles/l. Since the concentration of H_2O in dilute aqueous solutions is essentially unchanged from that in pure H_2O, this figure may be taken as a constant. It is, in fact, usually incorporated into the expression for the dissociation of water, to give

$$C_{H^+}C_{OH^-} = 1.8 \times 10^{-16} \times 55.5 = 1.01 \times 10^{-14}$$
$$= K_w = 1.01 \times 10^{-14} \tag{1-4}$$
$$\text{at } 25°C$$

This new constant K_w, termed the ion product of water, expresses the relation between the concentration of H^+ and OH^- ions in aqueous solutions; for example, this relation may be used to calculate the concentration of H^+ in pure water. To do this, let x equal the concentration of H^+. Since in pure water one OH^- is produced for every H^+ formed on dissociation of a molecule of H_2O, x must also equal the concentration of OH^-. Substituting in equation 1-4, we have

$$x \cdot x = 1.01 \times 10^{-14}$$
$$x^2 = 1.01 \times 10^{-14}$$
$$x = C_{H^+} = C_{OH^-} = 1.0 \times 10^{-7} \text{ mole/l}$$

pH

In 1909, Sörensen introduced the term pH as a convenient manner of expressing the concentration of H^+ ion by means of a logarithmic function. pH may be defined as:

$$pH = \log \frac{1}{a_{H^+}} = -\log a_{H^+} \qquad (1\text{-}5)$$

where a_{H^+} is defined as the activity of H^+. In this text no distinction is made between activities and concentrations, and so

$$pH = \log \frac{1}{[H^+]} = -\log [H^+] \qquad (1\text{-}6)$$

Moreover, to indicate that we are dealing with concentrations, we use brackets [ ] to indicate them. Thus the concentration of H^+ (C_{H^+}) is represented as $[H^+]$. We may point out the difference between activities and concentrations by the following example. The pH of $0.1M$ HCl when measured with a pH meter is 1.09. This value can be substituted in equation 1-5, as the pH meter measures activities and not concentrations (see Appendix 3)

$$1.09 = \log \frac{1}{a_{H^+}}$$

$$a_{H^+} = 10^{-1.09}$$

$$a_{H^+} = \text{antilog } \bar{2}.91$$

$$a_{H^+} = 8.1 \times 10^{-2} \text{ mole/l}$$

Since the concentration of H^+ in $0.1M$ HCl is 0.1 mole/l, the activity coefficient γ may be calculated:

$$\gamma = \frac{a_{H^+}}{[H^+]}$$

$$= \frac{0.081}{0.1}$$

$$= 0.81$$

It is important to stress that the pH is a logarithmic function; thus, when the pH of a solution is decreased one unit from 5 to 4, the H^+ concentration has increased tenfold from $10^{-5}M$ to $10^{-4}M$. When the pH has increased three-tenths of a unit from 6 to 6.3, the H^+ concentration has decreased from $10^{-6}M$ to $5 \times 10^{-7}M$.

If we now apply the term of pH to the ion product expression for pure water, we obtain another useful expression:

$$[H^+] \times [OH^-] = 1.0 \times 10^{-14}$$

We take the logarithms of this equation:

$$\log[H^+] + \log[OH^-] = \log(1.0 \times 10^{-14})$$
$$= -14$$

and multiply by -1.

$$-\log[H^+] - \log[OH^-] = 14$$

If we now define $-\log[OH^-]$ as pOH, a definition similar to that of pH, we have an expression relating the pH and pOH in any aqueous solution:

$$pH + pOH = 14 \tag{1-7}$$

Dissociation of Strong Electrolytes

Next we wish to consider the application of the Law of Mass Action to the dissociation of electrolytes. Strong electrolytes are substances that, in aqueous solution, are dissociated almost completely into charged particles known as ions. Sodium chloride (common table salt), even in its solid, crystalline form, exists as Na^+ ions and Cl^- ions. We may represent the dissociation of NaCl in solution as being complete.

$$Na^+Cl^- \longrightarrow Na^+ + Cl^-$$

Strong acids and bases are electrolytes that, in aqueous solution, are almost completely dissociated into their corresponding ions. Thus hydrochloric acid (HCl), a familiar mineral acid which incidentally is not dissociated in its gaseous state, is completely dissociated in H_2O.

$$HCl \longrightarrow H^+ + Cl^- \tag{1-8}$$

We should represent the dissociation of HCl in H_2O more accurately as follows:

$$HCl + H_2O \longrightarrow H_3O^+ + Cl^-$$

This indicates that the electrically neutral HCl has reacted with H_2O to form Cl^- anion and the hydronium ion H_3O^+. Indeed, both the Cl^- anion and the proton H^+ are hydrated, but is it common practice to omit the water of hydration in a chemical reaction and represent the dissociation of a strong acid like HCl as we did in reaction 1-8. It is important to remember that in aqueous solutions water is always associated with the dissolved particles and that this association may greatly influence the properties of the substance in solution.

The strong bases such as NaOH are also completely dissociated:

$$NaOH \longrightarrow Na^+ + OH^-$$

Dissociation of Weak Electrolytes

Of particular importance in biochemistry are weak acids and bases, which, in contrast to strong acids and bases, exhibit only a slight tendency to dissociate. Consider the dissociation of the weak, organic acid, acetic acid:

$$CH_3COOH \longrightarrow H^+ + CH_3COO^- \qquad (1\text{-}9)$$

The equilibrium constant that describes the extent of this dissociation quantitatively may be written:

$$\frac{[H^+][CH_3COO^-]}{[CH_3COOH]} = K_{eq} \qquad (1\text{-}10)$$

The equilibrium constant for this type of reaction is more commonly referred to as the ionization constant K_a or K_{ion} since the process involves the formation of a proton H^+ and acetate anions CH_3COO^-. At $25°C$, the K_a or K_{ion} is 1.8×10^{-5} mole/l. That is,

$$K_a = K_{ion} = 1.8 \times 10^{-5} \text{ mole/l}$$

$$\frac{[H^+][CH_3COO^-]}{[CH_3COOH]} = 1.8 \times 10^{-5}$$

This useful relation permits us to calculate the concentration of H^+ in a solution of acetic acid of known concentration. As an example, let us calculate the concentration of H^+ in $1.0M$ CH_3COOH and thus determine the extent of ionization of a solution of acetic acid of this concentration. If we let x equal the concentration of H^+ formed by the ionization of the acetic acid, then x will also be the concentration of CH_3COO^-, because these two ions are formed in equal amounts when acetic acid ionizes. The amount of CH_3COOH remaining after the ionization equilibrium has been established will then be $1 - x$. Therefore,

Initially	At Equilibrium after Ionization
$[CH_3COOH] = 1.00$ mole/l	$[CH_3COOH] = (1.00 - x)$ mole/l
$[H^+] = 0.00$	$[H^+] = x$
$[CH_3COO^-] = 0.00$	$[CH_3COO^-] = x$

Substituting the values that exist at equilibrium in the expression for the ionization of acetic acid we have:

$$\frac{x^2}{1 - x} = 1.8 \times 10^{-5} \qquad (1\text{-}11)$$

This quadratic equation, when solved for x (see Appendix 1), is found to equal $0.0042M$. Thus $[H^+] = [CH_3COO^-] = 0.0042M$. The concentration of the undissociated CH_3COOH will therefore be $1.00 - 0.0042$ or $0.9958M$. At $25°$, a $1M$ solution of acetic acid is dissociated or ionized to the extent of only 0.4 per cent. The pH of this solution, which is $0.0042M$ in hydrogen ion, may be calculated from equation 1-6.

$$\begin{aligned} pH &= -\log 0.0042 = -\log (4.2 \times 10^{-3}) \\ &= -\log 4.2 - \log 10^{-3} \\ &= -0.62 + 3 \\ &= 2.38 \end{aligned}$$

It is possible to simplify the solution of equation 1-11 above. In considering the ionization of relatively concentrated solutions of weak electrolytes the term in the denominator $(1 - x)$ may be simplified by not correcting for the amount of acid (x) which dissociated, provided x is small. In the example just given, the amount that dissociated was negligible (only 0.4 per cent) and may be ignored. When this approximation is made,

$$\begin{aligned} x^2 &= 1.8 \times 10^{-5} \\ x &= \sqrt{18 \times 10^{-6}} \\ x &= 4.2 \times 10^{-3} \\ [H^+] &= [CH_3COO^-] = 0.0042M \end{aligned}$$

Another important relation is emphasized by calculating the H^+ concentration when the concentration of anion is equal to the concentration of unionized weak acid. Such a relation would exist in a solution prepared by mixing 0.1 mole of sodium acetate (8.2 g) with 0.1 mole of acetic acid (6 g) in sufficient water to make a liter of solution. Under these conditions, $[CH_3COO^-] = [CH_3COOH] = 0.1M$, and when these are substituted in equation 1-10,

$$\frac{[H^+][CH_3COO^-]}{[CH_3COOH]} = 1.8 \times 10^{-5}$$

$$\frac{[H^+][0.1]}{[0.1]} = 1.8 \times 10^{-5}$$

$$[H^+] = 1.8 \times 10^{-5}$$

$$pH = 5 - \log 1.8$$

$$pH = 4.74$$

Thus $H^+ = K_a$ when the concentration of the anion of the acid is equal to the concentration of the unionized acid. Since different weak acids have different K_a's, equimolar mixtures of these acids and their corresponding salts will each have a different pH.

The Henderson-Hasselbalch Equation

Henderson and Hasselbalch have rearranged the Mass Law as it applies to the ionization of weak acids into a useful expression known as the Henderson-Hasselbalch equation. If we consider the ionization of a generalized weak acid HA:

$$HA \rightleftharpoons H^+ + A^-$$

$$K_{ion} = K_a = \frac{[H^+][A^-]}{[HA]}$$

Rearranging terms, we have

$$[H^+] = K_a \frac{[HA]}{[A^-]}$$

Taking logarithms, we find

$$\log[H^+] = \log K_a + \log \frac{[HA]}{[A^-]}$$

and multiplying by -1,

$$-\log[H^+] = -\log K_a - \log \frac{[HA]}{[A^-]}$$

If $-\log K_a$ is defined as pK_a and $\log[A^-]/[HA]$ is substituted for $-\log[HA]/[A^-]$, we obtain

$$pH = pK_a + \log \frac{[A^-]}{[HA]} \tag{1-12}$$

This is the expression known as the Henderson-Hasselbalch equation, an expression of great use in calculating the pH of mixtures of weak acids and their salts. For example, in the preceding section we determined the pH of a mixture of $0.1M$ sodium acetate and $0.1M$ acetic acid as 4.74. We could have used the Henderson-Hasselbalch expression for this same calculation. In this case equation 1-12 becomes:

$$pH = pK_{a_{HAc}} + \log \frac{[CH_3COO^-]}{[CH_3COOH]} \tag{1-13}$$

The acetic acid concentration $[CH_3COOH]$ in this mixture will be $0.1M$ *minus* the small amount a of CH_3COOH that dissociates, and the acetate ion concentration $[CH_3COO^-]$ will be $0.1M$ plus the small amount a of acetate ion produced in the dissociation just mentioned. Equation 1-13 therefore becomes

$$pH = pK_{a_{HAc}} + \log \frac{(0.1 + a)}{(0.1 - a)} \tag{1-14}$$

Although it is possible to calculate a, the quantity is usually negligible and can be ignored. This approximation, together with the approximation previously introduced by substituting concentrations for activities (p. 4), can be incorporated into the expression for the equilibrium constant by the use of a corrected *equilibrium constant*, K_{eq}'. This constant will vary, of course, with the concentration of the reactants, and the conditions for its use must be specified, usually in terms of the ionic strength.

The K_a for acetic acid is 1.8×10^{-5} mole/l; pK_a is therefore $-\log (1.8 \times 10^{-5})$ or 4.74. Substituting this value and neglecting a, we find that equation (1-14) becomes:

$$pH = 4.74 + \log \frac{0.1}{0.1}$$

$$= 4.74$$

The student should be thoroughly familiar with calculations involving the Henderson-Hasselbalch equation. Appendix 1 contains problems illustrating the use of the equation.

Titration Curves

The titration curve obtained when 100 ml of $0.1N$ CH_3COOH is titrated with $0.1N$ NaOH is shown in Figure 1-1. This curve can be obtained experimentally in the laboratory by measuring the pH of $0.1N$ CH_3COOH before and after addition of different aliquots of $0.1N$ NaOH. The curve may also be calculated by the Henderson-Hasselbalch equation for all the points except the first, where no NaOH has been added, and the last, where a stoichiometric amount (100 ml) of $0.1N$ NaOH has been added. Clearly the Henderson-Hasselbalch equation cannot be used to determine the pH at the limits of the titration where the ratio of salt to acid is either zero or infinite.

In considering the grosser aspects of the titration curve of acetic acid, we see visually that the change in pH for unit of alkali added is greatest at the beginning and end of the titration, whereas the smallest change in pH for unit of alkali added is obtained when the titration is half complete. In other words, an equimolar mixture of sodium acetate and acetic acid shows less change in pH initially when acid or alkali is added than a solution consisting mainly of either acetic acid or sodium acetate. We refer to the ability of a solution to resist a change in pH as its *buffer action,* and it can be shown that a buffer exhibits its *maximum* action when the titration is half complete or when the pH is equal to the pK_a (equation 1-12). In Figure 1-1 the point of maximum buffer action is at the pH of 4.74.

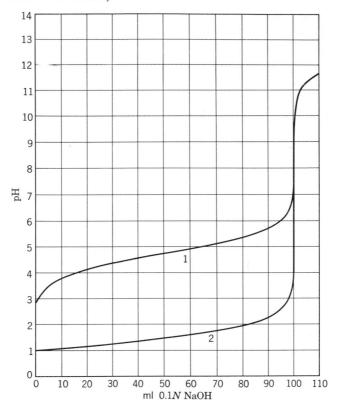

Fig. 1-1.   Titration curve of 100 ml of 0.1N CH$_3$COOH (1) and 100 ml of 0.1N HCl (2) with 0.1N NaOH.

Another way of representing the condition which exists when the pH of a mixture of acetic acid and sodium acetate is at the pK_a is to state that the acid at this pH is half ionized.   That is, half the "total acetate" species is present as undissociated CH$_3$COOH while the other half is in the form of CH$_3$COO$^-$ anion.   Since at the pK_a any weak acid will be half ionized, this is one of the most useful ways of distinguishing between individual weak acids.   The pK_a is also a characteristic property of each acid, because the ionization constant is a function of the inherent properties of the weak acid (to be discussed later).

The titration curve of 0.1N HCl is also represented in Figure 1-1. The Henderson-Hasselbalch equation is of no value in calculating the curve for HCl as it applies only for weak electrolytes, but the pH at any point on the HCl curve can be calculated by determining the milliequivalents of HCl remaining and correcting for the volume.   Thus when 30 ml of 0.1N NaOH have been added, 7.0 meq of HCl will remain in a volume of 130 ml. The concentration of H^+ will therefore be 7.0 divided by 130 or $0.054M$. If the activity coefficient is neglected, the pH may be calculated from equation 1-6 as 1.27.

Up to this point we have considered only the monobasic acid, acetic acid. Polybasic or *polyprotic* acids, commonly encountered in biochemistry, are acids capable of ionizing to form more than one proton per molecule of acid. In each case the extent of dissociation of the individual protons may be described by a K_{ion} or K_a. In the case of phosphoric acid (H_3PO_4) three protons may be furnished on complete ionization of a mole of this acid.

$$H_3PO_4 \rightleftharpoons H^+ + H_2PO_4^- \qquad K_{a_1} = 7.5 \times 10^{-3} \qquad pK_{a_1} = 2.12$$
$$H_2PO_4^- \rightleftharpoons H^+ + HPO_4^{2-} \qquad K_{a_2} = 6.23 \times 10^{-8} \qquad pK_{a_2} = 7.21$$
$$HPO_4^{2-} \rightleftharpoons H^+ + PO_4^{3-} \qquad K_{a_3} = 2.2 \times 10^{-13} \qquad pK_{a_3} = 12.66$$

This means that at the pH of 2.12 the first ionization of H_3PO_4 is half complete; the pH must be 12.66, however, before the third and final ionization of H_3PO_4 is 50 per cent complete. At the pH of 7.0, which is frequently encountered in the cell, the second proton of phosphoric acid ($pK_{a_2} = 7.2$) will be about half dissociated. At this pH both the mono- and di-anions of phosphoric acid or phosphate esters will be present in approximately equal concentrations. For phosphoric acid the two predominant ionic species will be $H_2PO_4^-$ and HPO_4^{2-}. In the case of α-glycerol phosphate the two following ions will be present in about equal concentration at pH 7.0.

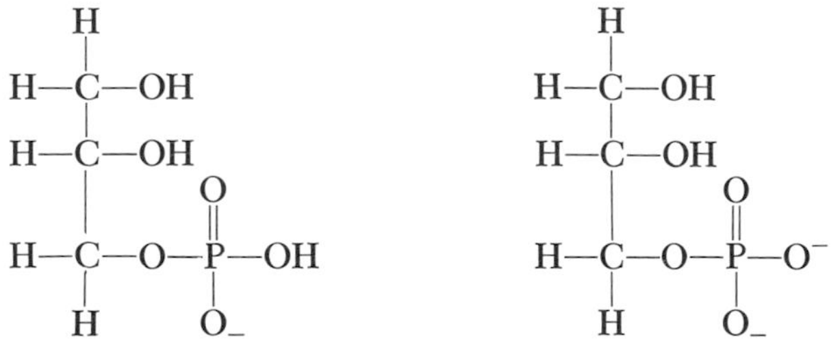

Many of the common organic acids encountered in intermediary metabolism are polyprotic; for example, succinic acid ionizes according to the following:

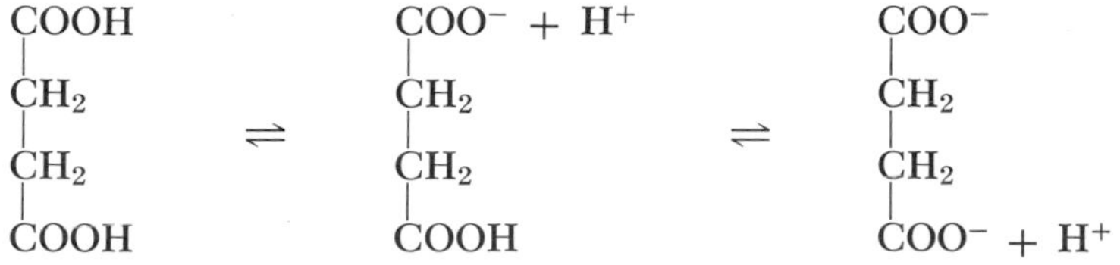

At pH 7.0 in the cell, succinic acid will exist predominantly as the di-anion $^-$OOC—CH$_2$—CH$_2$—COO$^-$. Furthermore, most of the organic acids which serve as metabolites (palmitic, lactic, and pyruvic acids, for example) will be present as their anions (palmitate, lactate, and pyruvate). This has led to the use of the names of the ions when these compounds are discussed in biochemistry. In writing chemical reactions, however, it will be the practice in this text to use the formulas for the undissociated acid.

Table 1-1 lists the pK_a's for several of the organic acids commonly encountered in intermediary metabolism.

If he has not already done so, the student is urged to review his knowledge of chemical stoichiometry. The meanings of gram molecular weight and gram equivalent weight (mole and equivalent, respectively) and the significance of molarity, molality, and normality must be thoroughly understood. Biochemistry is a quantitative science, and the student must recognize immediately such terms as millimole and micromole. In connection with titrations it is also important to remind the student that the H$^+$ concentrations of 0.1N H$_2$SO$_4$ and 0.1N CH$_3$COOH are by no means similar but that 1 liter of each of these solutions contains the same amount of total titratable acid.

Table 1-1. The pK_a of Some Organic Acids

	pK_a	pK_{a_2}	pK_{a_3}
Acetic acid (CH$_3$COOH)	4.74		
Acetoacetic acid (CH$_3$—CO—CH$_2$—COOH)	3.58		
Citric acid (HOOC—CH$_2$—C(OH) (COOH)—CH$_2$—COOH)	3.09	4.75	5.41
Formic acid (HCOOH)	3.62		
Fumaric acid (HOOC—CH=CH—COOH)	3.03	4.54	
DL-Glyceric acid (CH$_2$OH—CHOH—COOH)	3.55		
DL-Lactic acid (CH$_3$—CHOH—COOH)	3.86		
DL-Malic acid (HOOC—CH$_2$—CHOH—COOH)	3.40	5.26	
Pyruvic acid (CH$_3$—CO—COOH)	2.50		
Succinic acid (HOOC—CH$_2$—CH$_2$—COOH)	4.18	5.56	

Ionization of Weak Bases

The ionization of a weak base, defined in the chemical sense as a substance that furnishes OH^- ions on dissociation, can be represented as:

$$BOH \rightleftharpoons B^+ + OH^-$$

$$K_{eq} = K_b = \frac{[B^+][OH^-]}{[BOH]}$$

For NH_4OH, the K_b is given in chemical handbooks as 1.8×10^{-5}. It is therefore important to realize that the extent of dissociation of NH_4OH is identical with that of CH_3COOH. The important difference, of course, is that NH_4OH dissociates to form hydroxyl ions (OH^-) whereas CH_3COOH dissociates to form protons (H^+), and that the pH of $0.1M$ solutions of these two substances is by no means similar.

We can rearrange the equilibrium expression for the dissociation of a weak base and obtain an expression similar to that for weak acids.

$$pOH = pK_b + \log \frac{[B^+]}{[BOH]} \qquad (1\text{-}15)$$

With reference to the acidity of this solution, note that pH is not a term in this equation, and that pOH is encountered instead, where

$$pOH = -\log[OH^-]$$
$$pK_b = -\log K_b$$

Thus in a manner analogous to that for the titration of acetic acid, this expression can be used to calculate the theoretical curve for the titration of $0.1N$ NH_4OH with $0.1N$ HCl. This calculation gives curve 1 in Figure 1-2.

The very great disadvantage of equation 1-15 is that the results are expressed in terms of pOH. It is of course true that $pH = 14 - pOH$ and that we can calculate the pH of solutions of different NH_4OH and NH_4Cl concentrations when we know the pOH. In order to convert curve 1 in Figure 1-2 to the familiar pH scale, we must subtract all these values from 14. The subtraction provides curve 2 of Figure 1-2. It can be seen again that the minimum change in pH occurs at the point where the NH_4OH is half neutralized, that is, when $pH = 14 - pK_b$. Thus it is important to stress that with weak bases whose ionization constant (K_b) is expressed in the classical sense of a substance furnishing OH^- anions, the pH at half-neutralization will be known only after the pK_b (calculated from the K_b) is subtracted from 14.

It is unfortunate that the term pK_b remains in textbooks and in

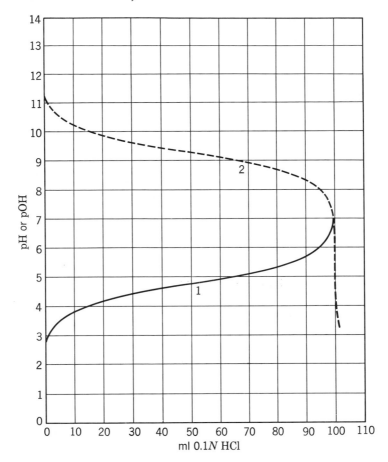

Fig. 1-2. Titration curve of 100 ml of 0.1N NH$_4$OH with 0.1N HCl plotted as pOH (1) and pH (2).

chemical handbooks. In biochemistry the term is particularly inconvenient in dealing with the titration of amino acids and proteins, compounds having weak acid groups [such as the carboxyl (—COOH) group], and weak basic functions such as the amino (—NH$_2$) group. To avoid the confusion introduced by the use of K_b, it is desirable to use Brönsted's definition of acids and bases.

In the foregoing discussion we have considered acids as substances that can furnish H$^+$ in aqueous solution and bases as furnishing OH$^-$ ions. There are other definitions of acids and bases: For example, an acid is a substance that has a sour, vinegary taste, and a base has a slick touch to the skin.

Brönsted Acids

A most useful definition of acids and bases in biochemistry is that proposed by Brönsted. He defined an acid as any substance that can *donate* a proton, and a base as a substance that can *accept* a proton. Although other definitions of acids, notably one proposed by G. N. Lewis, are even more general, the Brönsted concept should be thoroughly understood by students of biochemistry.

The following underlined substances are examples of Brönsted acids:

$$\underline{HCl} \longrightarrow H^+ + Cl^-$$
$$\underline{CH_3COOH} \longrightarrow H^+ + CH_3COO^-$$
$$\underline{NH_4^+} \longrightarrow NH_3 + H^+$$

and the generalized expression would be

$$\underline{HA} \longrightarrow H^+ + A^-$$

The corresponding bases are:

$$\underline{Cl^-} + H^+ \longrightarrow HCl$$
$$\underline{CH_3COO^-} + H^+ \longrightarrow CH_3COOH$$
$$\underline{NH_3} + H^+ \longrightarrow NH_4^+$$

The corresponding base for the generalized weak acid HA is

$$\underline{A^-} + H^+ \longrightarrow HA$$

It is customary to refer to the acid-base pair as follows: HA is the *Brönsted acid* because it can furnish a proton; the anion A^- is called the *conjugate base* because it can accept the proton to form the acid HA.

In applying the Henderson-Hasselbalch equation to the dissociation of a weak acid, we have previously seen that:

$$pH = pK_a + \log \frac{[A^-]}{[HA]}$$

If we recognize that A^- would represent the Brönsted conjugate base and HA the Brönsted acid, we would have, as a generalized expression,

$$pH = pK_a + \log \frac{[\text{Brönsted conjugate base}]}{[\text{Brönsted acid}]} \qquad (1\text{-}16)$$

The Brönsted definition is especially useful when we consider the dissociation of ammonium ions and substituted amino groups found in amino acids. In this consideration NH_4^+ is considered the Brönsted acid, and it dissociates to form a proton; thus we may write

$$NH_4^+ \longrightarrow NH_3 + H^+$$

$$K_a = \frac{[NH_3][H^+]}{[NH_4^+]}$$

and we may solve for H^+ and convert to pH in the manner of Henderson-Hasselbalch:

$$pH = pK_a + \log \frac{[NH_3]}{[NH_4^+]} \tag{1-17}$$

If we appreciate that NH_3 is the Brönsted base, capable of accepting protons, and NH_4^+ the Brönsted acid, we see that an expression of the ionization of NH_4^+ becomes completely general in keeping with equation 1-16:

$$pH = pK_a + \log \frac{[\text{Base or } NH_3]}{[\text{Acid or } NH_4^+]}$$

The important thing to remember is that the ionization constant of ammonium hydroxide in most handbooks is expressed as the classical base K_b. Thus to convert to a term useful in equation 1-17 we may recall that the inflection point on the pH scale in Figure 1-2 was obtained by subtracting pK_b from 14. That is, $pK_a = 14 - pK_b$. Fortunately the pK_a's for the amino groups of amino acids are listed in many chemical handbooks, along with the pK_b's.

Determination of pK_a

A valuable property of many biological compounds is their ability to ionize. Organic acids, amino acids, proteins, purines, pyrimidines, and phosphate esters are examples of biochemicals which are ionized to varying degrees in biological systems. Since the pH of most biological fluids is near 7, the extent of dissociation of some of these compounds may be complete there. The first ionization of H_3PO_4 will likewise be complete; the second ionization ($pK_{a_2} = 7.2$) will be approximately half complete.

One of the characteristic qualitative properties of a molecule is the pK_a of any dissociable group it may possess. The experimental determination of the pK_a of dissociable groups is therefore an important procedure in describing properties of an unknown substance. The pK_a may be determined in the laboratory by measuring the titration curve experimentally with a pH meter. As known amounts of alkali or acid are added to a solution of the unknown the pH is determined, and the titration curve can be plotted. From this curve the inflection point (pK_a) may be determined by suitable procedures. The student should become familiar with the glass-electrode system, which is commonly used to measure H^+ activity (see Appendix 3).

Buffers

With a thorough understanding of the ionization of weak electrolytes it is possible to discuss buffer solutions. *A buffer solution is one that resists a change in pH on the addition of acid or alkali.* Most commonly, the buffer solution consists of a mixture of a weak Brönsted acid and its conjugate base; for example, mixtures of acetic acid and sodium acetate or of ammonium hydroxide and ammonium chloride are buffer solutions.

There are many examples of the significance of buffers in biology; the ability to prevent large changes in pH is an important property of most intact biological organisms. The cytoplasmic fluids which contain dissolved proteins, organic substrates, and inorganic salts resist excessive changes in pH. The blood plasma is a highly effective buffer solution almost ideally designed to keep the range of the pH of blood within 0.2 pH unit of 7.2–7.3; values outside this range are not compatible with life. Further appreciation of the buffered nature of the living cell results from recognizing that many of the metabolites constantly being produced and utilized in the cell are weak Brönsted acids. In addition, enzymes responsible for the catalysis of reactions in which these metabolites participate exhibit their maximum catalytic action at some definite pH (Chapter 7).

In the laboratory the biochemist also wishes to examine reactions *in vitro* under conditions where the change in pH is minimal. He obtains these conditions by using efficient buffers, preferably inert ones, in the reactions under investigation. The buffers may include weak acids such as phosphoric, acetic, glutaric, and tartaric acids or weak bases such as ammonia, pyridine, and tris-(hydroxymethyl)-amino methane.

Let us consider the mechanism by which a buffer solution exerts control over large pH changes. When alkali (for instance, $NaOH$) is added to a mixture of acetic acid (CH_3COOH) and potassium acetate (CH_3COOK), the following reaction occurs:

$$OH^- + CH_3COOH \longrightarrow CH_3COO^- + H_2O$$

This reaction states that OH^- ion reacted with protons furnished by the dissociation of the weak acid and formed H_2O.

$$CH_3COOH \rightleftharpoons CH_3COO^- + H^+$$
$$\searrow OH^-$$
$$\searrow H_2O$$

On the addition of alkali there is a further dissociation of the available CH_3COOH to furnish additional protons and thus to keep the H^+ concentration or pH unchanged.

When acid is added to an acetate buffer the following reaction occurs:

$$H^+ + CH_3COO^- \longrightarrow CH_3COOH$$

The protons added (in the form of HCl, for example) combine instantly with the CH_3COO^- anion present in the buffer mixture (as potassium acetate) to form the undissociated weak acid CH_3COOH. Consequently the resulting pH change is much less than would occur if the conjugate base were absent.

In discussing the quantitative aspects of buffer action we should point out that two factors determine the effectiveness or *capacity* of a buffer solution. Clearly the molar concentration of the buffer components is one of them. The buffer capacity is directly proportional to the concentration of the buffer components. Here we encounter the convention used in referring to the concentration of buffers. The concentration of a buffer refers to the *sum* of the concentration of the weak acid and its conjugate base. Thus a $0.1M$ acetate buffer could contain 0.05 mole of acetic acid and 0.05 mole of sodium acetate in 1 l of H_2O. It could also contain 0.065 mole of acetic acid and 0.035 mole of sodium acetate in a liter of H_2O.

The second factor influencing the effectiveness of a buffer solution is the *ratio* of the concentration of the conjugate base to the concentration of the weak acid. Quantitatively it should seem evident that the most effective buffer would be one with *equal concentrations* of basic and acidic components since such a mixture could furnish *equal quantities* of basic or acidic components to react, respectively, with acid or alkali. An inspection of the titration curve for acetic acid (Figure 1-1) similarly shows that the minimum change in pH resulting from the addition of a unit of alkali (or acid) occurs at the pK_a for acetic acid. At this pH we have already seen that the ratio of CH_3COO^- to CH_3COOH is 1. On the other hand, at values of pH far removed from the pK_a (and therefore at ratios of conjugate base to acid greatly differing from unity), the change in pH for unit of acid or alkali added is much larger.

Having stated the two factors that influence the buffer capacity, we may consider the decisions involved in selecting a buffer to be effective at the desired pH value, for example pH = 5. Clearly it would be most desirable to select a weak acid having a pK_a of 5.0. If this cannot be done, the weak acid whose pK_a is closest to 5.0 is the first choice. In addition it is evident that we should want to use as high a concentration as is compatible with other features of the system. Too high a concentration of salt frequently inhibits the activity of enzymes or other phys-

Table 1-2. Buffers

Compound	pK_{a_1}	pK_{a_2}	pK_{a_3}	pK_{a_4}
Acetic acid	4.7			
Ammonium chloride	9.3			
Carbonic acid	6.1	10.3		
Citric acid	3.1	4.8	5.4	
Diethanolamine	8.9			
Ethanolamine	9.5			
Fumaric acid	3.0	4.4		
Glycine	2.4	9.6		
Glycylglycine	3.1	8.1		
Histidine	1.8	6.1		
Maleic acid	1.9	6.2		
Phosphoric acid	2.1	7.2	12.7	
Pyrophosphoric acid	—	2.0	6.5	8.4
Triethanolamine	7.8			
Tris-(hydroxymethyl)- amino methane	8.0			
Veronal (sodium diethylbarbituate)	8.0			
Versene (ethylenediamino- tetra-acetic acid)	2.0	2.7	6.2	10.3

iological systems, however. The solubility of the buffer components may also limit the concentration which can be employed.

Table 1-2 lists the pK_a for some buffers commonly encountered in biochemistry.

Let us consider the practical problem of making 1 l of 0.1M acetate buffer, pH 5.22. The first step is to determine the ratio of the conjugate base (acetate ion) to the weak acid (acetic acid) in this buffer solution. It may be calculated by means of the Henderson-Hasselbalch equation:

$$pH = pK_a + \log \frac{[CH_3COO^-]}{[CH_3COOH]}$$

$$5.22 = 4.74 + \log \frac{[CH_3COO^-]}{[CH_3COOII]}$$

$$\log \frac{[CH_3COO^-]}{[CH_3COOH]} = 5.22 - 4.74 = 0.48$$

$$\frac{[CH_3COO^-]}{[CH_3COOH]} = \text{antilog } 0.48$$

$$\frac{[CH_3COO^-]}{[CH_3COOH]} = 3$$

In this solution, then, there will be 3 moles of CH_3COO^- for every mole of CH_3COOH; that is, 75 per cent of the buffer component is present as the conjugate base CH_3COO^-. Since 1 l of $0.1M$ acetate buffer will contain 0.1 g mole of acetate and acetic acid combined, 0.75×0.1 or 0.075 mole of acetate ion will be present.

This amount of acetate ion is contained in 6.15 g of sodium acetate. The acidic component will, of course, be 0.25×0.1 or 0.025 mole of acetic acid, which amounts to 1.5 g of acetic acid. When mixed with sodium acetate in final volume of 1 l, this amount of acetic acid will give a liter of buffer of the desired pH and concentration.

It is an experimental fact that when such a solution is carefully prepared and its pH is measured accurately with a pH meter the observed value will not be 5.22. The chief reason for the discrepancy is that in our calculations we have chosen to deal with concentrations rather than activities. Since the pH meter accurately measures H^+ activity, a discrepancy is not surprising. If necessary, the pH of the buffer can be adjusted by the addition of acid or alkali to obtain the desired pH. More frequently we may adjust the pH of the concentrated buffer so that, when it is diluted ten- to fiftyfold in an experiment, the pH of the final reaction mixture is known precisely.

It is a common practice to prepare a buffer mixture by starting with one component of the desired buffer and preparing the other component by the addition of acid or alkali. For example, the primary amine tris-(hydroxymethyl)-amino methane, or "Tris," has found extensive use as a buffer in biochemistry. This amine reacts with acid to form the corresponding salt of the amine:

$$(CH_2OH)_3CNH_2 + H^+ \rightleftharpoons (CH_2OH)_3CNH_3^+$$

The pK_a for the dissociation of the acid formed is 8.0. Consider therefore the preparation of 500 ml of $0.5M$ Tris buffer, pH 7.4. The ratio of the conjugate base to acid in this buffer will be found by solving:

$$pH = pK_a + \log \frac{\text{Base}}{\text{Acid}}$$

$$7.4 = 8.0 + \log \frac{[(CH_2OH)_3CNH_2]}{[(CH_2OH)_3CNH_3^+]}$$

$$-0.6 = \log \frac{[\text{Free Amine}]}{[\text{Acid Salt}]} \tag{1-16}$$

$$0.6 = \log \frac{[\text{Acid Salt}]}{[\text{Free Amine}]}$$

$$4 = \frac{[\text{Acid Salt}]}{[\text{Free Amine}]}$$

Hence Tris buffer with this desired composition will have four-fifths or 80 per cent of the total buffer as the amine salt and 20 per cent as free amine. Since 500 ml of $0.5M$ buffer will contain 0.25 mole of Tris (salt and free amine), the buffer will contain 0.8×0.25 or 0.2 mole of acid salt and 0.05 mole of free amine. To prepare the buffer, we would weigh out 0.25 mole (30.2 g) of solid amine (mol wt, 121), add 0.20 mole of HCl (200 ml of $1N$ HCl) to it, and dissolve in a final volume of 500 ml.

Additional buffer problems may be found in Appendix 1.

REFERENCES

1. J. B. Neilands and Paul K. Stumpf, *Outlines of Enzyme Chemistry*, John Wiley and Sons, New York, 2nd edition, 1958.

    A good treatment of chemical and hydrogen ion equilibria will be found in Chapter 2, pp. 7–27.

2. I. M. Kolthoff and E. B. Sandell, *Textbook of Quantitative Inorganic Analysis*, The MacMillan Co., New York, 3rd Edition, 1952.

    Chapters 2, 4, and 29 discuss the fundamental aspects of chemical stoichiometry, the Law of Mass Action, and the theory of acidimetry and alkalimetry, respectively.

3. *Data for Biochemical Research*, edited by R. M. C. Dawson et al., Oxford University Press, Oxford, 1959.

4. *Biochemisches Taschenbuch*, edited by H. M. Rauen, Springer Verlag, Berlin, 1956.

    These two handbooks are particularly useful as a source of information on the numerous properties of biochemicals, including dissociation constants.

Two

Carbohydrates

Introduction

Together with lipids and proteins, carbohydrates play a fundamental role in the life of animals and plants. They are an important source of energy for living organisms as well as a means by which chemical energy can be stored. In addition, some carbohydrates can function as structural units within the cell. Examples of carbohydrates which participate in the energy economy of the cell are the polysaccharides starch and glycogen; cellulose and chitin are typical structural carbohydrates.

Carbohydrates may be defined as polyhydroxy aldehydes or ketones, or as substances that yield one of these compounds on hydrolysis. Glucose ($C_6H_{12}O_6$) and fructose ($C_6H_{12}O_6$) are samples, respectively, of an *aldose* and a *ketose*.

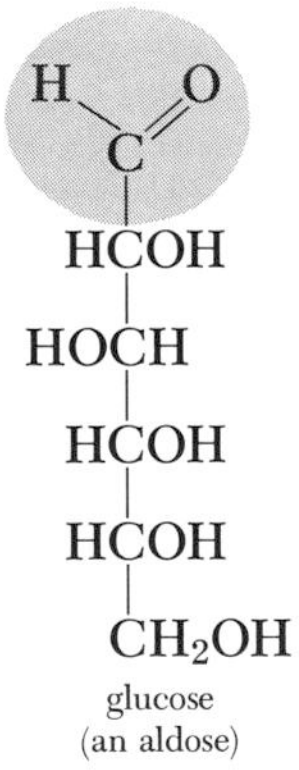

glucose
(an aldose)

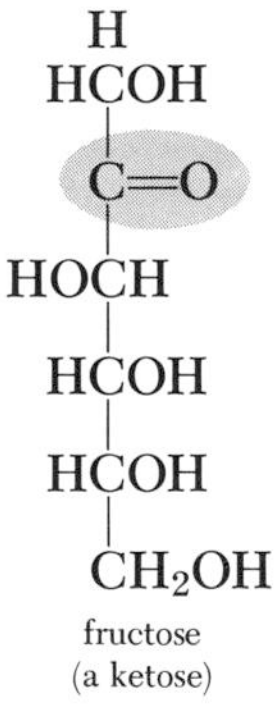

fructose
(a ketose)

The word carbohydrate originally indicated the belief that compounds of this group could be represented as *hydrates of carbon,* that is, as $C_x(H_2O)_y$. It became clear that this definition was not suitable when other compounds having the properties of carbohydrates did not have the required ratio of hydrogen to oxygen (2 to 1). One example of such a compound is the sugar deoxyribose ($C_5H_{10}O_4$), which is a constituent of deoxyribonucleic acid, a component of every cell.

In addition, we know that other carbohydrates contain nitrogen and sulfur in addition to carbon, hydrogen, and oxygen. These compounds obviously do not agree with the general formula $C_x(H_2O)_y$. Thus, as is frequently the case with definitions, the term carbohydrate is convenient rather than exact.

Carbohydrates can be classified in three main groups: monosaccharides, oligosaccharides, and polysaccharides. Monosaccharides are simple sugars that cannot be hydrolyzed into smaller units under reasonably mild conditions. The monosaccharides, in turn, are classified according to the number of carbon atoms they possess; trioses $(C_3H_6O_3)$ have three carbon atoms, tetroses, four carbon atoms, and so on up to octoses or nonoses.

Oligosaccharides are compound sugars that yield two to six molecules of simple sugars on hydrolysis. Thus disaccharides are oligosaccharides which hydrolyze to yield *two* molecules of monosaccharides, and pentosaccharides yield *five* molecules of monosaccharides on hydrolysis. For the most part the sugars that may be classified as monosaccharides or oligosaccharides are crystalline compounds which are readily soluble in water and usually have a sweet taste.

The term polysaccharide refers to a group of compounds that yield a large number of monosaccharides on hydrolysis. Some of the monosaccharides that are bound together by glycosidic bonds to form polysaccharides are glucose, xylose, and arabinose. Polysaccharides are frequently tasteless, insoluble, amorphous compounds with very high molecular weights.

Stereoisomerism

The study of carbohydrates and their chemistry immediately introduces the topic of stereoisomerism. It is desirable therefore to review the subject of isomerism as it is treated in organic chemistry.

The subject of isomerism may be divided into *structural isomerism* and *stereoisomerism*. Structural isomers have the same molecular formula but differ from each other by having different structures; stereoisomers have the same molecular formula and the same structure, but they differ in *configuration*, that is, in the arrangement of their atoms in space. Structural isomers, in turn, can be of three types. One type is that of the *chain isomers,* in which the isomers have different arrangements of the carbon atoms. As an example, *n*-butane is a chain isomer of isobutane. Another type of structural isomers is that of

$$CH_3-CH_2-CH_2-CH_3$$

n-butane

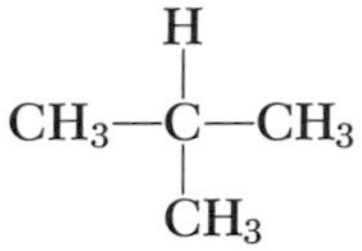

$$CH_3-\overset{\overset{\displaystyle H}{|}}{\underset{\underset{\displaystyle CH_3}{|}}{C}}-CH_3$$

isobutane

the *positional isomers;* n-propyl chloride and isopropyl chloride, in which the two compounds involved have the same carbon chain but differ in the position of a substituent group, are positional isomers. The

$$CH_3-CH_2-CH_2-Cl$$

n-propyl chloride

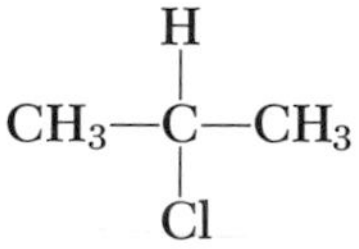

$$CH_3-\overset{\overset{\displaystyle H}{|}}{\underset{\underset{\displaystyle Cl}{|}}{C}}-CH_3$$

isopropyl chloride

third type of structural isomer is that of the *functional-group* isomers in which the compounds have different functional groups. Examples are ethyl alcohol and dimethyl ether.

$$CH_3-CH_2OH$$

ethyl alcohol

$$CH_3-O-CH_3$$

dimethyl ether

The subject of stereoisomerism can be divided into the smaller areas of *optical isomerism* and *geometrical* (or *cis-trans*) *isomerism.* The latter type of isomerism is illustrated by the *cis-trans* pair, fumaric and maleic acids.

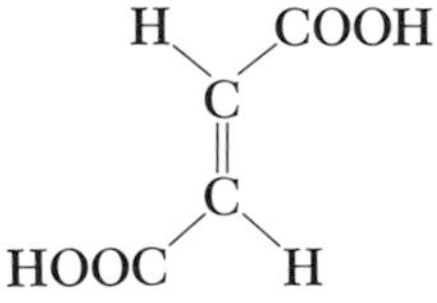

fumaric acid
(*trans*)

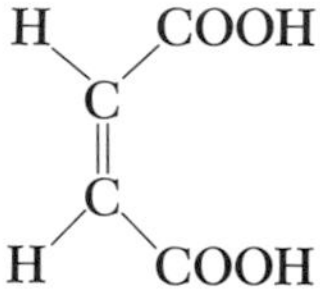

maleic acid
(*cis*)

Optical isomerism, the type of isomerism commonly found in carbohydrates, is usually encountered when a molecule contains one or more *asymmetric* carbon atoms. The subject of stereoisomerism was extensively developed after van't Hoff and LeBel introduced the concept of the *tetrahedral carbon atom.* Today it is recognized that the carbon atom has the shape of a tetrahedron in which the carbon nucleus sits in the center of the tetrahedron and the four covalent bondings go out to the corners of the tetrahedron. When four different groups are attached to those bonds, the carbon atom is said to be *asymmetric.* This is indicated in the following structure, where the compound C(ABDE), containing a single asymmetric carbon atom, is represented as having the four groups A, B, D, and E attached.

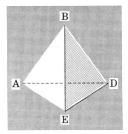

These groups may be arranged in space in two different ways so that *two* different compounds are formed.

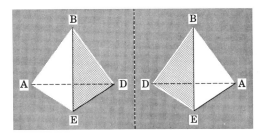

The compounds are obviously different; they cannot be superimposed on each other. Instead, one compound resembles the other by being its *mirror image* or *optical antipode*. If one model is held before a mirror, the image in the mirror corresponds to the other model. These two compounds which are mirror image isomers of each other are said to be an *enantiomorphic* pair; one member of the pair is said to be the *enantiomorph* of the other.

Many of the properties of the two members of an enantiomorphic pair are identical—they have the same boiling point, the same melting point, the same solubility in various solvents. They also exhibit optical activity; in this property they differ in one important manner. One member of the enantiomorphic pair will rotate a plane of polarized light in a clockwise direction and is therefore said to be *dextro*rotatory. Its mirror image isomer or enantiomorph will rotate the plane of polarized light to the *same extent* but in the *opposite* or counterclockwise direction. This isomer is said to be *levo*rotatory.

The subject of optical activity and the ability of optically active compounds to rotate plane-polarized light is dealt with in introductory organic chemistry. The student should review the principles of light refraction that make it possible to construct a Nicol prism which can polarize light into two planes. The student should also review the construction of the polarimeter, the device which measures quantitatively the extent to which plane-polarized light is rotated when it passes through optically active materials.   Finally, the student should review the meaning of *specific rotation* [α], which is given by the formula

$$[\alpha] = \frac{\text{Observed Rotation (degrees)}}{\text{Length of Tube (dm)} \times \text{Concentration (g/ml)}}$$

In the study of carbohydrates many examples of optical isomerism are encountered, and it is necessary to have a means for representing the different possible isomers.   One way of representing them is to use the *projection formula* introduced in the nineteenth century by the distinguished German organic chemist, Emil Fischer.   The projection formula represents the four groups attached to the carbon atom as being projected onto a plane.   This projection can be represented for the asymmetric carbon atoms depicted previously as

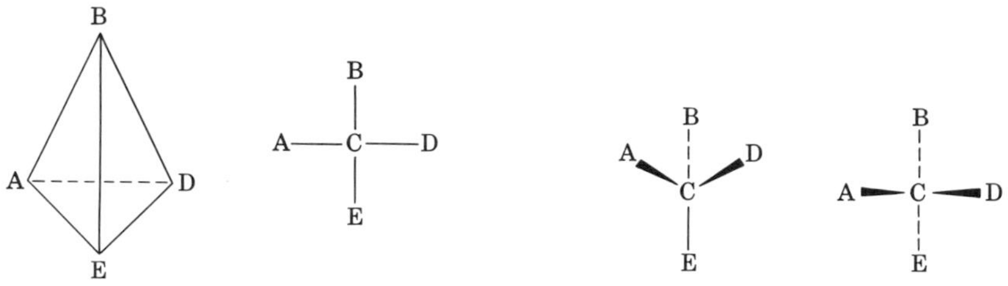

projection formula   perspective representation

In the perspective representation, ordinary lines indicate bonds in the plane of the page and dashed lines indicate bonds extending below the plane of the page.   Solid wedges identify bonds standing above the plane of the page.   The projection and perspective formulas can be used to distinguish between the compound just shown and its mirror image isomer below.   These two pairs of formulas represent all the enan-

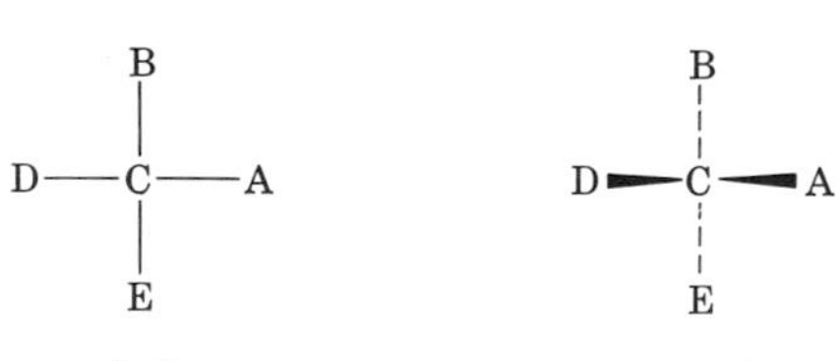

projection   perspective

tiomorphs.   There can be no possibility of confusing the two compounds as long as the rule for representing the carbon atom by the Fischer formula is observed.   This rule is that the formula as represented on a plane of paper can only be moved in that plane.   If the formula is lifted out of that plane, there is a possibility of confusion.

With the existence of a large number of optical isomers in carbohydrates it is also necessary to have a reference compound.   The simplest monosaccharide that possesses an asymmetric carbon atom has been chosen as the reference standard; this compound is triose *glycerose* or *glyceraldehyde*. Since this compound has one asymmetric carbon atom it can exist in two optically active forms. These are represented as:

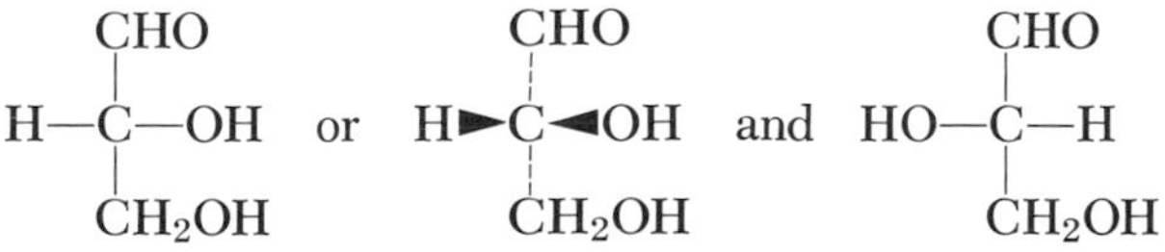

$$\begin{array}{ccccccc}
\text{CHO} & & \text{CHO} & & & \text{CHO} & \\
| & & | & & & | & \\
\text{H--C--OH} & \text{or} & \text{H}\blacktriangleright\text{C}\blacktriangleleft\text{OH} & \text{and} & \text{HO--C--H} \\
| & & | & & & | & \\
\text{CH}_2\text{OH} & & \text{CH}_2\text{OH} & & & \text{CH}_2\text{OH} &
\end{array}$$

It is clear that these two forms are related to each other as mirror image isomers; they will have the same melting point, boiling point, and solubility in H_2O. But they will differ in the direction in which they rotate plane-polarized light. The isomer that rotates light in the clockwise direction has been assigned the symbol D($+$) as a prefix to indicate that it is the dextrorotatory compound. The symbol ($+$) describes the sign of rotation and the letter D indicates the configuration shown next; in this representation the hydroxy group on the asymmetric carbon atom is on the right when the aldehyde group is at the top of the formula:

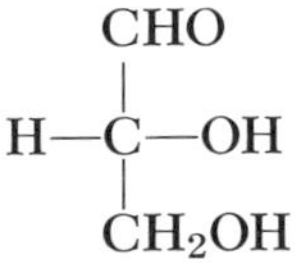

$$\begin{array}{c}
\text{CHO} \\
| \\
\text{H--C--OH} \\
| \\
\text{CH}_2\text{OH}
\end{array}$$

D($+$)-glyceraldehyde

As an illustration of the use of D-glyceraldehyde as a reference compound, consider the formation of tetrose sugars from a triose by the *Kiliani* cyanohydrin synthesis. This synthesis is a process by which the chain length of a carbohydrate may be increased. In the initial reaction the triose glyceraldehyde is allowed to react with HCN to form a cyanohydrin:

$$CH_2OH\text{--}CHOH\text{--}CHO + HCN \longrightarrow$$

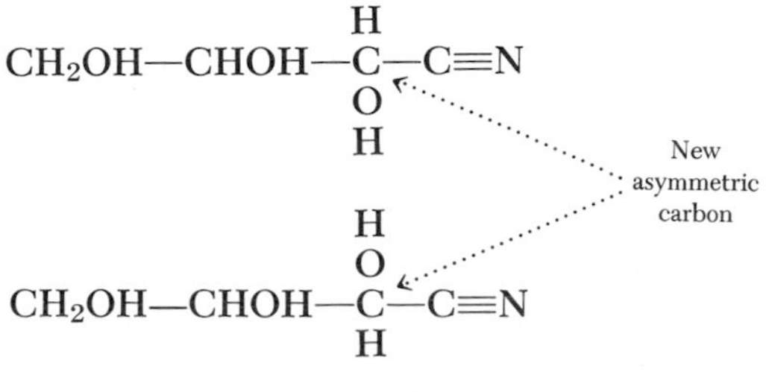

$$\begin{array}{l}
\phantom{CH_2OH\text{--}CHOH\text{--}C}\text{H} \\
CH_2OH\text{--}CHOH\text{--}C\text{--}C\equiv N \\
\phantom{CH_2OH\text{--}CHOH\text{--}C}O \\
\phantom{CH_2OH\text{--}CHOH\text{--}C}\text{H} \\[4pt]
\phantom{CH_2OH\text{--}CHOH\text{--}C}\text{H} \\
\phantom{CH_2OH\text{--}CHOH\text{--}C}O \\
CH_2OH\text{--}CHOH\text{--}C\text{--}C\equiv N \\
\phantom{CH_2OH\text{--}CHOH\text{--}C}\text{H}
\end{array}$$

New asymmetric carbon   (2-1)

This process creates a new asymmetric carbon atom, as indicated. *Two different compounds differing in the configuration about the newly*

formed asymmetric atom will result in this reaction. These two cyanohydrins can be hydrolyzed to carboxylic acids:

$$CH_2OH-CHOH-C^\circ HOH-C\!\!=\!\!N \xrightarrow[H_2O]{H^+}$$

$$CH_2OH-CHOH-C^\circ HOH-COOH$$

and then converted to the γ-lactones:

$$CH_2OH-CHOH-C^\circ HOH-COOH \xrightarrow{-H_2O}$$

$$\underset{\rule{3.5em}{0.4pt}O\rule{3.5em}{0.4pt}}{CH_2-CHOH-C^\circ HOH-C\!\!=\!\!O}$$

Finally, the lactones can be reduced to the corresponding aldose with
sodium amalgam:

$$\underset{\rule{3.5em}{0.4pt}O\rule{3.5em}{0.4pt}}{CH_2-CHOH-C^\circ HOH-C\!\!=\!\!O} \xrightarrow{(2H)}$$

$$CH_2OH-CHOH-C^\circ HOH-CHO$$

Since the cyanohydrin synthesis introduces a new asymmetric center (in
reaction 2-1) two new sugars are produced from a single monosaccharide.

The application of the cyanohydrin synthesis to D-glyceraldehyde is
shown in Figure 2-1. In the initial step two cyanohydrins are formed
in which the configuration at the carbon atom adjacent to the nitrile
group is reversed. When hydrolysis, lactonization, and reduction are
complete, two new sugars, the tetroses D-erythrose and D-threose, are
formed. Note that these tetroses differ only in the position of the hydroxyl group on carbon atom 2, the carbon atom adjacent to the
aldehyde group. They do not differ in the configuration on the asymmetric carbon atom 3, the asymmetric carbon atom which was present
initially in D-glyceraldehyde. Since they have the same configuration
on this *reference carbon atom*, the asymmetric carbon atom furthest
removed from the functional group (CHO), these two tetroses are
known as D-sugars. Similarly two new L-sugars, L-threose and L-erythrose, are formed in the cyanohydrin synthesis from L-glyceraldehyde
(Figure 2-1).

At this point it is profitable to consider the stereochemical relations
that exist between these four tetroses and the reference compound
D-glyceraldehyde. First, these four tetroses have the same structural
formula, $CH_2OH-CHOH-CHOH-CHO$, and they are therefore
stereoisomers rather than structural isomers. Second, with regard to

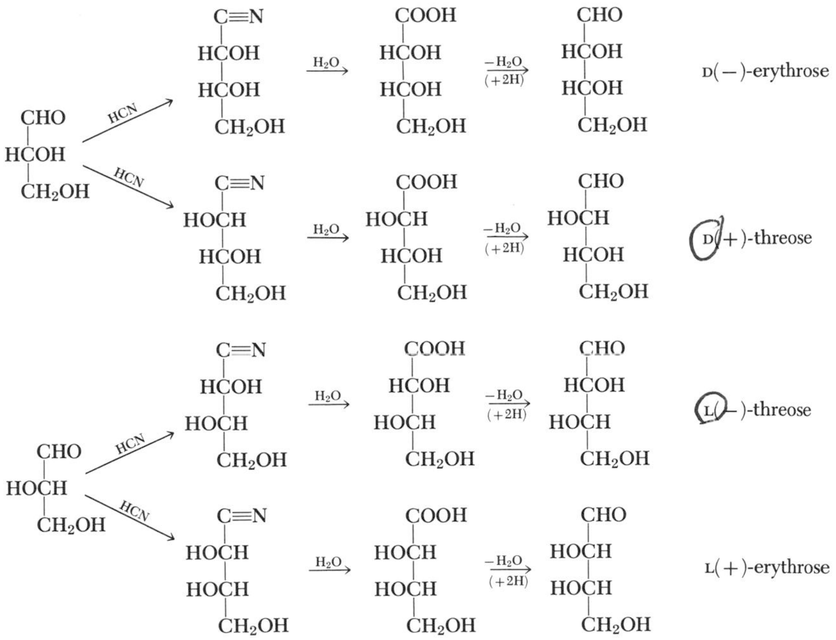

Fig. 2-1. Application of the cyanohydrin synthesis to D-glyceraldehyde.

their stereoisomerism, they obviously belong to the class of optical isomers rather than that of geometric isomers. Third, there are two pairs of enantiomorphs among the four tetroses: D-erythrose is the mirror image isomer of L-erythrose. The same relation exists between D-threose and L-threose. Fourth, the two D-sugars are related structurally to D-glyceraldehyde because they have the same configuration about the *penultimate* carbon atom, the carbon atom next to the last carbon from the functional or aldehyde group. Fifth, note that the symbols D and L *bear no relation* to whether the tetrose is dextrorotatory or levorotatory. D-erythrose is levorotatory, whereas D-threose is dextrorotatory. The direction in which light is rotated is a specific property of the molecule under consideration and is not related directly to the configuration about the penultimate carbon atom (except in the glyceraldehydes).

As the number of asymmetric carbon atoms increases in a carbohydrate molecule the number of optical isomers also increases. In the trioses, where there is one asymmetric carbon atom, there are two optical isomers; in the tetroses, where there are two asymmetric carbon atoms, there are four optical isomers; in the aldohexoses, where there are four asymmetric carbon atoms, there are sixteen optical isomers. van't Hoff established that 2^n represents the number of possible optical isomers, where n is the number of asymmetric carbon atoms.   In the ketohexoses, where n is 3, there are eight possible optical isomers.

Consider the four common hexoses whose projection formulas are:

$$
\begin{array}{cccc}
\text{CHO} & \text{CHO} & \text{CHO} & \text{CH}_2\text{OH} \\
\text{HCOH} & \text{HOCH} & \text{HCOH} & \text{C}{=}\text{O} \\
\text{HOCH} & \text{HOCH} & \text{HOCH} & \text{HOCH} \\
\text{HCOH} & \text{HCOH} & \text{HOCH} & \text{HCOH} \\
\text{HCOH} & \text{HCOH} & \text{HCOH} & \text{HCOH} \\
\text{CH}_2\text{OH} & \text{CH}_2\text{OH} & \text{CH}_2\text{OH} & \text{CH}_2\text{OH} \\
\text{D}(+)\text{-glucose} & \text{D}(+)\text{-mannose} & \text{D}(+)\text{-galactose} & \text{D}(-)\text{-fructose}
\end{array}
$$

The following statements can be made about their isomerism: all four sugars are D-sugars, because they have the same configuration as D-glyceraldehyde on the penultimate carbon atom; the use of the term D has no bearing on whether these sugars are dextro- or levorotatory.

D-fructose is a structural isomer of the other three hexoses.   Although it has the same molecular formula ($C_6H_{12}O_6$) it has a different functional group; it is a ketose rather than an aldose.

The three aldohexoses are stereoisomers, more specifically optical isomers.   Because no one of the three is an enantiomorph of either of the other two, they are related as *diastereomers*.   If two optical isomers are not enantiomorphs, they are related as diastereomers.   Since these isomers are diastereomers they have different melting points, different boiling points, different solubilities, different specific rotations, and, in general, different chemical properties.   Clearly the three aldoses are only three of the possible *sixteen* optical isomers; there are eight pairs of enantiomorphs in the sixteen aldohexoses.

D(+)-glucose may be said to be an *epimer* of D(+)-mannose because these compounds differ from each other by their configuration on a single asymmetric carbon atom.   Similarly, D(+)-glucose is an epimer of D(+)-galactose.   On the other hand there is no epimeric relationship between D(+)-mannose and D(+)-galactose.

Ring Structure of Glucose

We have considered the sugars as simple aldehydes or ketones with open-chain structures.   There is abundant evidence, however, to indicate that other forms (of glucose, for example) exist and indeed predominate both in the solid phase and in solution.   For instance, many sugars undergo the Kiliani cyanohydrin synthesis with difficulty, although cyanohydrin formation with simple aldehydes is usually rapid.   Glucose and other aldoses fail to give the Schiff test for aldehydes.   Solid glucose is quite inert to oxygen, and yet aldehydes are notoriously autoxidizable.   Finally, it is possible to show that two crystalline forms of D-glucose exist.   When D-glucose is dissolved in water and allowed to crystallize out by evaporation of the water, a form designated as α-D-glucose is obtained.   If glucose is crystallized from acetic acid or pyridine, another form, β-D-glucose, is obtained.   These two forms of D-glucose show the phenomenon of *mutarotation*.   A freshly prepared aqueous solution of α-D-glucose has a specific rotation $[\alpha]_D^{20}$ of $+113°$; when the solution is left standing it changes to $+52.5°$.   A fresh solution of β-D-glucose, on the other hand, has an $[\alpha]_D^{20}$ of $+19°$; on standing it also changes to the same value, $+52.5°$.

The explanation of the existence of the two forms of glucose, as well as the other anomalous properties described, is found in the fact that the aldohexoses and other sugars tend to form cyclic molecules.   The angles of the tetrahedral carbon atom tend to bend the glucose molecule, for example, into a ring.   Thus the ends of the six-carbon chain of glucose tend to approach each other.   A ring is readily formed because the aldehydes are able to form hemiacetals with alcohols:

$$R—CHO + R'—OH \longrightarrow R—\underset{\underset{H}{\overset{|}{\underset{O}{|}}}}{\overset{\overset{H}{|}}{C}}—O—R'$$

In the hexoses, the proximity of the alcoholic hydroxyl on the fourth and fifth carbon atoms causes these structures to form a hemiacetal with the aldehyde of carbon-1.   In this instance the reaction between

the aldehyde and C-5 hydroxyl of the hexose has resulted in a six-membered ring; if the C-4 hydroxyl had participated, the ring would be five membered.   A seven-membered ring is too strained to permit participation of the C-6 hydroxyl of aldohexoses in ring formation.

The six-membered ring sugars are considered derivatives of pyran, but the five-membered rings are considered related to furan:

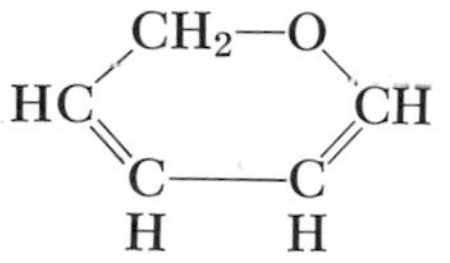

$$\underset{\alpha\text{-pyran}}{\overset{\displaystyle CH_2\!-\!O}{HC \diagdown \diagup CH}} \qquad \underset{furan}{\overset{\displaystyle O}{HC \diagdown \diagup CH}}$$

α-pyran 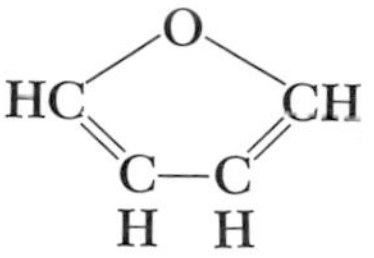   furan

Hence it is customary to refer to the *pyranose* or *furanose* form of the monosaccharide. Furanose forms of the free sugar are less stable than the pyranose forms in solution; combined forms of furanose sugars (as in the fructose unit of sucrose) are found in nature, however.

The projection formulas of the two forms of glucose and the open-chain formula may be represented as:

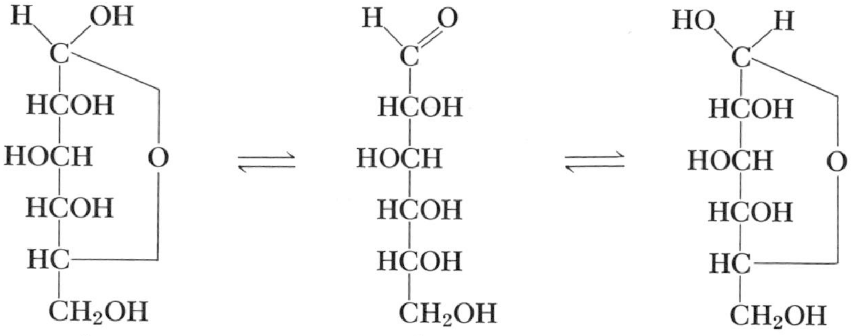

α-D-glucose   D-glucose   β-D-glucose

Whenever either pure α- or pure β-D-glucose is freshly dissolved in H_2O, the form initially available is converted to the other form through the open-chain structure. The attainment of equilibrium is known as mutarotation. The equilibrium mixture in aqueous solution with specific rotation of $+52.5°$ consists of 37 per cent α and 63 per cent β with only a very small amount (about 0.1 per cent) of the straight-chain compound. Thus it is apparent that the phenomenon of mutarotation is not a unique property of α- or β-D-glucose, but is rather a property exhibited by all crystalline sugars that exist in ring structures and have a potentially free aldehyde or ketone group in their molecule.

As we have shown the α- and β- forms of D-glucose are optical isomers; they are diastereomers however, rather than enantiomorphs, for the α-form of D-glucose is clearly not the mirror image isomer of β-D-glucose. They are also known as *anomers* because they differ only in the configuration about the terminal asymmetric carbon atom. Since the cyclic forms of the aldohexoses have five asymmetric carbon atoms, there are thirty-two optical isomers consisting of sixteen pairs of enantiomorphs of the cyclic aldohexoses.

The convention in representing the α and β anomers is the following: The isomer that has the higher specific rotation in the positive sense is called the α-form whereas the isomer with the lower rotation is called β. In the case of the pyranose forms of D-glucose, the isomer with specific rotation of $+113°$ is therefore α-D-glucose. This is experimentally known to be the form in which the hydroxyl group attached to the aldehydic carbon atom is on the same side (*cis*) as the hydroxyl on the adjacent carbon atom. For sugars in the L-series the anomer that has the lower rotation is designated as α. Thus the enantiomorph of α-D-glucose will have a specific rotation of $-113°$ and will be designated as α-L-glucose. Its structure is

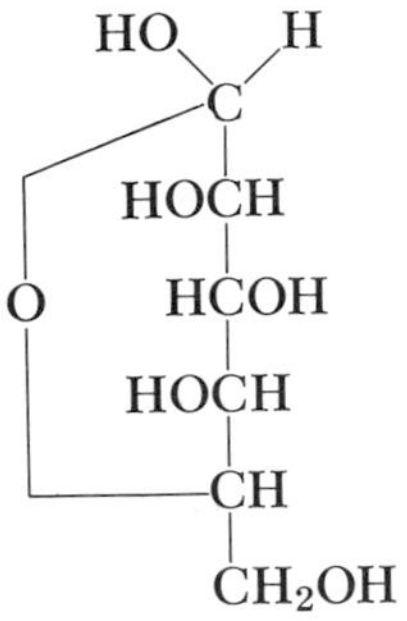

α-L-glucose

Although the Fischer projection formulas are accurate they are somewhat cumbersome to draw. The English chemist W. H. Haworth proposed that the cyclic forms of the carbohydrate be represented in another manner that emphasizes their structural relationship to furan and pyran. In the Haworth formula the first five carbon atoms of the aldohexoses and the oxygen atom of the ring are represented as a hexagon in a plane that projects from the paper on which the formula is written. The thicker lines at the bottom of the Haworth formula represent those atoms of the hexagon which are nearer the reader.

If this formula is used, it is possible to represent the substituents on the carbon atoms as extending above or below the plane of the six-membered ring. The carbon atoms not involved in ring formation (C-6 in the aldopyranoses) also sit above or below the plane of the ring.

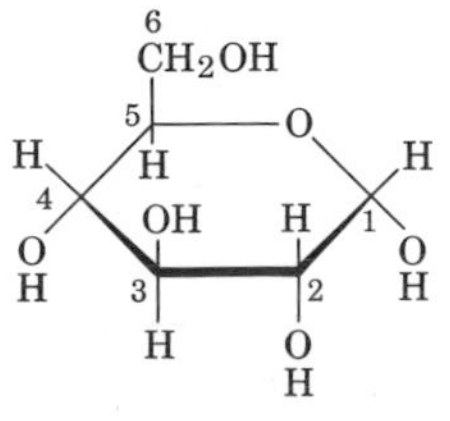

α-D-glucose

When the carbon atoms in the ring of the Haworth formula are numbered clockwise, as in α-D-glucopyranose, the group written on the right-hand side of the asymmetric carbon atoms in the Fischer projection are represented as projecting below the plane of the ring in the Haworth perspective formula. Similarly those groups on the left of the asymmetric carbon atoms in the Fischer formula will be shown as extending above the plane of the Haworth formula. There is an apparent discrepancy in the groups on carbon atom 5 in that the hydrogen atom which is clearly on the left in the Fischer formula is *below* the plane of the ring in the Haworth structure. This is the result of *torsion* required to effect ring closure. In forming the pyranose form of glucose from the straight-chain aldehyde form, the fifth carbon atom must be rotated so that the oxygen atom in the hydroxyl group on this carbon atom is brought into the plane of the first five carbon atoms. As a result, the hydrogen atom on carbon atom 5 is shifted to the other side of the chain because that atom has been rotated through more than 90°.

The Haworth structures for β-D-glucopyranose, α-D-xylopyranose, α-L-arabinopyranose, and β-D-fructopyranose are shown in the accompanying diagram. Although the pyranose form of fructose is the com-

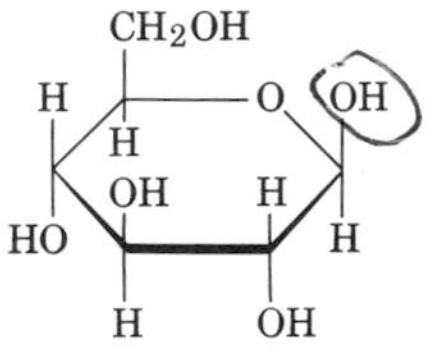

β-D-glucopyranose

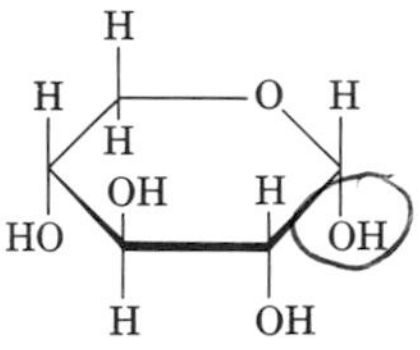

α-D-xylopyranose

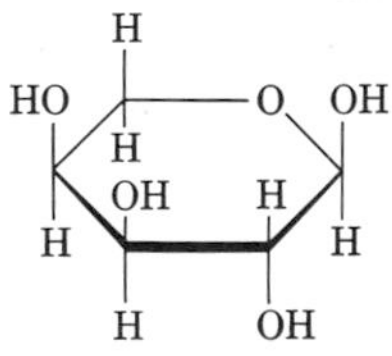

α-L-arabinopyranose

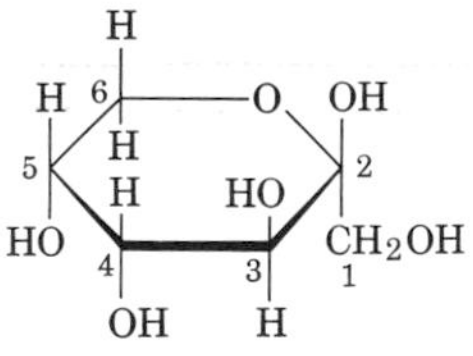

β-D-fructopyranose

mon ring form of the cyclic sugar, the *furanose* or five-membered ring of fructose is the one encountered when the anomeric hydroxyl group of the hemiketal is substituted, as in D-methyl-fructofuranoside.

Monosaccharides

The number of known monosaccharides is approximately 70. About twenty of these occur naturally; the remainder are synthetic. In general these sugars are very soluble in H_2O, sparingly soluble in ethanol, and insoluble in ether. The structures of a number of important monosaccharides have already been presented in this chapter; these include D-glucose, D-fructose, D-mannose, D-galactose, D-erythrose, α-D-xylopyranose, and α-L-arabinopyranose. Additional important monosaccharides are dihydroxyacetone and dihydroxyacetone phosphate.

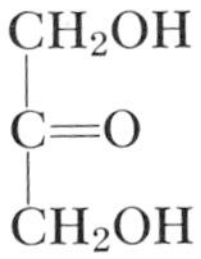

$$CH_2OH$$
$$|$$
$$C{=}O$$
$$|$$
$$CH_2OH$$

dihydroxyacetone

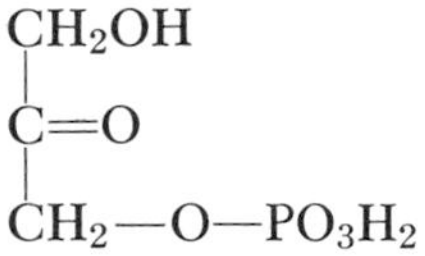

$$CH_2OH$$
$$|$$
$$C{=}O$$
$$|$$
$$CH_2{-}O{-}PO_3H_2$$

dihydroxyacetone phosphate

Dihydroxyacetone, a triose, occurs as a phosphorylated intermediate, dihydroxyacetone phosphate, in the metabolism of monosaccharides.

In this connection we should mention that many of the naturally occurring sugars exist as phosphorylated derivatives. Such compounds are of immense metabolic importance as intermediates in many different biochemical processes. These phosphorylated sugars exist both as mono- and as diesters.

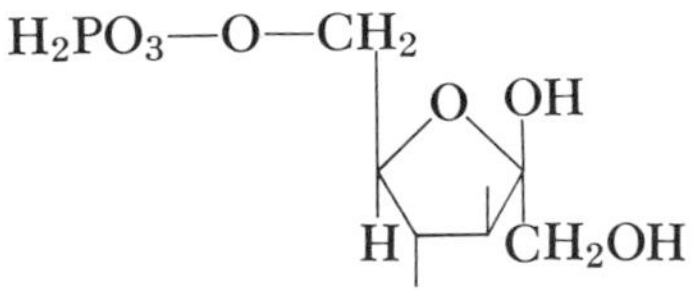

β-D-fructose-6-phosphate
a monoester

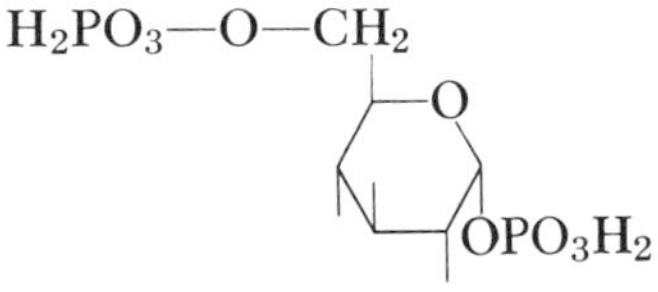

α-D-glucose-1,6-diphosphate
a diester

The two types of nucleic acid that are found in all living cells contain the two pentoses D-ribose and 2-deoxy-D-ribose, respectively. These sugars occur in the nucleic acids in the furanose configuration. Ribose is also a constituent of several coenzymes.

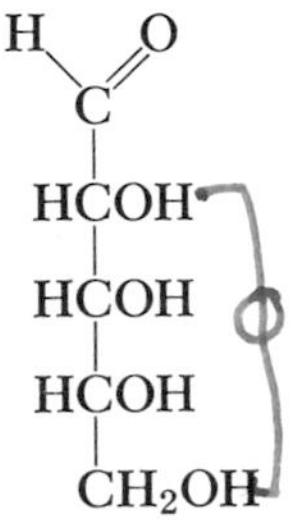

D-ribose

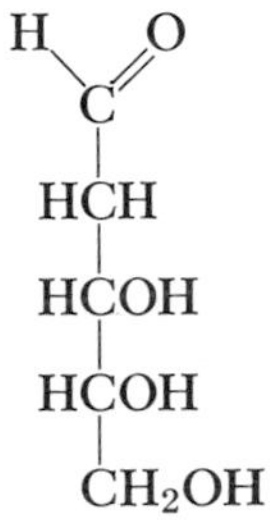

2-deoxy-D-ribose

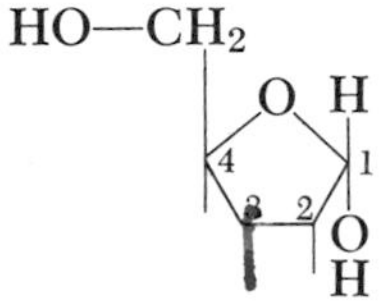

α-D-ribofuranose

Another pentose involved (as a phosphate ester) in intermediary metabolism is xylulose.

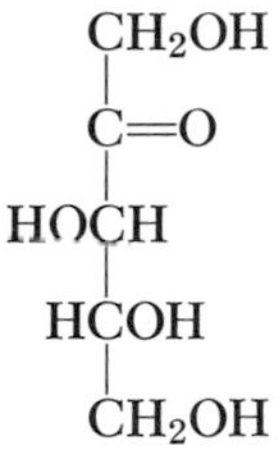

$$CH_2OH$$
$$C{=}O$$
$$HOCH$$
$$HCOH$$
$$CH_2OH$$

D-xylulose

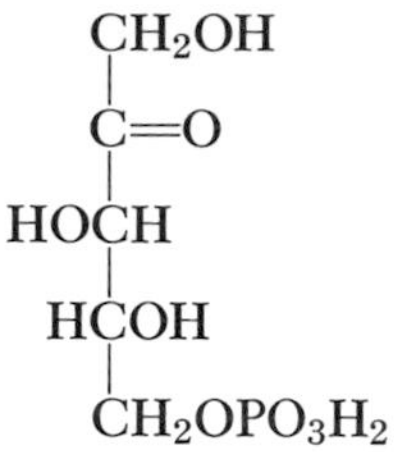

$$CH_2OH$$
$$C{=}O$$
$$HOCH$$
$$HCOH$$
$$CH_2OPO_3H_2$$

D-xylulose-5-phosphate

A similarly important heptose in metabolism is sedoheptulose, which occurs in nature both free and as its mono- and diphosphate esters.

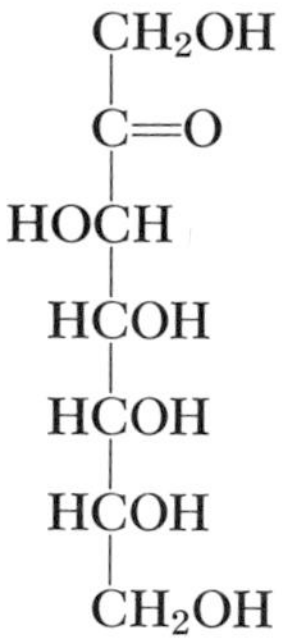

$$CH_2OH$$
$$C{=}O$$
$$HOCH$$
$$HCOH$$
$$HCOH$$
$$HCOH$$
$$CH_2OH$$

D-sedoheptulose

$$CH_2OH$$
$$C{=}O$$
$$HOCH$$
$$HCOH$$
$$HCOH$$
$$HCOH$$
$$CH_2OPO_3H_2$$

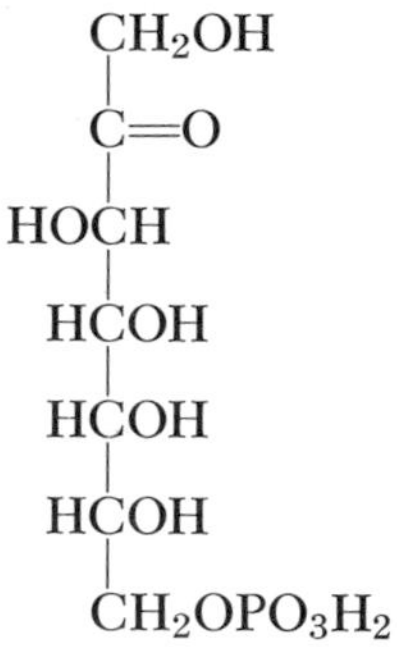

D-sedoheptulose-7-phosphate

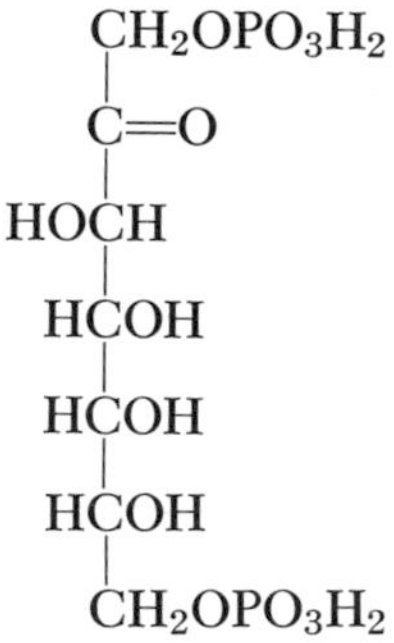

$$CH_2OPO_3H_2$$
$$C{=}O$$
$$HOCH$$
$$HCOH$$
$$HCOH$$
$$HCOH$$
$$CH_2OPO_3H_2$$

D-sedoheptulose-
1,7-diphosphate

In addition to the aldoses and ketoses we have described, some sugar alcohols exist that do not possess the general formula $C_x(H_2O)_y$ but are properly classified as carbohydrates because of their chemical and physical properties.   One example is the hexitol sorbitol, which is the most common of the sugar alcohols.   Sorbitol is found in the berries of

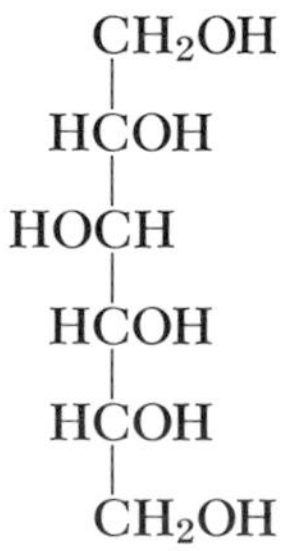

$$CH_2OH$$
$$HCOH$$
$$HOCH$$
$$HCOH$$
$$HCOH$$
$$CH_2OH$$

D-sorbitol

higher plants and in seaweeds.   It is a crystalline solid at room temperature but possesses a low melting point.   Sorbitol and other sugar alcohols are readily soluble in H_2O and have a sweet taste.

Amino sugars are sugars in which a hydroxyl group is replaced by an amino group or a substituted amino group. The most common amino sugar is D-glucosamine, which is found as a component of mucopolysac-

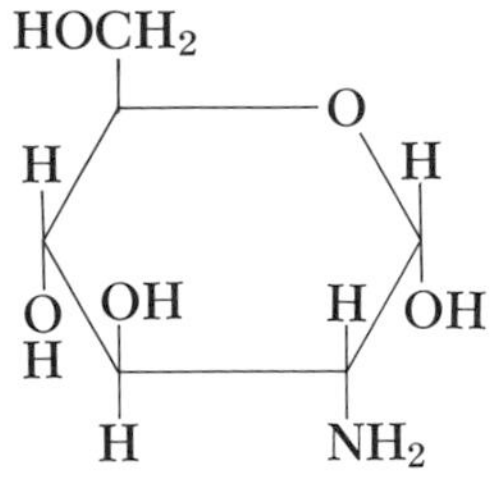

$$HOCH_2$$

α-D-glucosamine

charides and glycoproteins, proteins found in saliva and in eggs. Chitin, which is the material of the hard shell of insects and crustaceans, is a polymer of N-acetyl-D-glucosamine in which one of the hydrogens on the amino group is replaced by an acetyl group.

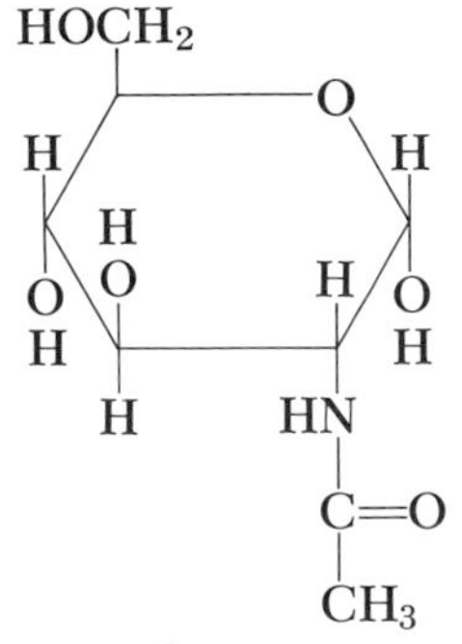

$$HOCH_2$$

N-acetyl-D-glucosamine

PROPERTIES OF MONOSACCHARIDES

Carbohydrates may be classified as either reducing or nonreducing sugars. The reducing sugars, which are the more common, are able to function as reducing agents because free or potentially free aldehyde and ketone groups are present in the molecule. The reducing proper- ties of these carbohydrates are usually observed by their ability to reduce metal ions, notably copper or silver, in alkaline solution. Fehling's solution is the most common reagent for detecting reducing sugars; in this reagent Cu^{2+} is maintained in solution as its tartrate com- plex. When the Cu^{2+} is reduced, the resulting Cu^+ ion is less soluble and Cu_2O precipitates out of the alkaline solution as a brick red solid.

Monosaccharides are also readily oxidized in acid in the presence of mild oxidizing agents. Under these conditions the aldehyde group is oxidized to form a monocarboxylic acid. In the presence of an excess of a strong oxidizing agent like HNO_3 the sugar will be further oxidized to a dicarboxylic acid.

$$CH_2OH—(CHOH)_4—CHO \xrightarrow{(O)}$$

$$CH_2OH—(CHOH)_4—COOH \xrightarrow{(O)} COOH—(CHOH)_4—COOH$$

<table>
<tr><td>"onic" acid,
e.g., gluconic acid
galactonic acid</td><td>"aldaric" acid,
e.g., saccharic acid</td></tr>
</table>

When aldohexoses are heated with strong mineral acid, a furfural derivative is formed.

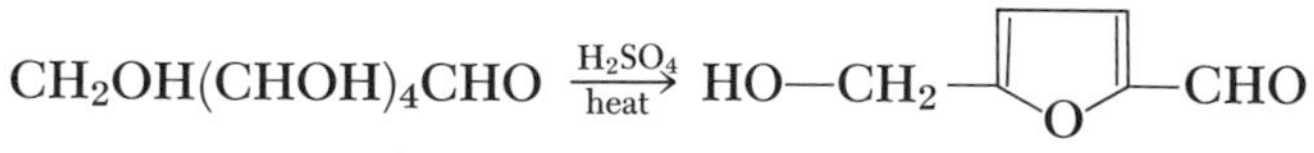

$$CH_2OH(CHOH)_4CHO \xrightarrow[\text{heat}]{H_2SO_4} HO—CH_2\text{—}\boxed{}\text{—CHO}$$

hydroxymethyl furfural

Under the same conditions pentoses yield furfural itself.

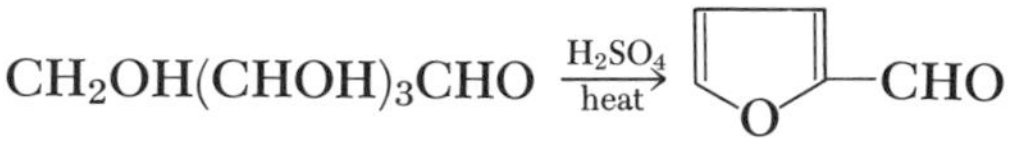

$$CH_2OH(CHOH)_3CHO \xrightarrow[\text{heat}]{H_2SO_4} \boxed{}\text{—CHO}$$

furfural

If the furfurals are in turn reacted with certain amines or α-napthol colored products are formed; these reactions are the basis for certain qualitative tests for carbohydrates.

One of the most important properties of monosaccharides is their ability to form glycosides or acetals. Consider as an example the formation of the methyl glycoside of glucose. When D-glucose in solution is treated with methanol and HCl, two compounds are formed. Determination of their structure has shown that these two compounds are the α- and β-methyl-D-glucosides. These glucosides, and glycosides in gen-

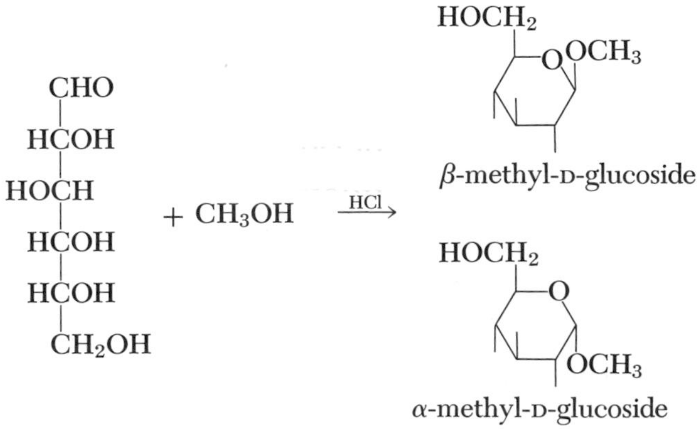

HOCH$_2$
OCH$_3$

β-methyl-D-glucoside

CHO
|
HCOH
|
HOCH
| + CH$_3$OH $\xrightarrow{\text{HCl}}$
HCOH
|
HCOH
|
CH$_2$OH

HOCH$_2$
O

OCH$_3$

α-methyl-D-glucoside

eral, are acid labile but are relatively stable at alkaline pH. Since the formation of the methyl glucoside converts the aldehydic group to an acetal group, the glycoside is not a reducing sugar and does not show the phenomenon of mutarotation.

Mutarotation is another property of the monosaccharides that possess a free or potentially free aldehyde or ketone group. Moreover, the process of mutarotation is catalyzed by small amounts of alkali.

When the aldose glucose is exposed to dilute alkali for several hours the resulting mixture can be shown to contain both fructose and mannose. If either of these sugars is treated with dilute alkali, the equilibrium mixture will contain the other sugar as well as glucose. This reaction, known as the *Lobry de Bruyn-von Ekenstein transformation,* is due to the enolization of these sugars in the presence of alkali. An enediol intermediate that is common to all three sugars is responsible for the establishment of the equilibrium.

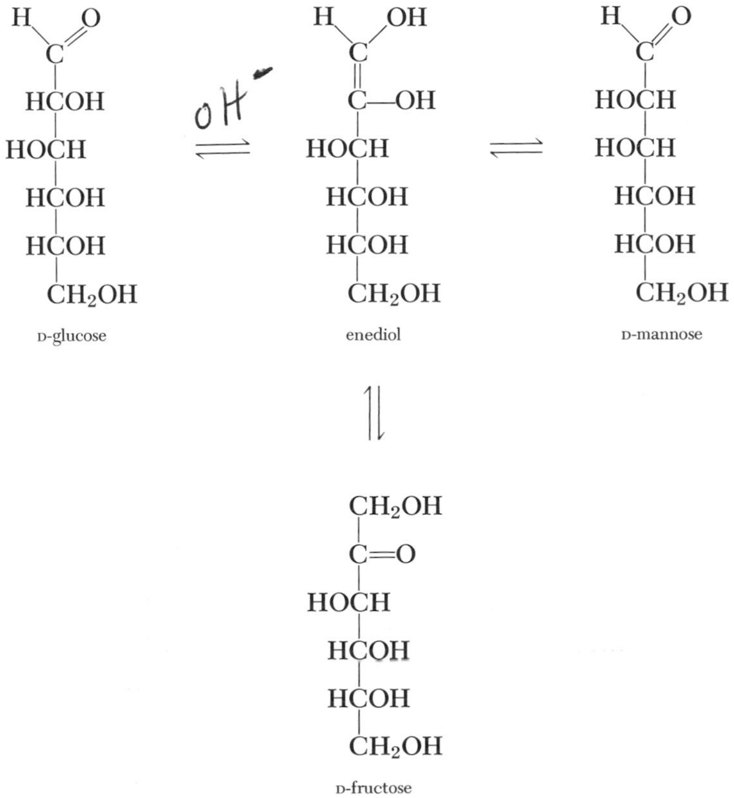

D-glucose   enediol   D-mannose

D-fructose

The reaction of monosaccharides with phenylhydrazine is one of the classic reactions of organic chemistry. One mole of phenylhydrazine will react with 1 mole of aldose or ketose to form a hydrazone. In the

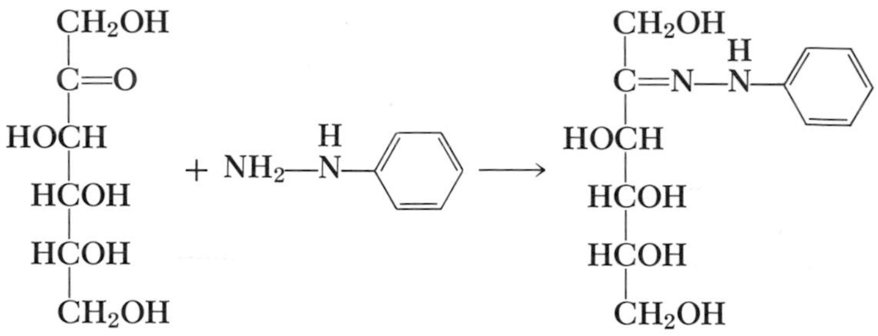

$$
\begin{array}{l}
\text{CH}_2\text{OH} \\
\text{C}=\text{O} \\
\text{HOCH} \\
\text{HCOH} \\
\text{HCOH} \\
\text{CH}_2\text{OH}
\end{array}
\quad + \text{NH}_2\text{—N—} \langle\ \rangle\ \longrightarrow
\quad
\begin{array}{l}
\text{CH}_2\text{OH} \\
\text{C}=\text{N—N—}\langle\ \rangle \\
\text{HOCH} \\
\text{HCOH} \\
\text{HCOH} \\
\text{CH}_2\text{OH}
\end{array}
$$

fructose   fructose hydrazone

presence of excess phenylhydrazine the hydrazone is oxidized and the phenylhydrazine is reduced to aniline and NH_3. Finally, a third mole

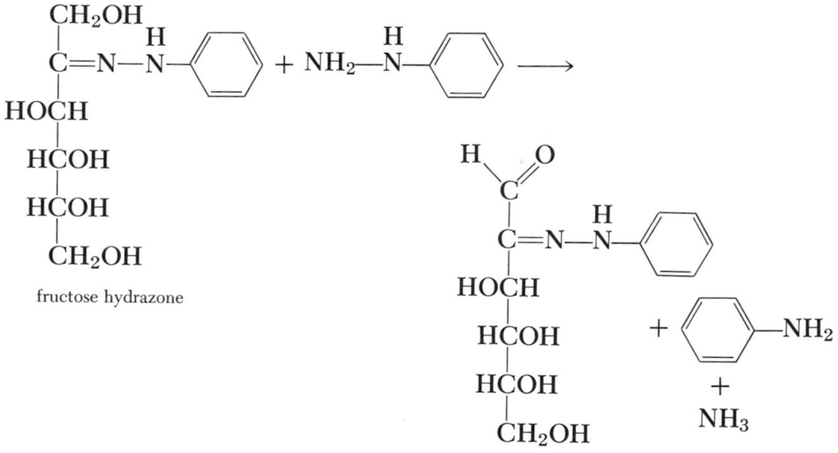

$$
\begin{array}{l}
\text{CH}_2\text{OH} \\
\text{C}=\text{N—N—}\langle\ \rangle \\
\text{HOCH} \\
\text{HCOH} \\
\text{HCOH} \\
\text{CH}_2\text{OH}
\end{array}
\quad + \text{NH}_2\text{—N—}\langle\ \rangle \longrightarrow
$$

fructose hydrazone

$$
\begin{array}{l}
\text{H—C}=\text{O} \\
\text{C}=\text{N—N—}\langle\ \rangle \\
\text{HOCH} \\
\text{HCOH} \\
\text{HCOH} \\
\text{CH}_2\text{OH}
\end{array}
\quad + \langle\ \rangle\text{—NH}_2 \; + \; NH_3
$$

ketohydrazone

of phenylhydrazine will react with the ketohydrazone to yield an ozazone. These latter compounds are colored, possess characteristic crystalline forms, and may be used for tentative identification of the parent carbohydrate.

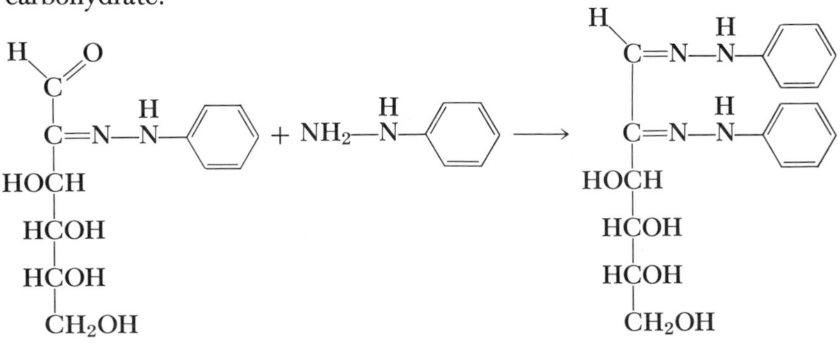

$$
\begin{array}{l}
\text{H—C}=\text{O} \\
\text{C}=\text{N—N—}\langle\ \rangle \\
\text{HOCH} \\
\text{HCOH} \\
\text{HCOH} \\
\text{CH}_2\text{OH}
\end{array}
\quad + \text{NH}_2\text{—N—}\langle\ \rangle \longrightarrow
\quad
\begin{array}{l}
\text{H—C}=\text{N—N—}\langle\ \rangle \\
\text{C}=\text{N—N—}\langle\ \rangle \\
\text{HOCH} \\
\text{HCOH} \\
\text{HCOH} \\
\text{CH}_2\text{OH}
\end{array}
$$

ketohydrazone   ozazone

In determining the structure of unknown carbohydrates it sometimes is desirable to react all the free hydroxyl groups with some reagent that effectively blocks or otherwise converts the hydroxyls to a known substitution. A suitable reagent for the sugar is acetic anhydride used in the presence of a catalyst. When it is so employed every hydroxyl group will be acetylated to form the acetate polyester of the parent carbohydrate. Similarly, when sugars are reacted with dimethyl sulfate

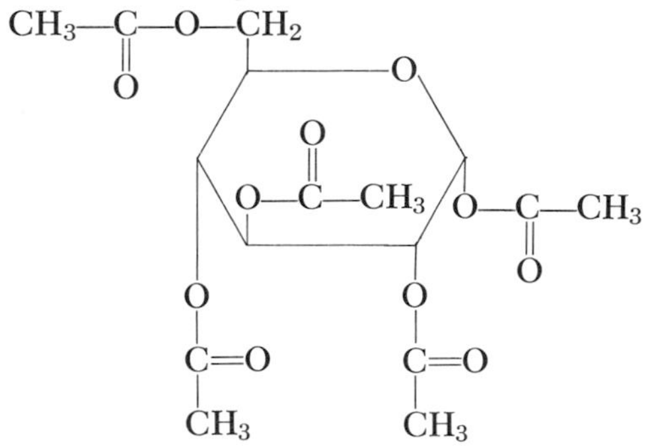

D-glucose penta-acetate

and alkali, all the free hydroxyl groups are converted to methyl ethers. The stability of the O-methyl ether renders these derivatives extremely useful in the structural analysis of carbohydrates. It is also possible to methylate selectively certain hydroxyl groups in monosaccharides; such compounds are utilized as reference compounds in investigating the structure of oligosaccharides and polysaccharides.

An additional important reagent that is useful in carbohydrate chemistry is periodic acid, HIO_4. This oxidant will cleave carbon-carbon bonds if both carbons have hydroxyl groups or if a hydroxyl and an amino group are on adjacent carbon atoms. Thus α-methyl-D-glucose would react as shown in the diagram. The carbon atoms whose bonds

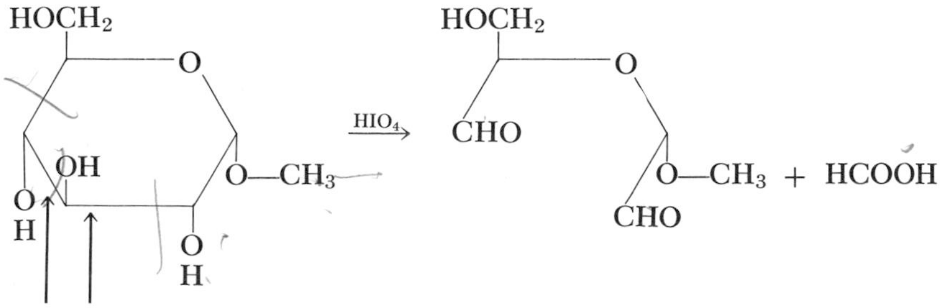

are severed are converted to aldehydes (R—CHO). If there happen to be three hydroxyl groups on adjacent carbon atoms, as in this case, the central carbon atom is released as formic acid.

Oligosaccharides

The oligosaccharides most frequently encountered in nature are disaccharides which on hydrolysis yield 2 moles of monosaccharides. Among the disaccharides encountered is the sugar *maltose*. In this sugar one

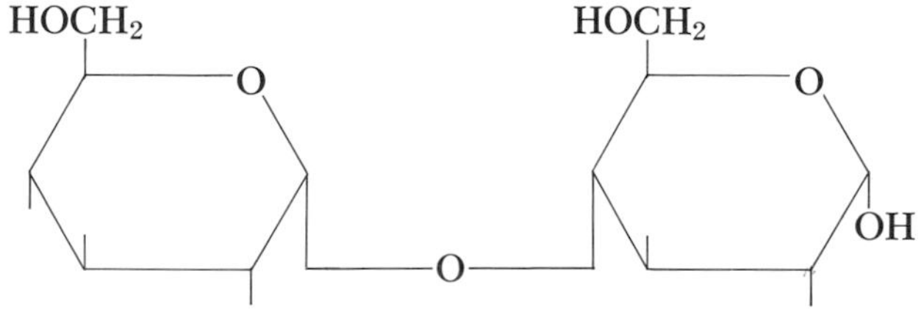

α-maltose

molecule of glucose is bonded through the hydroxyl group on C-1 carbon atom to the hydroxyl group on C-4 of a second molecule of glucose. The disaccharide is said to have an α-1-4 glucosidic linkage. Maltose is a reducing sugar since it has a potentially free aldehyde group; it therefore shows the phenomenon of mutarotation. Maltose is not found in nature to any extent but is a product obtained during the degradation of starch.

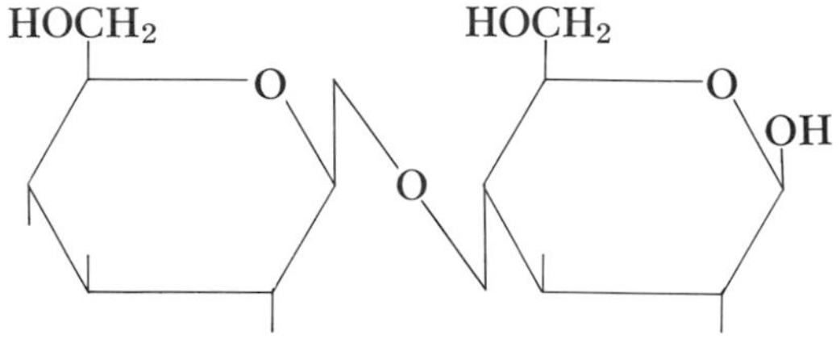

β-cellobiose

The disaccharide *cellobiose* is identical with maltose except that the former compound has a β-1-4 glucosidic linkage. Cellobiose is also a disaccharide formed during hydrolysis of a polysaccharide, specifically cellulose. Cellobiose is a reducing sugar and undergoes mutarotation.

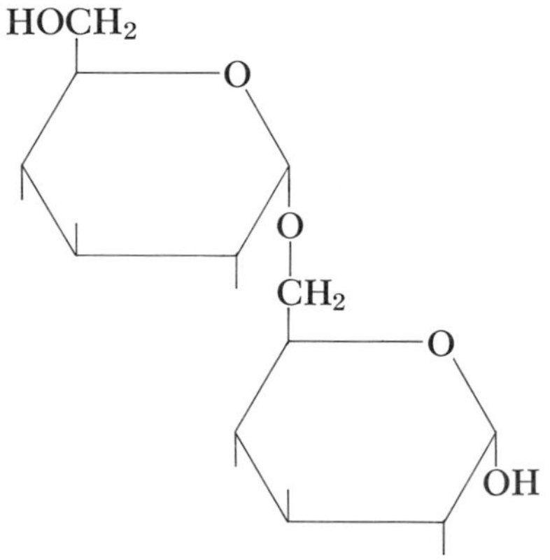

α-isomaltose

Isomaltose, another disaccharide obtained during the hydrolysis of certain polysaccharides, is similar to maltose except that it has an α-1-6 glucoside linkage.

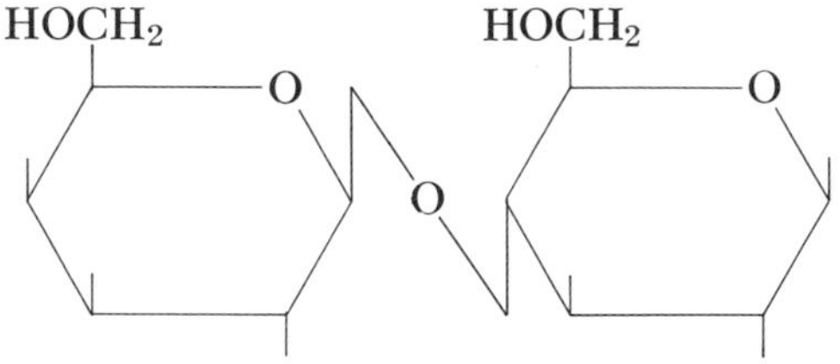

HOCH$_2$ ... HOCH$_2$

O ... O

O

β-lactose

Lactose is a disaccharide found in milk; on hydrolysis it yields one mole of D-glucose and one of D-galactose. The configuration about the bond involved in the glycosidic linkage is β.

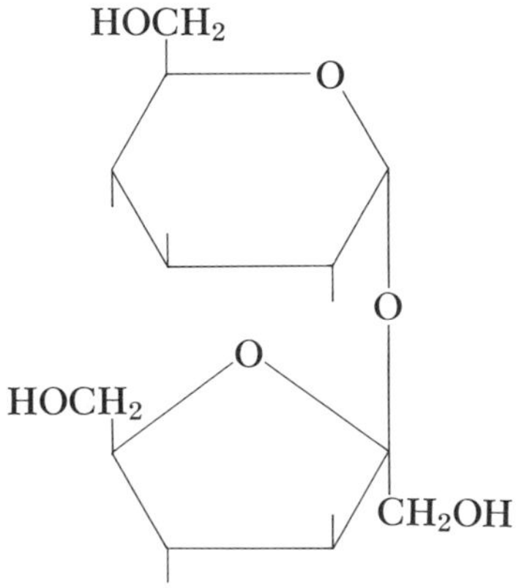

HOCH$_2$

O

O

O

HOCH$_2$

CH$_2$OH

sucrose

Sucrose, a naturally occurring disaccharide, is the chief constituent of beet and cane sugar; on hydrolysis 1 mole each of D-glucose and D-fructose are formed. In contrast to the other disaccharides sucrose is non-reducing. Hence the reducing groups in both of the monosaccharides must be involved in the linkage between the two sugar units. Since the reducing groups are found on the C-1 and C-2 carbon atoms, respectively, of glucose and fructose, the glycosidic bond of the disaccharide must be between these two carbon atoms. Note that fructose possesses the furanose ring structure in the disaccharide although the pyranose ring predominates in the free ketohexose.

Polysaccharides

As noted earlier, the polysaccharides found in nature serve either a structural or a nutrient function. The plant starches and animal glycogens are important examples of the latter type of polysaccharides. The fundamental unit of starch and glycogen is D-glucose, as this is the only monosaccharide obtained on total hydrolysis of the polysaccharide.

The starches consist of two components, amylose and amylopectin, which are present in varying amounts; the former gives a blue color with iodine, and amylopectin produces a purple to red color with the halogen. Enzymatic hydrolysis of the amylose component of potato starch with amylases yields maltose as the chief product. The linkage in amylose hence may be seen to be of the α-1-4 type. Other studies have shown that potato amylose is a linear polysaccharide with a molecular weight ranging from 4000 to 150,000. Its structure may therefore be represented as:

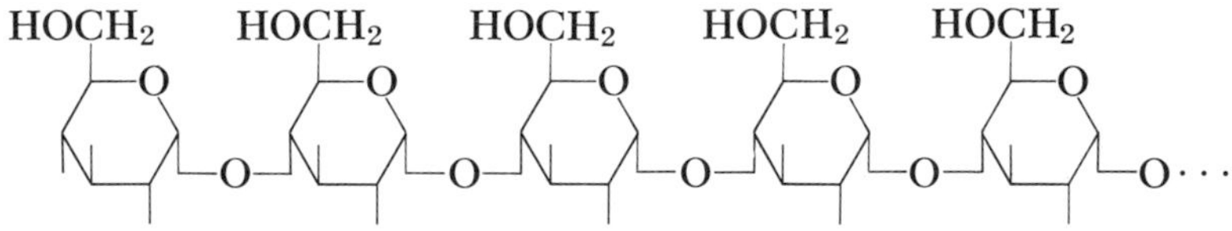

amylose

Structural studies on potato amylopectin have also shown that this component of starch is a branched polysaccharide. In this molecule shorter (about thirty-unit) chains of glucose linked by α-1-4 linkages are also joined to each other by α-1-6 linkages (from which isomaltose can be obtained). The branching point may be represented as in our diagram. The molecular weight of amylopectin may vary greatly

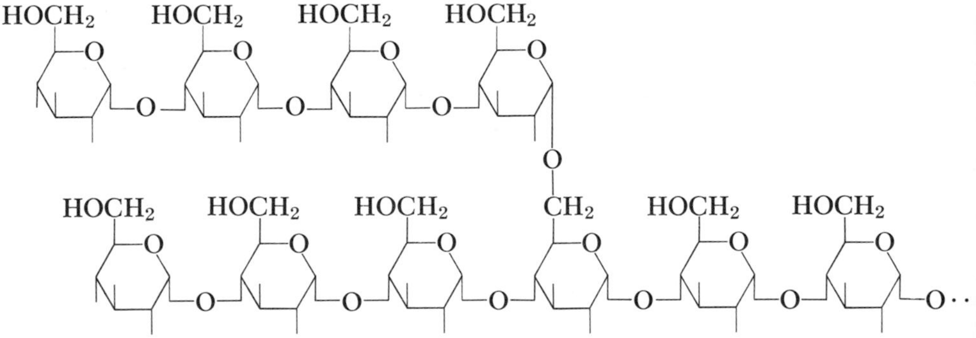

amylopectin

within one sample of starch and may be 500,000 or larger.

The nutrient polysaccharide of animal tissues is glycogen; its structure is similar to that of amylopectin in that it is a branched molecule. Its chain length, however, is usually shorter (ten to twenty glucose units) and hence it is even more highly branched. Its structure may be represented as we show it, where each bead of the chain represents a glucose molecule.

glycogen

A final example of a nutrient polysaccharide will suffice. This is *inulin*, a storage carbohydrate found in the bulbs of many plants (dahlias, Jerusalem artichokes). Inulin consists chiefly of fructo-furanose units joined together by β-2-1 glycosidic linkages.

The most abundant structural polysaccharide is cellulose, a major component of higher plants. Total hydrolysis by acid of cellulose yields D-glucose; partial hydrolysis gives cellobiose. Studies seem to indicate that cellulose is a linear polysaccharide consisting of β-1-4-linked glucose units. The molecular weights of cellulose samples vary from 200,000 to 2,000,000.

Other interesting structural carbohydrates are known. The fruits of many plants contain pectins, which are polymers of galactose, arabinose, and galacturonic acid. Pectic acids consisting of D-galacturonic acids have the following structure:

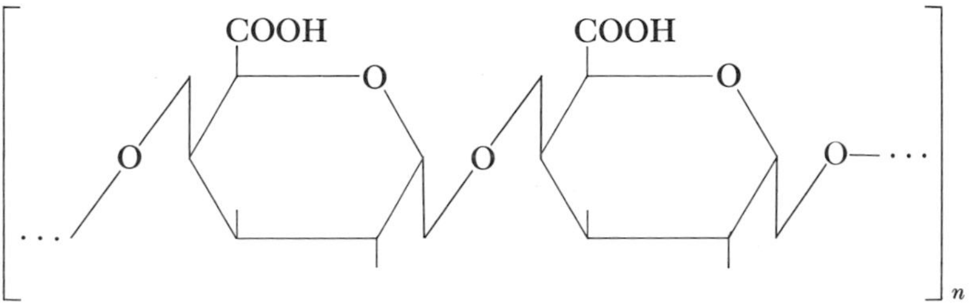

The shells of crustaceans contain chitin, a polymer of N-acetyl-D-glucosamine.

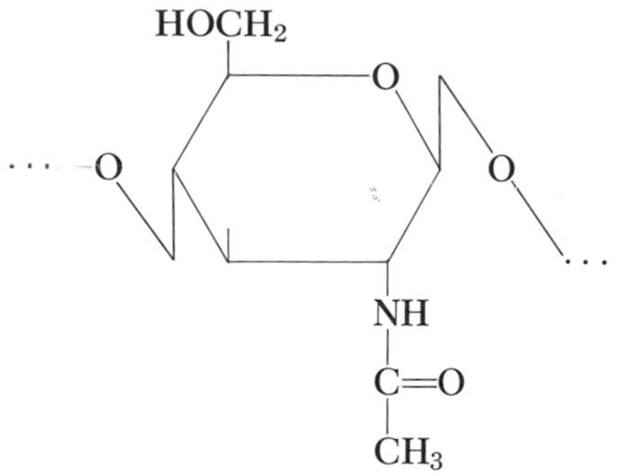

$$HOCH_2$$

chitin

One example of a structural polysaccharide in higher animals may be cited; this is hyaluronic acid.   Hyaluronic acid refers to a mucopolysaccharide found in such tissues as the eye and the umbilical cord.   It may have a molecular weight as large as 5,000,000 and consists of repeating units of D-glucuronic acid and N-acetyl-D-glucosamine.   The mucopoly-

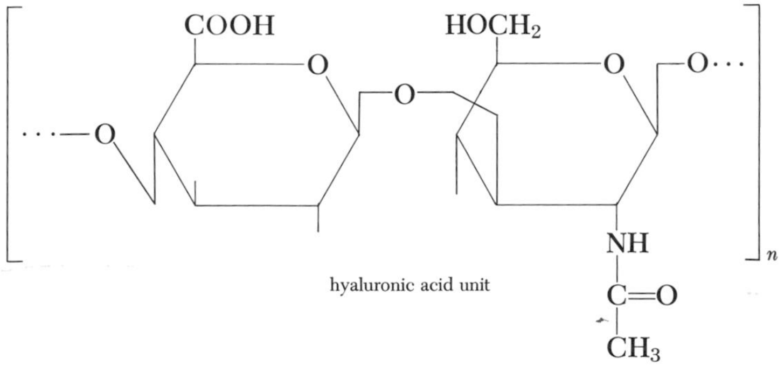

hyaluronic acid unit

saccharides may also contain sulfate ester groups on the C-6 position of the N-acetyl-D-glucosamine.   These polymers, known as chondroitins, are found in cartilage, tendons, and skin.   In the cell the mucopolysaccharides may exist as carbohydrate-protein complexes known as glycoproteins.

REFERENCES

1. *The Carbohydrates*, edited by W. Pigman, Academic Press, New York, revised edition, 1957.
2. E. G. V. Percival, *Structural Carbohydrate Chemistry*, Prentice-Hall, New York, 1950.
    These two books are valuable sources of detailed information about the structure and chemical properties of carbohydrates.

Three

Lipids ✓ ~~read~~

Introduction

Lipids are characterized by their sparing insolubility in water and considerable solubility in organic solvents, physical properties which reflect their hydrophobic, hydrocarbon nature. Lipids, a rather heterogeneous class of compounds, are traditionally classified as (a) simple lipids, (b) compound lipids, and (c) derived lipids. All classes are widely distributed in nature.

Simple Lipids

FATTY ACIDS

Acid or base hydrolysis of simple lipids releases 3 moles of long-chain *fatty acids* and 1 mole of the trihydroxyl alcohol *glycerol*. The esters are called triglycerides and their structure is:

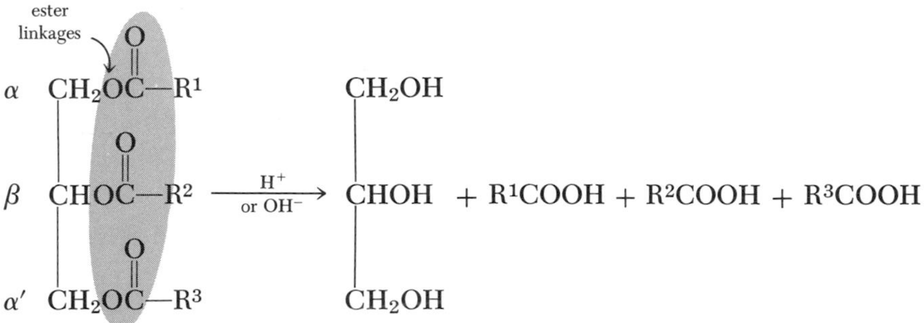

$$
\begin{array}{llll}
 & \overset{\displaystyle O}{\underset{\displaystyle \parallel}{}} & & \\
\alpha & CH_2OC-R^1 & & CH_2OH \\
 & \overset{\displaystyle O}{\underset{\displaystyle \parallel}{}} & & \\
\beta & CHOC-R^2 & \xrightarrow[\text{or } OH^-]{H^+} & CHOH \; + R^1COOH + R^2COOH + R^3COOH \\
 & \overset{\displaystyle O}{\underset{\displaystyle \parallel}{}} & & \\
\alpha' & CH_2OC-R^3 & & CH_2OH \\
\end{array}
$$

ester linkages (pointing to O)

triglyceride   [in base called saponification]   glycerol   fatty acids

The great majority of lipids are triglycerides, which may exist in the solid or liquid form depending on the nature of the constituent fatty acids. Thus most plant oils contain a large proportion of unsaturated fatty acids such as oleic, linoleic, or linolenic acid with low melting points and are liquid, whereas in many animals a high proportion of saturated fatty acids, such as palmitic and stearic acid, of higher melting points, confers at room temperature a semisolid or solid property to the fat.   Table 3-1 collects some of the naturally occurring fatty acids, their structures, and their melting points.

Far less widespread but equally important are the waxes, esters of long-chain fatty acids and monohydroxy alcohols.   The alcohols include high-molecular-weight hydrocarbon compounds ranging from C_{16} to C_{36}; the acids range from C_{24} to C_{36}.   Being highly insoluble and having a fully reduced hydrocarbon chain, these waxes are unusually inert

Table 3-1.   Structure

Acid	Structure	Melting Point
Saturated Fatty Acids		
Lauric acid	$CH_3CH_2CH_2CH_2CH_2CH_2CH_2CH_2CH_2$ $-CH_2CH_2COOH$	44°
Myristic acid	$CH_3(CH_2)_{12}COOH$	54°
Palmitic acid	$CH_3(CH_2)_{14}COOH$	63°
Stearic acid	$CH_3(CH_2)_{16}COOH$	70°
Arachidic acid	$CH_3(CH_2)_{18}COOH$	75°
Behenic acid	$CH_3(CH_2)_{20}COOH$	80°
Lignoceric acid	$CH_3(CH_2)_{22}COOH$	84°
Unsaturated Fatty Acids		
Oleic acid	$CH_3(CH_2)_7CH\overset{cis}{=\!=}CH(CH_2)_7COOH$	
Vaccenic acid	$CH_3(CH_2)_5CH\overset{cis}{=\!=}CH(CH_2)_9COOH$	
Ricinoleic acid	$CH_3(CH_2)_5CHOHCH_2CH\!=\!\!CH(CH_2)_7COOH$	
Linoleic acid	$CH_3(CH_2)_4(CH\!=\!\!CHCH_2)_2(CH_2)_6COOH$	
Linolenic acid	$CH_3CH_2(CH\!=\!\!CHCH_2)_3(CH_2)_6COOH$	
Arachidonic acid	$CH_3(CH_2)_4(CH\!=\!\!CHCH_2)_4(CH_2)_2COOH$	
Unusual Fatty Acids		
α Elaeostearic acid	$CH_3(CH_2)_3CH\overset{trans}{=\!=}CHCH\overset{trans}{=\!=}CHCH\overset{cis}{=\!=}CH$ $-(CH_2)_7COOH$ (conjugated)	
Tauric acid	$CH_3(CH_2)_{10}C\!\equiv\!C(CH_2)_4COOH$	
Isanic acid	$CH_2\!=\!\!CH(CH_2)_4C\!\equiv\!C\!-\!C\!\equiv\!C(CH_2)_7COOH$	
Lactobacillic acid	$CH_3(CH_2)_5\overset{\displaystyle CH_2}{\overset{\diagup\ \diagdown}{CH\!-\!\!CH}}(CH_2)_9COOH$	
9,10 Epoxyoctadecanoic acid	$CH_3(CH_2)_7\overset{\displaystyle O}{\overset{\diagup\ \diagdown}{CH\!-\!\!CH}}(CH_2)_7COOH$	

chemically.   Beeswax, sperm-whale wax, and carnauba wax are typical examples.

REACTIVITIES

The chemical reactivities of simple lipids reflect the reactivity of the ester linkage and the degree of unsaturation in the hydrocarbon chain. Since free fatty acids occur only to a very limited extent in the cell, the major proportion is found bound as esters (triglycerides).

Ester bonds are susceptible to both acid and base hydrolysis.   Acid hydrolysis differs from base hydrolysis in that the former is reversible and the latter irreversible.   The last step in base hydrolysis is irrevers-

acid hydrolysis:

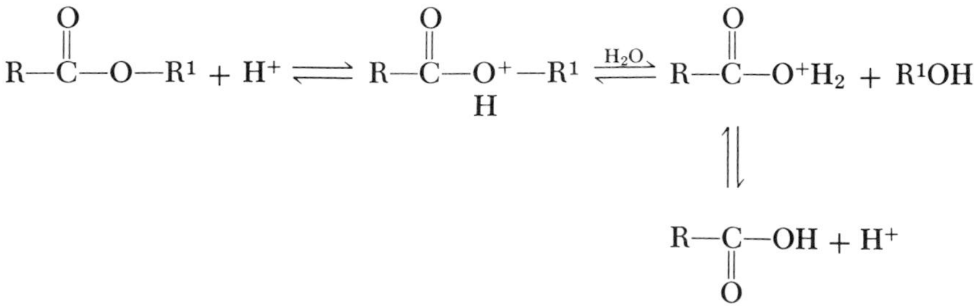

$$R-\overset{\overset{\displaystyle O}{\|}}{C}-O-R^1 + H^+ \rightleftharpoons R-\overset{\overset{\displaystyle O}{\|}}{C}-\underset{H}{O^+}-R^1 \xrightarrow{H_2O} R-\overset{\overset{\displaystyle O}{\|}}{C}-O^+H_2 + R^1OH$$

$$\updownarrow$$

$$R-\underset{\underset{\displaystyle O}{\|}}{C}-OH + H^+$$

base hydrolysis:

$$R-\underset{\underset{\displaystyle O}{\overset{\displaystyle\|}{\,}}}{C}-O-R^1 \longleftrightarrow R-\underset{O\delta^-}{\overset{\delta+}{C}}-O-R^1 \xrightarrow{OH^-} \left[R-\underset{O\delta^-}{\overset{\overset{\displaystyle H}{\overset{\displaystyle O}{|}}}{C}}-O-R^1 \right]$$

$$\updownarrow$$

$$R^1O^- + R-\underset{\underset{\displaystyle O}{\|}}{\overset{\overset{\displaystyle H}{\overset{\displaystyle O}{|}}}{C}} \xrightarrow[\text{irreversible}]{\text{in base}} R-\overset{\overset{\displaystyle O^-}{|}}{C}=O$$
$$+$$
$$R^1OH$$

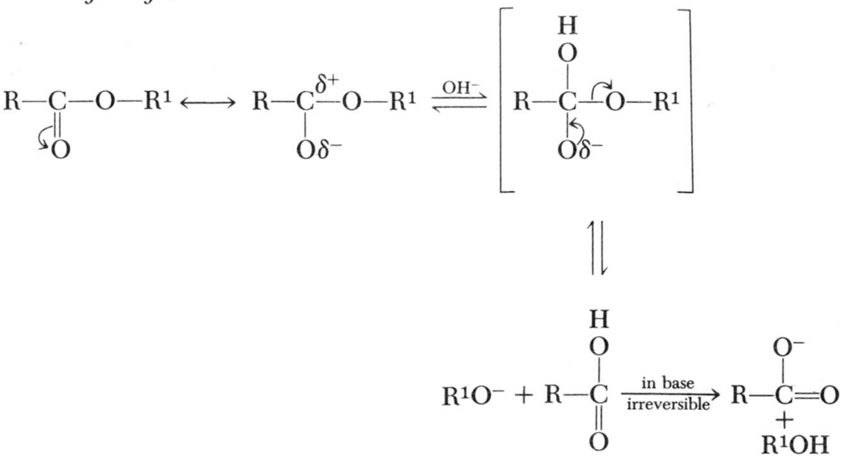

ible because in the presence of excess base the acid occurs as the fully dissociated anion which has no tendency to react with alcohols.   In acid hydrolysis the system is essentially reversible in all its steps and reaches an equilibrium rather than going to completion. Thus strong bases are used for saponification to hydrolyze the ester bonds in the simple and complex lipids.

Free fatty acids undergo dissociation in water:

$$RCOOH \rightleftharpoons RCOO^- + H^+$$

$$K_a = \frac{[H^+][RCOO^-]}{[RCOOH]}$$

Since $pK_a = -\log K_a$, the acid strength is determined by the dissociation. Thus the pK_a of most fatty acids is about 4.76–5.0. Stronger acids have lower pK_a values and weaker acids have higher pK_a values. The effective concentration of an acid is also an important factor. Since acetic acid is very soluble in water, its acid properties are readily measured. On the other hand, palmitic acid with its long, hydrophobic, hydrocarbon side chain is highly insoluble in water; consequently, its acid properties are not readily measurable. See Chapter 1 for a thorough discussion of acid dissociation and Appendix 2 for a consideration of acid-strengthening groups.

Other properties of fatty acids reflect the nature of their hydrocarbon chains. Naturally occurring saturated fatty acids that have from one to eight carbon atoms are liquid, whereas those with more carbon atoms are solids. Stearic acid has a melting point of 70°C but, with the introduction of one double bond, as in oleic acid, the melting point drops to 14°C, and the addition of more double bonds further lowers the melting point. When a double bond is found in the hydrocarbon chain of a fatty acid, geometric isomerism occurs. Most unsaturated fatty acids are found as the unstable *cis* isomers rather than as the more stable *trans* isomers.

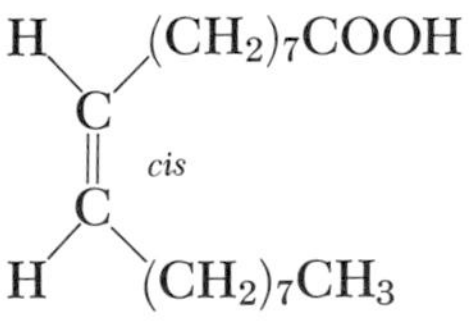

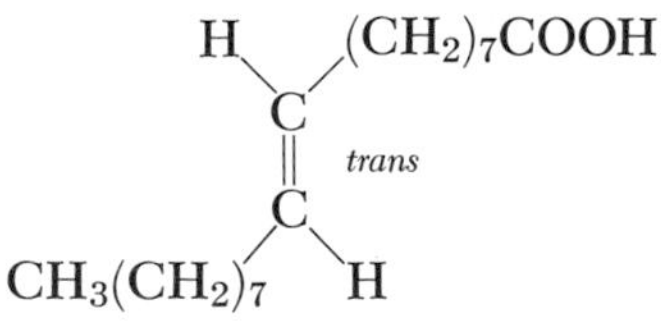

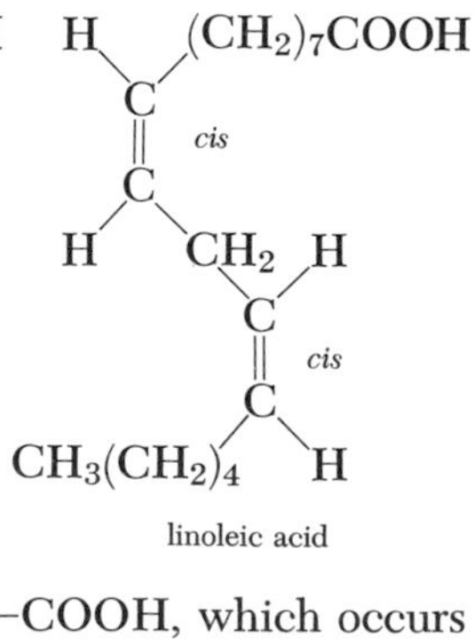

Vaccenic acid $CH_3-(CH_2)_5-CH=CH(CH_2)_9-COOH$, which occurs in animal fats in small quantities, is the *trans* isomer. In addition to the isomeric double-bond property, another typical structural property of the naturally occurring fatty acids is the nonconjugated double-bond system of the polyunsaturated fatty acids.   Linoleic acid is an example of the nonconjugated type.

$$-CH_2-CH=CH-CH_2-CH=CH-CH_2-$$ Nonconjugated double-bond system

$$-CH_2-CH=CH-CH=CH-CH=CH-CH_2-$$ Conjugated double-bond system

These two types of double-bond system exhibit important differences in chemical reactivity.   The nonconjugated or 1,4 pentadiene system has a *methylene* group flanked by double bonds on both sides and is directly attacked by oxygen.

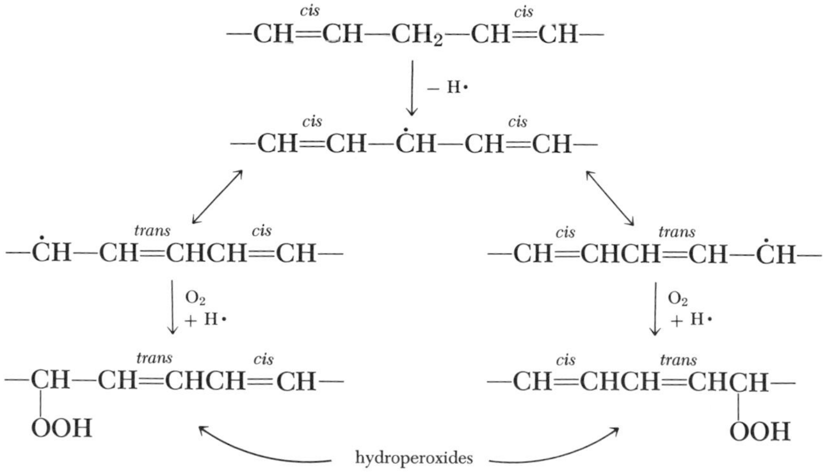

During autoxidation isomerization of the *cis* to the *trans* configuration occurs, and a conjugated system develops.   This structure is then attacked by molecular oxygen to yield hydroperoxides, which in turn undergo secondary reactions yielding epoxides

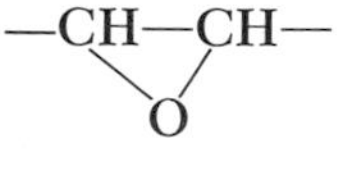

and glycols:

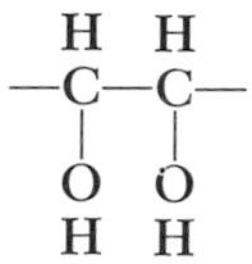

An important polyunsaturated fatty acid is α-elaeostearic acid, the chief acid in tung oil, which is isomeric with linolenic acid but differs from it in having a conjugated triene system.   Its structure is as shown,

$$\overset{trans}{CH_3(CH_2)_3CH}=\overset{trans}{CHCH}=\overset{cis}{CHCH}=CH(CH_2)_7COOH$$

and it has valuable properties as a drying oil since it polymerizes readily.

SOME INTERESTING FATTY ACIDS

Several unusual fatty acids have been isolated and characterized from different sources. Chaulmoogric acid, for example, found in the seeds of a tropical plant family (*Flacourtiaceae*), has a cyclopentenyl ring with the structure:

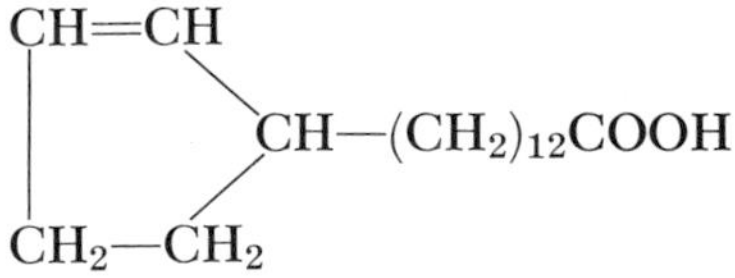

$$
\begin{array}{c}
CH=CH \\
| \qquad \diagdown \\
\qquad CH-(CH_2)_{12}COOH \\
| \qquad \diagup \\
CH_2-CH_2
\end{array}
$$

chaulmoogric acid

Lactobacillic acid, which is found in the lipids of some bacteria, including *Lactobacillus arabinosus,* is an acid with a cyclopropane ring.

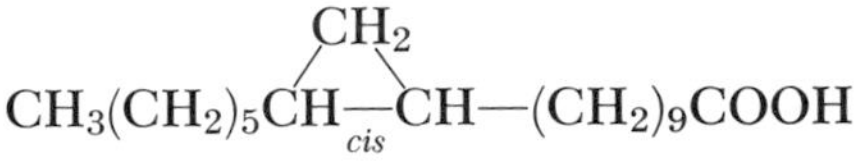

$$
\begin{array}{c}
CH_2 \\
\diagup \quad \diagdown \\
CH_3(CH_2)_5CH-CH-(CH_2)_9COOH \\
\qquad \textit{cis}
\end{array}
$$

lactobacillic acid

A most unusual acid, nemotinic acid, is excreted into the growth medium by a *Basidiomycete* mold. It is remarkable because it contains every known form of carbon-to-carbon linkage and is the first example of a naturally occurring compound that is optically active by reason of the allene group. Another acid of interest is the 9,10 epoxyoctadecanoic

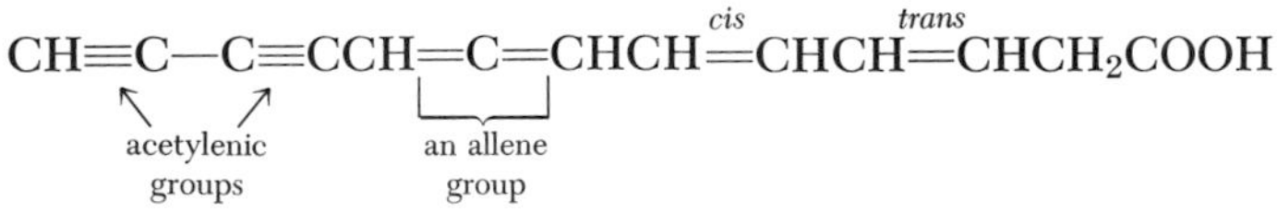

$$CH\equiv C-C\equiv CCH=C=\overset{cis}{CHCH}=\overset{trans}{CHCH}=CHCH_2COOH$$

acetylenic   an allene
groups   group

nemotinic acid

acid which makes up 20 per cent of the total fatty acids in the spores of certain rusts.

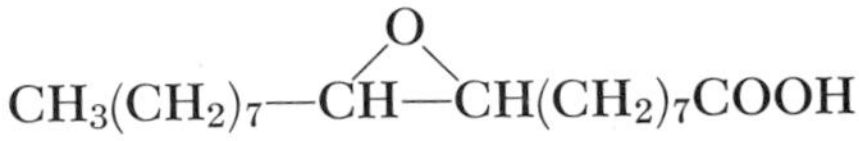

$$
\begin{array}{c}
O \\
\diagup \diagdown \\
CH_3(CH_2)_7-CH-CH(CH_2)_7COOH
\end{array}
$$

epoxyoctadecanoic acid

SEPARATION AND ISOLATION OF LIPIDS AND
FATTY ACIDS

Much can be written about the techniques at present available for separation and isolation. For the separation of classes of lipids, silicic acid column chromatography developed by Hanahan and others has found extensive use. In principle, the lipids are adsorbed onto the silicic acid and then differentially eluted by solvents such as methanol and chloroform. By this technique triglycerides can be separated from phospholipids and steroids. These techniques have of course been greatly refined to permit careful fractionation of a lipid mixture.

The components of a mixture of fatty acids can be analyzed by two general techniques. One is reverse-phase paper chromatography in which free fatty acids, when placed on siliconized filter paper, move at different rates when the developing solvent is 85 per cent acetic acid. The other extremely powerful procedure is the well-known method of gas-liquid chromatography. This method is described in detail in Appendix 3. Because gas-liquid chromatography can so readily resolve a complex mixture of fatty acids into its individual components, the older methods of iodine number and saponification value that were formerly employed to characterize a mixture of fatty acids or triglycerides are rapidly falling into disuse and will not be discussed further.

Phosphatides

As the name implies, these complex lipids are so named because they contain phosphate. In addition they usually contain glycerol, fatty acids, and a nitrogenous base. Several phosphatides, which are considered as derivatives of phosphatidic acid, are listed in Table 3-2. The structure of phosphatidic acid is:

$$
\begin{array}{l}
CH_2OCOR^1 \\
| \\
CHOCOR^2 \\
| \qquad\qquad OH \\
\qquad\qquad\quad + \;\diagup \\
CH_2{-}O{-}P{-}O^- \\
\qquad\qquad\quad \diagdown OH
\end{array}
$$

phosphatidic acid

Phospholipids are widespread in both animal and plant tissues, and their general structures, regardless of their sources, are quite similar. Phospholipids, namely phosphatidyl aminoethanol, choline, and serine, are frequently associated with membranes. Indeed they must play a

Table 3-2.

Phosphatide	Usual Fatty Acid	Base	Common Name
Phosphatidyl choline: 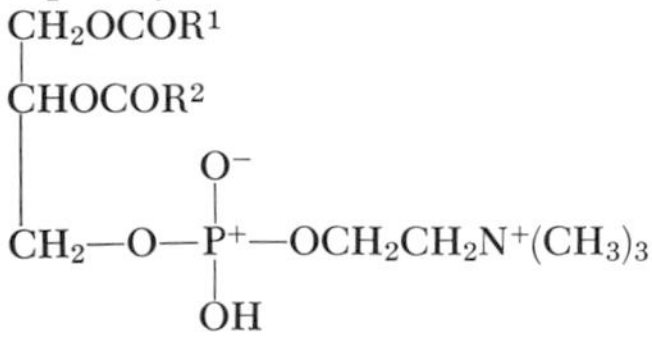 CH_2OCOR^1 $CHOCOR^2$ $CH_2-O-P^+-OCH_2CH_2N^+(CH_3)_3$ (with O^- and OH on P)	Oleic and Palmitic	Choline	Lecithin
Phosphatidyl aminoethanol: 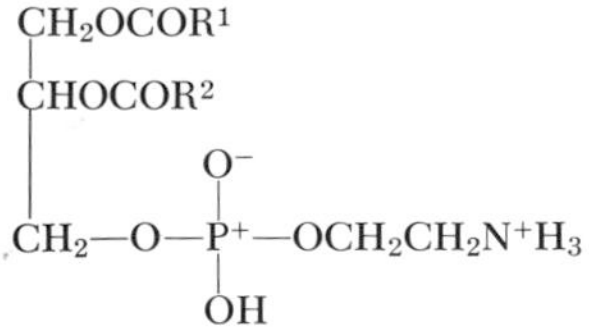 CH_2OCOR^1 $CHOCOR^2$ $CH_2-O-P^+-OCH_2CH_2N^+H_3$ (with O^- and OH on P)	Oleic and Palmitic	Aminoethanol	A cephalin
Phosphatidyl serine: 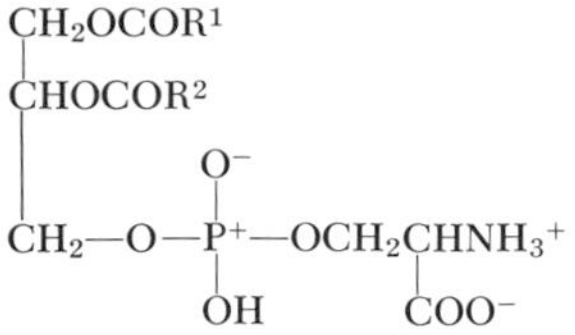 CH_2OCOR^1 $CHOCOR^2$ $CH_2-O-P^+-OCH_2CHNH_3^+$ (with O^- and OH on P; COO^-)	Oleic and Palmitic	Serine	A cephalin
Phosphatidal aminoethanol: 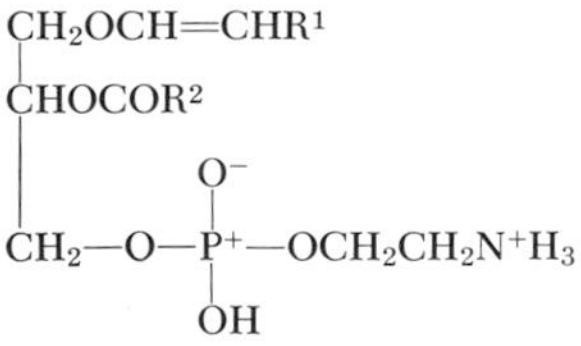 $CH_2OCH=CHR^1$ $CHOCOR^2$ $CH_2-O-P^+-OCH_2CH_2N^+H_3$ (with O^- and OH on P)	Palmityl α,β unsaturated ether; linoleic acid	Aminoethanol	Plasmalogen
Sphingomyelin: 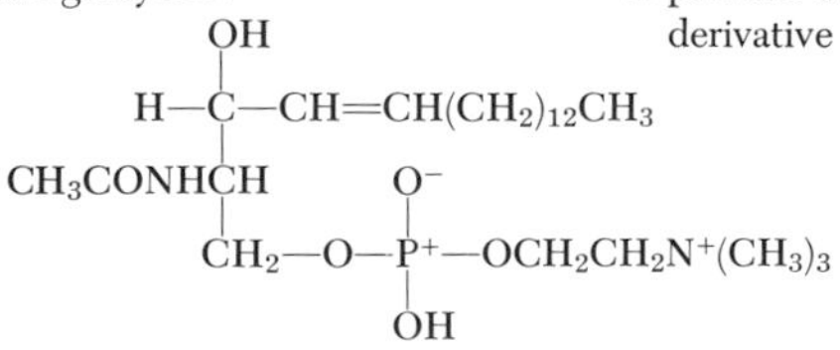 OH $H-C-CH=CH(CH_2)_{12}CH_3$ $CH_3CONHCH$ $CH_2-O-P^+-OCH_2CH_2N^+(CH_3)_3$ (with O^- and OH on P)	A palmitic acid derivative	Choline	

structural role in the membranous portion of the endoplasmic reticulum and of the mitochondrion.

The sphingomyelins are closely associated with brain tissue. They differ from the lecithins and cephalins in not containing glycerol; on hydrolysis, compounds of this group yield fatty acids, phosphoryl choline and sphingosine.

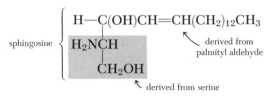

sphingosine $\begin{cases} \text{H—C(OH)CH=CH(CH}_2)_{12}\text{CH}_3 \\ \text{H}_2\text{NCH} \\ \text{CH}_2\text{OH} \end{cases}$

derived from palmityl aldehyde

derived from serine

Lipoproteins

In mammalian blood plasma much of the lipid material is associated with the plasma proteins in the form of lipoproteins. The lipid components consist of cholesterol esters and phospholipids and are held to the protein molecule by noncovalent forces.

Lipoproteins are also found in mitochondria, microsomes, and nuclei. The electron transport system in the mitochondria appears to contain large amounts of lipoprotein. Lamellar lipoprotein systems are also found in the myelin sheath of nerves, photoreceptive structures, chloroplasts, and retinal rods. These systems have a high degree of order in their complex organization.

REFERENCES

1. F. D. Gunstone, *The Chemistry of Fats and Fatty Acids,* John Wiley and Sons, New York, 1958.

    A good but brief account of lipid chemistry with a classical approach.

2. D. J. Hanahan, *Lipide Chemistry,* John Wiley and Sons, New York, 1960.

    Hanahan examines the progress of lipid chemistry in recent years and evaluates its status. A sound survey of the various topics of this field.

Four

Amino Acids and Proteins

Introduction

In this chapter a few of the more important properties of amino acids and proteins will be considered. Proteins are molecules of large molecular weight ranging from a few thousand to a million or more. The fundamental structural unit of proteins is the amino acid, as may be easily demonstrated by hydrolyzing purified proteins by chemical or enzymatic procedures. For example, a protein may be hydrolyzed to its constituent amino acids by refluxing with $6N$ HCl for 18 to 24 hours. Under refluxing the individual amino acids are released and may be isolated from the acid hydrolysate as their hydrochloride salts. All the naturally occurring amino acids are stable to this treatment with strong acid except tryptophan. This amino acid is obtained in very poor yield because it condenses, under the acidic conditions employed, with aldehydes (glucose and decomposition products of other amino acids) to form a black, insoluble residue. Proteins may also be hydrolyzed by boiling in alkali ($2N$ NaOH) for several hours. This procedure has two disadvantages, however; several of the amino acids (cystine, cysteine, serine, threonine, and arginine) are destroyed by alkaline hydrolysis and therefore cannot be isolated from the hydrolysate. In addition, treatment with alkali leads to the racemization of the amino acids. As we shall see, almost all the amino acids that occur naturally in proteins have the L-configuration. On hydrolysis with alkali the L-compound may be converted to a mixture of the D- and L-enantiomorphs.

The general formula for the naturally occurring amino acids may be represented as:

$$R-\underset{\underset{\text{H}}{|}}{\overset{\overset{\text{NH}_2}{|}}{C}}-\text{COOH}$$

Because the amino group is on the carbon atom adjàcent to the carboxyl group (the α-carbon), the amino acids having this general formula are known as alpha (α) amino acids. It is also apparent that if R in this formula is not equal to H, the α-carbon atom is asymmetric. Thus two different compounds that have this chemical formula may exist; one having the general formula shown, and the other being the enantiomorph or mirror image isomer of the first compound. It is clearly established that all the naturally occurring amino acids found in proteins have the same configuration. With reference to D-glyceraldehyde as a standard, the naturally occurring amino acids have the opposite or L-configuration. This relationship may be represented as follows for the amino acid L-serine.

$$\begin{array}{cc}
\underset{\substack{|\\ \text{H}-\text{C}-\text{OH}\\ |\\ \text{CH}_2\text{OH}}}{\overset{\text{H}\diagdown\diagup\text{O}}{\text{C}}} &
\underset{\substack{|\\ \text{NH}_2-\text{C}-\text{H}\\ |\\ \text{CH}_2\text{OH}}}{\overset{\text{HO}\diagdown\diagup\text{O}}{\text{C}}}\\
\text{D-glyceraldehyde} & \text{L-serine}
\end{array}$$

The determination of the relative configuration of the amino acids is one of the major accomplishments of synthetic organic chemistry. To determine it the groups attached to the asymmetric α-carbon atom had to be modified without changing the configuration about that atom except in a known manner. This involved the use of chemical reactions in which the mechanism of the reaction was known precisely. A key compound in interrelating L-serine and D-glyceraldehyde was D-lactic acid. Thus by known reactions, the details of which we shall not specify, D-glyceraldehyde was converted to D-lactic acid without disturbing the spatial configuration around the α-carbon atom.

$$\begin{array}{ccc}
\underset{\substack{|\\ \text{H}-\text{C}-\text{OH}\\ |\\ \text{CH}_2\text{OH}}}{\overset{\text{H}\diagdown\diagup\text{O}}{\text{C}}} & \longrightarrow &
\underset{\substack{|\\ \text{H}-\text{C}-\text{OH}\\ |\\ \text{CH}_3}}{\overset{\text{HO}\diagdown\diagup\text{O}}{\text{C}}}\\
\text{D-glyceraldehyde} & & \text{D-lactic acid}
\end{array}$$

When L-serine was converted to lactic acid, the lactic acid formed was found to be L-lactic acid, and thus the naturally occurring serine found in proteins was recognized to have the L-configuration with respect to D-glyceraldehyde.

$$\begin{array}{ccc}
\underset{\substack{|\\ \text{NH}_2-\text{C}-\text{H}\\ |\\ \text{CH}_2\text{OH}}}{\overset{\text{HO}\diagdown\diagup\text{O}}{\text{C}}} & \longrightarrow &
\underset{\substack{|\\ \text{HO}-\text{C}-\text{H}\\ |\\ \text{CH}_3}}{\overset{\text{HO}\diagdown\diagup\text{O}}{\text{C}}}\\
\text{L-serine} & & \text{L-lactic acid}
\end{array}$$

As with the carbohydrates, it is important to stress again that the use of L- and D- refers only to the absolute configuration of these compounds and does not provide any information regarding the direction in which these optically active compounds rotate polarized light.

Structure of the Naturally Occurring Amino Acids

The amino acids commonly obtained on hydrolysis of proteins may be conveniently classified into three groups, the aliphatic, aromatic, and heterocyclic amino acids, with appropriate subclasses. The structure of the common amino acids, together with certain of their distinctive features, are given next.

GROUP I. ALIPHATIC

Amino Acids Containing One Carboxyl Group and One Amino Group
1. Glycine

$$NH_2-CH_2-COOH$$

Glycine, the simplest amino acid, does not possess an asymmetric carbon atom. (In the general formula, R = H.)
2. L-Alanine

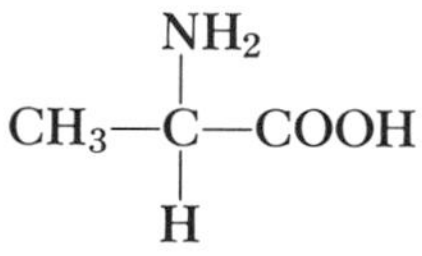

$$CH_3-\underset{\underset{H}{|}}{\overset{\overset{NH_2}{|}}{C}}-COOH$$

3. L-Valine

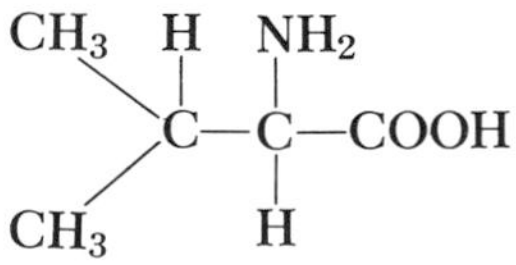

$$\underset{CH_3}{\overset{CH_3}{>}}C-\underset{\underset{H}{|}}{\overset{\overset{H}{|}}{C}}-\underset{\underset{H}{|}}{\overset{\overset{NH_2}{|}}{C}}-COOH$$

4. L-Leucine

$$\underset{CH_3}{\overset{CH_3}{>}}C-CH_2-\underset{\underset{H}{|}}{\overset{\overset{NH_2}{|}}{C}}-COOH$$

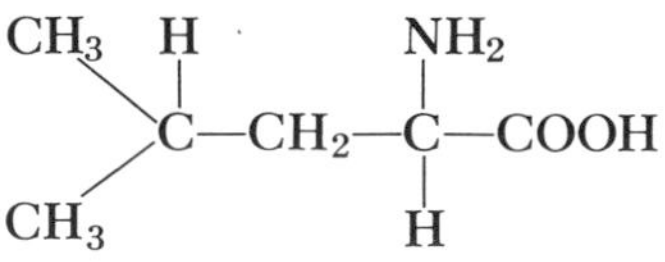

5. L-Isoleucine

$$\underset{CH_3}{\overset{CH_3-CH_2}{>}}C-\underset{\underset{H}{|}}{\overset{\overset{NH_2}{|}}{C}}-COOH$$

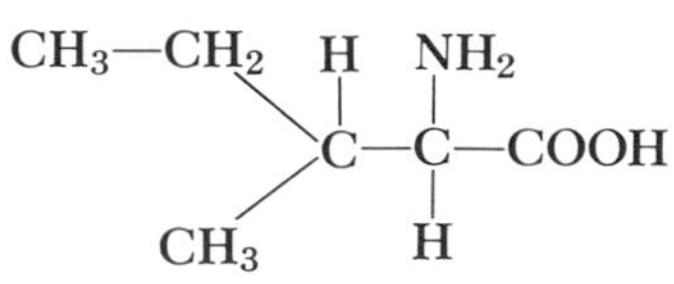

6. L-Serine

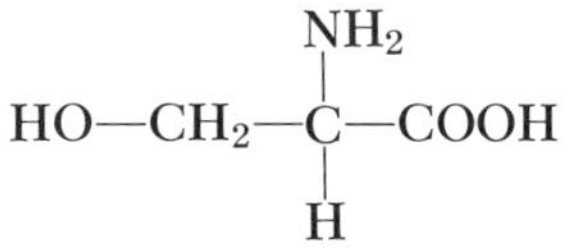

$$\text{HO—CH}_2\overset{\overset{\displaystyle NH_2}{|}}{\underset{\underset{\displaystyle H}{|}}{\text{C}}}\text{—COOH}$$

7. L-Threonine

$$\text{CH}_3\overset{\overset{\displaystyle H}{|}}{\underset{\underset{\displaystyle O}{|}}{\text{C}}}\overset{\overset{\displaystyle NH_2}{|}}{\underset{\underset{\displaystyle H}{|}}{\text{C}}}\text{—COOH}$$

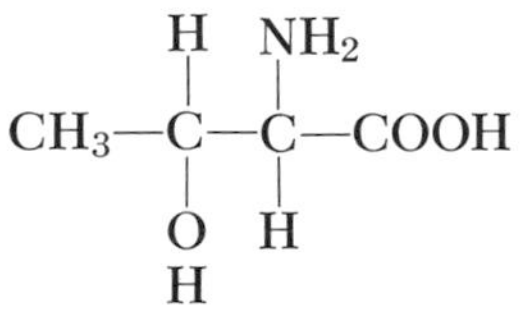

L-Threonine, together with L-isoleucine and L-hydroxyproline, contains an additional asymmetric carbon atom. Thus there are four possible isomers of isoleucine, hydroxyproline, and threonine. Of the four, only one is found to occur naturally in proteins.

Monamino-Monocarboxylic Amino Acids Containing Sulfur

8. L-Cysteine

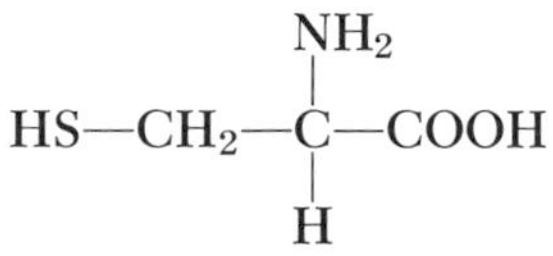

$$\text{HS—CH}_2\overset{\overset{\displaystyle NH_2}{|}}{\underset{\underset{\displaystyle H}{|}}{\text{C}}}\text{—COOH}$$

L-Cysteine, although naturally occurring in proteins, is readily oxidized during hydrolysis to its disulfide, cystine. The latter amino acid is also known to occur in native proteins and is most important in establishing protein structure. This oxidation reaction may be represented as:

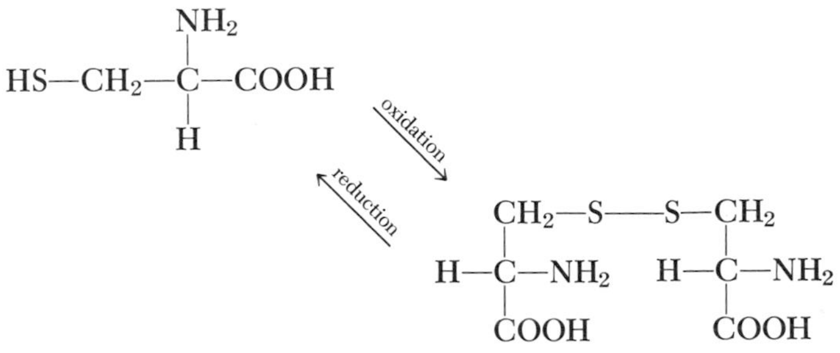

$$\text{HS—CH}_2\overset{\overset{\displaystyle NH_2}{|}}{\underset{\underset{\displaystyle H}{|}}{\text{C}}}\text{—COOH}$$

oxidation
reduction

$$\text{CH}_2\text{—S——S—CH}_2$$
$$\text{H—C—NH}_2 \quad \text{H—C—NH}_2$$
$$\text{COOH} \qquad \text{COOH}$$

9. L-Cystine

$$\text{CH}_2\text{—S——S—CH}_2$$
$$\text{H—C—NH}_2 \quad \text{H—C—NH}_2$$
$$\text{COOH} \qquad \text{COOH}$$

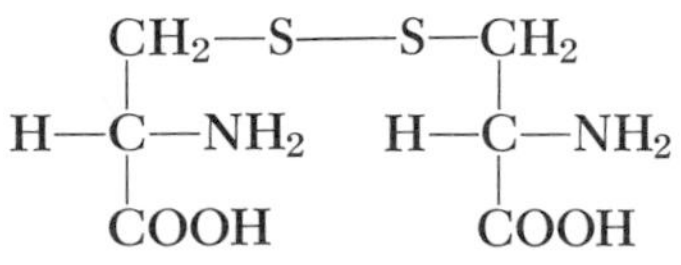

Cystine, in the presence of appropriate reducing agents, can be reduced to yield two molecules of L-cysteine.

10. L-Methionine

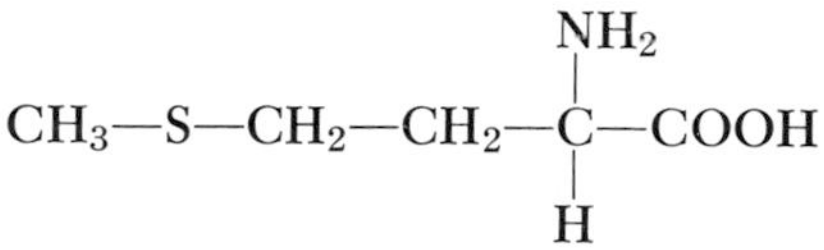

$$CH_3-S-CH_2-CH_2-\underset{\underset{H}{|}}{\overset{\overset{NH_2}{|}}{C}}-COOH$$

Dicarboxylic Amino Acids

Since these amino acids contain an additional carboxyl group, aqueous solutions of the free amino acid will be acidic.

11. L-Glutamic acid

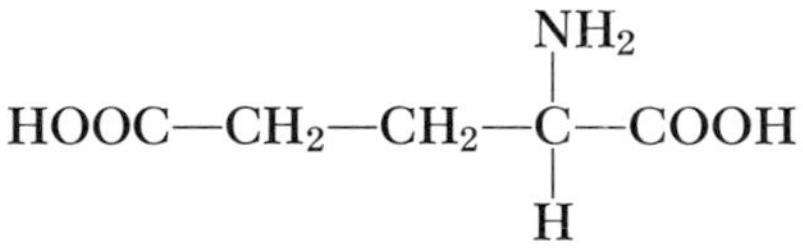

$$HOOC-CH_2-CH_2-\underset{\underset{H}{|}}{\overset{\overset{NH_2}{|}}{C}}-COOH$$

12. L-Aspartic acid

$$HOOC-CH_2-\underset{\underset{H}{|}}{\overset{\overset{NH_2}{|}}{C}}-COOH$$

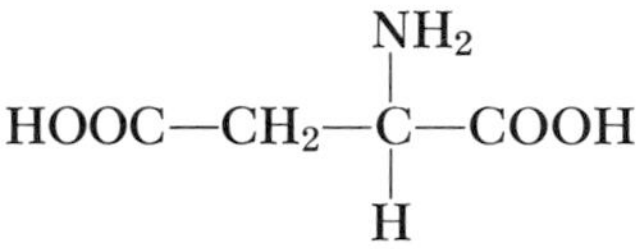

Basic Amino Acids

13. L-Lysine

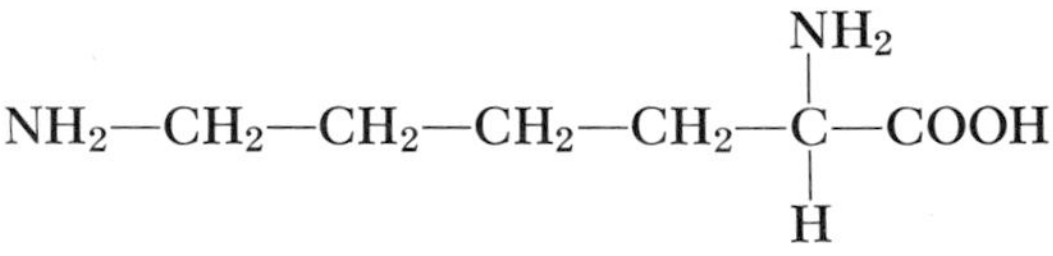

$$NH_2-CH_2-CH_2-CH_2-CH_2-\underset{\underset{H}{|}}{\overset{\overset{NH_2}{|}}{C}}-COOH$$

Aqueous solutions of lysine are basic because lysine has the additional amino group in its structure.

14. L-Arginine

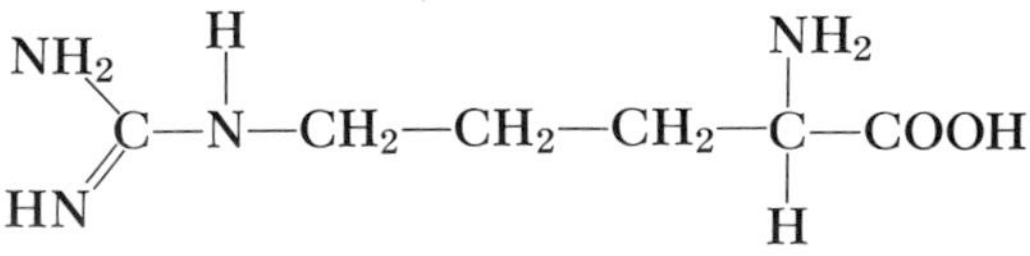

$$\underset{HN}{\overset{NH_2}{\diagdown}}C-\underset{\overset{|}{H}}{N}-CH_2-CH_2-CH_2-\underset{\underset{H}{|}}{\overset{\overset{NH_2}{|}}{C}}-COOH$$

This amino acid is strongly basic because of its guanidino group. It is a constituent of many proteins and especially of those basic proteins known as histones and protamines which are associated with nucleic acids in cell nuclei.

15. L-Histidine

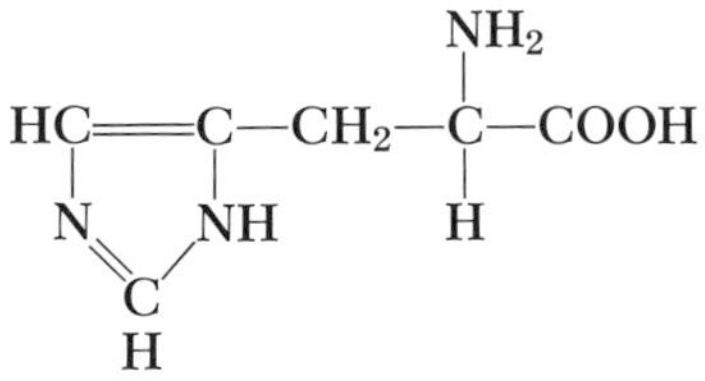

$$HC\!\!=\!\!\overset{\displaystyle |}{\underset{\displaystyle NH}{C}}\!-\!CH_2\!-\!\overset{\displaystyle NH_2}{\underset{\displaystyle H}{C}}\!-\!COOH$$

(imidazole ring with N, NH, and C—H below)

Histidine, which possess the weakly basic imidazole function, can also be classified as a heterocyclic amino acid.

GROUP II. AROMATIC AMINO ACIDS

These amino acids contain the aromatic or benzenoid ring.

16. L-Phenylalanine

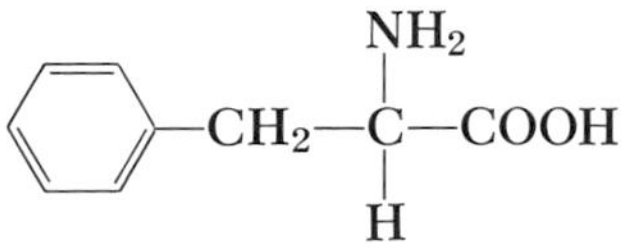

$$\text{(benzene ring)}\!-\!CH_2\!-\!\overset{\displaystyle NH_2}{\underset{\displaystyle H}{C}}\!-\!COOH$$

17. L-Tyrosine

$$HO\!-\!\text{(benzene ring)}\!-\!CH_2\!-\!\overset{\displaystyle NH_2}{\underset{\displaystyle H}{C}}\!-\!COOH$$

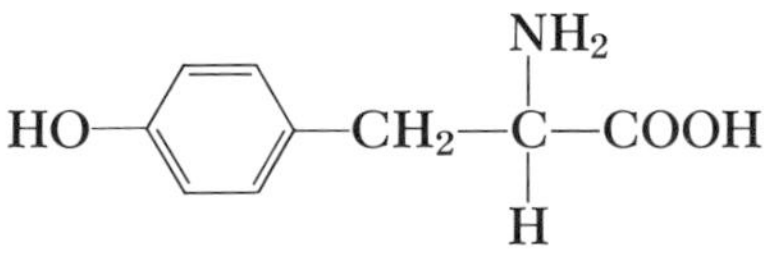

This amino acid, together with tryptophan, is responsible for the intense absorption of ultraviolet light in the region of 260–290 mμ that is exhibited by most proteins.   Tyrosine is also responsible for the xanthoproteic reaction, a familiar test for protein.   When tyrosine or proteins containing tyrosine are treated with HNO_3, the aromatic ring is readily nitrated and the product is yellow.   The intensity of the color is intensified in the presence of alkali.

GROUP III. HETEROCYCLIC AMINO ACIDS

18. L-Tryptophan

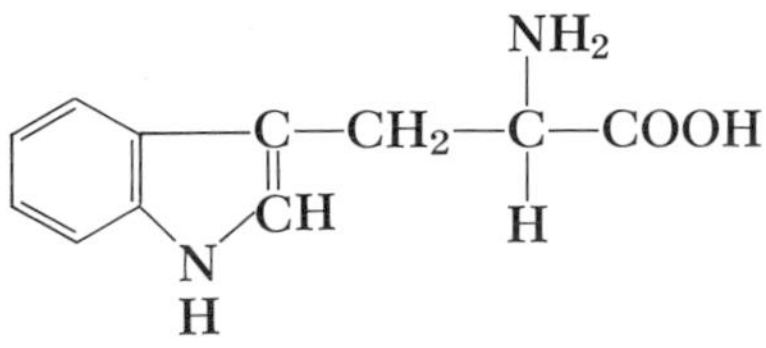

$$\text{(indole ring)}\!-\!C\!-\!CH_2\!-\!\overset{\displaystyle NH_2}{\underset{\displaystyle H}{C}}\!-\!COOH$$

19. L-Proline

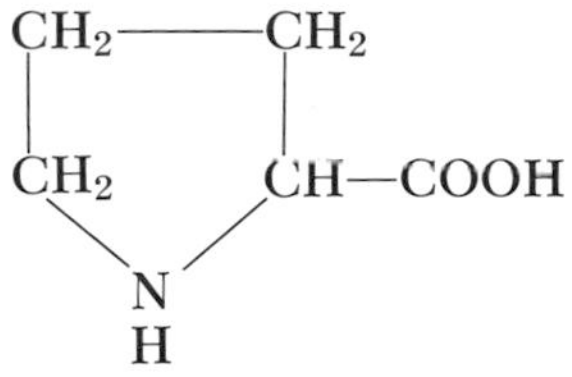

$$CH_2 \text{---} CH_2$$
$$CH_2 \qquad CH\text{---}COOH$$
$$N$$
$$H$$

20. L-Hydroxyproline

$$OH$$
$$CH \text{---} CH_2$$
$$CH_2 \qquad CH\text{---}COOH$$
$$N$$
$$H$$

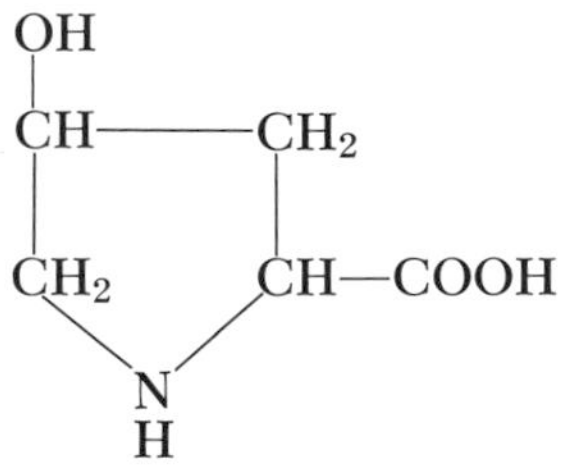

The heterocyclic nitrogen of the prolines is not a primary amino nitrogen atom but rather a secondary amine. Therefore the prolines are substituted α-amino acids.

The twenty amino acids are usually found as constituents of proteins. Some are limited in distribution, however, but may be present in high concentrations in a few proteins, and hence they warrant consideration as common amino acids. Hydroxyproline, for example, has a limited distribution but constitutes more than 12 per cent of the composition of collagen.

Two amide derivatives of amino acids are also found as constituents of proteins; these are the amides of aspartic and glutamic acids. Asparagine, the β-amide of aspartic acid, has been known since the beginning of the nineteenth century, when it was isolated from asparagus, in which it occurs as the free amide. The amide, which is a constituent of a great many proteins, may be readily hydrolyzed to aspartic acid and NH_3 by acid.

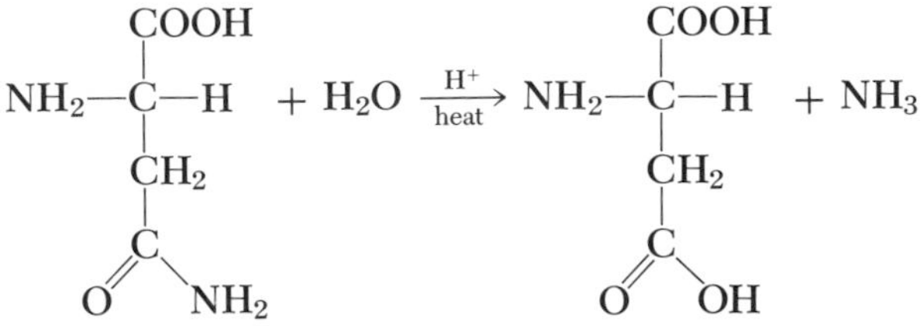

$$COOH \qquad\qquad\qquad COOH$$
$$NH_2\text{---}C\text{---}H \; + H_2O \xrightarrow[\text{heat}]{H^+} NH_2\text{---}C\text{---}H \; + NH_3$$
$$CH_2 \qquad\qquad\qquad CH_2$$
$$C \qquad\qquad\qquad\qquad C$$
$$O \quad NH_2 \qquad\qquad\quad O \quad OH$$

L-asparagine   L-aspartic acid

The γ-amide of glutamic acid, glutamine, also occurs both free in nature and as a constituent of numerous proteins.

$$NH_2—\overset{\displaystyle O}{\underset{\displaystyle}{\overset{\|}{C}}}—CH_2—CH_2—\overset{\displaystyle NH_2}{\underset{\displaystyle H}{C}}—COOH$$

An isomer of alanine, β-alanine, occurs in nature not as a constituent of proteins but as the free amino acid.   It is also a component of the important vitamin pantothenic acid and of coenzyme A, as well as of the peptides carnosine and anserine found in muscle.

Two other amino acids, ornithine and citrulline, are of interest as components of the metabolic sequence leading to the formation of urea. These amino acids are not usually found as constituents of proteins but do occur in the free form in animal tissues.   Citrulline, as the name implies, was first isolated from the watermelon.

Titration of Amino Acids

Two readily observable properties of amino acids provide information about their structure both in the solid state and in solution.   For example, the amino acids with certain exceptions are generally soluble in H_2O and are quite insoluble in nonpolar organic solvents such as ether, chloroform, and acetone.   This observation is not in keeping with the known properties of carboxylic acids and organic amines.   Aliphatic and aromatic carboxylic acids, particularly those having several carbon atoms, have limited solubility in H_2O but are readily soluble in organic solvents.   Similarly the higher amines are usually soluble in organic solvents but not in H_2O.

Another physical property of amino acids that relates to their structure is that their melting points are quite high and often result in decomposition; the melting points of the solid carboxylic acids and amines are usually low and sharp.   These two physical properties of the amino acids are not consistent with their general structural formula (p. 58), which represents them as containing nonpolar carboxyl and amino groups.   The solubilities and melting points rather suggest structures with charged, highly polar groups.

A deeper insight into the structure of amino acids in solution is gained from considering the behavior of amino acids as electrolytes. Since alanine, for example, contains both a carboxyl and an amino group, it should react with acids and alkalis.   Such compounds are referred to as *amphoteric substances.*   If a solid sample of alanine is dissolved in H_2O, the pH of this solution will be approximately neutral. If electrodes are placed in solution and a difference in potential is placed across the electrodes, the amino acid will not migrate in the electric field. This result is in keeping with the representation of the amino acid as a neutral, uncharged molecule. If alkali is added to the solution of the amino acid, alanine becomes negatively charged and will migrate to the positive anode. This might be represented as in reac-

$$
\begin{array}{c}
\text{COOH} \\
| \\
\text{NH}_2\text{—C—H} \\
| \\
\text{CH}_3
\end{array}
\quad
\begin{array}{c}
\overset{\text{OH}^-}{\nearrow} \\
\\
\underset{\text{H}^+}{\searrow}
\end{array}
\quad
\begin{array}{cc}
\begin{array}{c}
\text{COO}^- \\
| \\
\text{NH}_2\text{—C—H} + \text{H}_2\text{O} \\
| \\
\text{CH}_3
\end{array} & (4\text{-}1) \\
\\
\begin{array}{c}
\text{COOH} \\
| \\
\text{NH}_3{}^+\text{—C—H} \\
| \\
\text{CH}_3
\end{array} & (4\text{-}2)
\end{array}
$$

tion 4-1, where hydroxyl ions are shown accepting a proton from the carboxyl group of the amino acid. Similarly, when acid is added to the reaction mixture, as indicated in reaction 4-2, the amino group of the amino acid accepts the H^+. It is observed experimentally that alanine, in acid solution, is positively charged and migrates toward the negative cathode in an electric field.

The error in this representation is clear, however, when we consider the titration curve of alanine in Figure 4-1. If 20 ml of $0.1M$ alanine in solution is titrated with $0.1M$ NaOH, a curve with an inflection point (that is, a pK_a) at pH 9.7 is obtained when 10 ml of $0.1M$ NaOH are added. In other words, at pH 9.7 some group that is capable of furnishing protons to react with the added alkali is half neutralized. Similarly, if $0.1M$ HCl is added to the solution of alanine, the other half of the titration curve is obtained, and a pK_a of 2.3 is reached when 10 ml of $0.1M$ HCl have been added. When alkali and acid are added to a neutral solution of alanine, the carboxyl and amino groups would be expected to react. According to reactions 4-1 and 4-2, the group with the pK_a of 9.7 represents the carboxyl function while that with the pK_a of 2.3 corresponds to the amino group.

It is extremely difficult to argue, however, that the carboxyl group of alanine has a pK_a of 9.7 when the pK_a's for acetic and propionic acid are 4.74 and 4.85 respectively. The structure of alanine does not differ sufficiently from that of propionic acid to lead us to suggest that the carboxyl group of the amino acid should be 10^5 times less acidic. As for the amino group, the pK_a of $NH_4{}^+$ is 9.26, and it is difficult to ac-

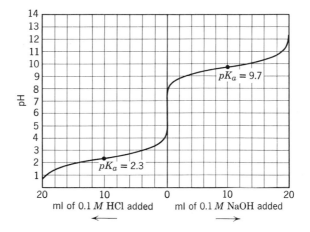

Fig. 4-1.   Titration curve obtained when 20 ml of 0.1M L-alanine is titrated with 0.1M NaOH and with 0.1M HCl.

count for the fact that, as presented in reaction 4-2, the amino group of alanine should be about 10^7 times as acidic as NH_4^+.

An alternative representation of the structure of the amphoteric amino acid in solution is the *Zwitterion* formula, first proposed by Bjerrum in 1923, in which the carboxyl group is represented as being ionized while the amino group, at neutral pH, is still protonated.   The *Zwitterionic* structure for alanine is

$$NH_3^+-\overset{\displaystyle COO^-}{\underset{\displaystyle CH_3}{C}}-H$$

The titration of the *Zwitterion* proceeds as follows: When alkali is added to a neutral solution of the amino acid it is the protons on the $-NH_3^+$ which are titrated, with the formula shown as a result.

$$NH_3^+-\overset{\displaystyle COO^-}{\underset{\displaystyle CH_3}{C}}-H$$

$$\xrightarrow{OH^-} NH_2-\overset{\displaystyle COO^-}{\underset{\displaystyle CH_3}{C}}-H \qquad (4\text{-}3)$$

$$\xrightarrow{H^+} NH_3^+-\overset{\displaystyle COOH}{\underset{\displaystyle CH_3}{C}}-H \qquad (4\text{-}4)$$

When acid is added to a neutral solution of the amino acid, the dissociated carboxyl group *accepts* the proton to form the protonated amino acid. When the *Zwitterion* is considered as the ionic form of the amino acid in solution, it is apparent that the amino group is the one furnishing the H^+ for neutralization of the alkali, and that its pK_a is 9.7. Similarly, the dissociated carboxyl group is the group titrated by acid and, at pH 2.3, the carboxyl group is half protonated. These observations are consistent with the observation that carboxylic acids have pK_a's less than 7 and organic amines have pK_a's greater than 7. Furthermore, the fact that the carboxyl group of alanine is a (hundredfold) stronger acid than acetic is due to the acid-strengthening properties of the α-amino group (see Appendix 2). It is the practice to assign the pK_a values in order of decreasing acidity; thus alanine has pK_1 of 2.3, which corresponds to the point of half neutralization of the carboxyl group. The pK_2 of 9.7 in turn corresponds to the pH of half neutralization of the protonated amino group ($-NH_3^+$).

From reaction 4-3 we see that the amino acid has a net charge of -1 in alkali; it will therefore migrate to the positively charged anode in an electric field. The amino acid will have a net charge of $+1$ in acid and will behave like a cation.

The titration curve constitutes evidence for the *Zwitterionic* nature of amino acids in solution. Observations on the physical properties of the solid amino acids are also consistent with amino acids being *Zwitterions* in the solid state. This accounts for their easy solubility in H_2O and their high melting points. The *Zwitterion* is essentially an internal salt, which should have a high melting point and be readily soluble in water. Additional evidence for the dipolar nature of the amphoteric amino acids is that the pK_a of 9.7 of alanine is lowered when the titration is performed in formaldehyde. It is lowered because formaldehyde forms a Schiff's base with amino groups which partially blocks the basic function of those groups. Other evidence of the *Zwitterionic* nature of all amino acids is found in their spectroscopic properties, their effects on the dielectric constant of aqueous solutions, and their titrations in organic solvents.

Those amino acids having more than one carboxyl or amino group will have corresponding pK_a values for them. Thus the pK_a for one of the carboxyl groups of aspartic is 2.1 while the pK_a for the second carboxyl and for the amino groups are 3.9 and 9.8 respectively. The titration curve for aspartic acid is shown in Figure 4-2.

It is informative to consider the various ionic species of aspartic acid that can exist at different pH values. We may start with the completely protonated form, that is, the form that will exist in strong acid where the concentration of H^+ is high. This form and its titration are

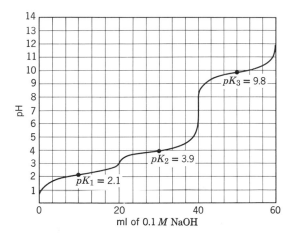

Fig. 4-2. Titration curve obtained when 20 ml of 0.1M aspartic hydrochloride is titrated with 0.1M NaOH.

represented in reaction 4-5 where alkali is added to react eventually with all the protons the amino acid can furnish. It is apparent, of course, that both the carboxyl groups and the protonated amino group are considered as Brönsted acids (Chapter 1, p. 17).

$$\begin{array}{ccccc}
\text{COOH} & & \text{COO}^- & & \\
| & & | & & \\
\text{NH}_3{}^+\!-\!\text{C}\!-\!\text{H} & \xrightarrow[\substack{\text{of} \\ \text{alkali} \\ \text{p}K_1 = 2.1}]{\text{1st eq.}} & \text{NH}_3{}^+\!-\!\text{C}\!-\!\text{H} & \xrightarrow[\substack{\text{of} \\ \text{alkali} \\ \text{p}K_2 = 3.9}]{\text{2nd eq.}} & \\
| & & | & & \\
\text{CH}_2 & & \text{CH}_2 & & \\
| & & | & & \\
\text{COOH} & & \text{COOH} & &
\end{array}$$

Net charge + 1   0

$$\begin{array}{ccccc}
& \text{COO}^- & & \text{COO}^- & \\
& | & & | & \\
\text{NH}_3{}^+\!-\!\text{C}\!-\!\text{H} & \xrightarrow[\substack{\text{of} \\ \text{alkali} \\ \text{p}K_3 = 9.8}]{\text{3rd eq.}} & \text{NH}_2\!-\!\text{C}\!-\!\text{H} & & (4\text{-}5) \\
& | & & | & \\
& \text{CH}_2 & & \text{CH}_2 & \\
& | & & | & \\
& \text{COO}^- & & \text{COO}^- &
\end{array}$$

-1 -2

The pK_a for half-neutralization of each of the protons that dissociate is listed in the diagram. Since there are two carboxyl groups, there is a question as to which of the two is more acidic and thus is to be assigned the pK_a of 2.1. The carboxyl group adjacent to the α-amino group is known to be the more acidic carboxyl function. Its acidity is due to the proximity of the charged NH_3^+ which, by repulsion of similar positive charges, increases the tendency of the proton on the α-carboxyl group to dissociate. In addition the net charge, which may be determined by visual inspection, is found under each form of the amino acid in reaction 4-5. The form having a net charge of 0 will not migrate in the electric field, of course. In the case of aspartic acid this form predominates when the stronger carboxyl group is ionized but the weaker is not. The ionic species with net charges of $+1$ and 0 will be present in equal amounts at pH 2.1 ($pK_1 = 2.1$). Similarly, at pH 3.9, the species with net charges of 0 and -1 will be present in equal quantity. At a pH intermediate between 2.1 and 3.9, that is at pH $= \dfrac{2.1 + 3.9}{2}$ or 3.0, the species with net charge of 0 will therefore predominate. This pH, at which the amino acid has a net charge of 0, is called the *isoionic point* or *pI*. The pI for a monocarboxy-monoamino acid is the average of the two pK_a's of that amino acid.

Some amino acids contain groups other than protonated carboxyl or amino groups which are capable of dissociating protons. Thus the sulfhydryl group of cysteine dissociates with a pK_a of 10.8.

$$
\begin{array}{ccc}
COO^- & & COO^- \\
| & & | \\
NH_2-C-H & \rightleftharpoons & NH_2-C-H + H^+ \\
| & & | \\
CH_2 & & CH_2 \\
| & & | \\
S & pK_3 = 10.8 & S_- \\
| & & \\
H & &
\end{array}
$$

Similarly, the guanidinium moiety of arginine dissociates to yield a proton at pH of 12.5.

$$
\begin{array}{ccc}
NH_2 & & NH_2 \\
\diagdown & & \diagdown \\
C=NH_2^+ & \rightleftharpoons & C=NH + H^+ \\
\diagup & & \diagup \\
HN & & HN \\
| & & | \\
R & pK_3 = 12.5 & R
\end{array}
$$

Other dissociable groups include the protonated nitrogen atom of the heterocyclic ring of histidine ($pK_a = 6.0$) and the phenolic hydroxyl ($pK_a = 10.1$) of tyrosine.

Reactions of Amino Acids

Probably the most important single chemical property of the amino acids is their ability to act as electrolytes due to the presence of dissociable groups in their molecules. We have discussed their ability to furnish and accept protons. Other properties dependent on the presence of carboxyl and amino groups in the amino acids will be described now.

The carboxyl groups of amino acids may be esterified with methyl or ethyl alcohol in the presence of acid catalysts. The esters so obtained are volatile, in contrast to the free amino acids; indeed, the preparation and fractional distillation of the methyl esters of the naturally occurring amino acids was one of the first procedures by which the amino acids were separated. Today gas chromatography may be used to separate and determine specially prepared esters of amino acids (Appendix 3). The esterification with ethanol may be given:

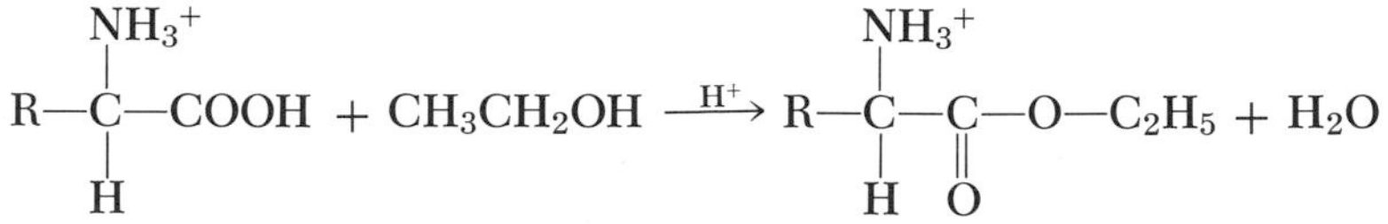

$$
\underset{\underset{H}{|}}{\overset{\overset{NH_3^+}{|}}{R-C-COOH}} + CH_3CH_2OH \xrightarrow{H^+} \underset{\underset{H}{|}\ \underset{O}{\|}}{\overset{\overset{NH_3^+}{|}}{R-C-C-O-C_2H_5}} + H_2O
$$

In protein molecules the carboxyl group of one amino acid is linked to the amino group of another amino acid. The structure linking the two amino acids is known as the peptide bond:

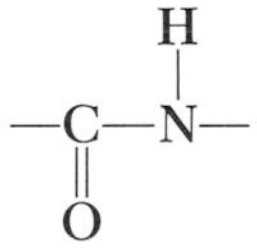

$$
\underset{\underset{O}{\|}}{\overset{\overset{H}{|}}{-C-N-}}
$$

This structure could be represented schematically as being formed in a reaction between the carboxyl group and a substituted amine (R_1-NH_2), where R_1 is the residue of a second amino acid.

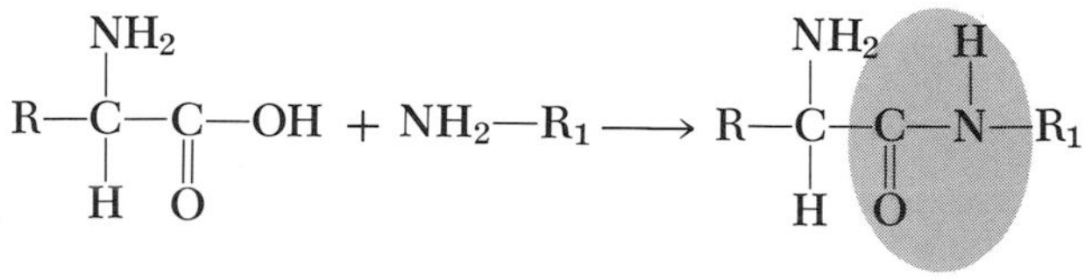

$$
\underset{\underset{H}{|}\ \underset{O}{\|}}{\overset{\overset{NH_2}{|}}{R-C-C-OH}} + NH_2-R_1 \longrightarrow \underset{\underset{H}{|}\ \underset{O}{\|}}{\overset{\overset{NH_2\quad H}{|\qquad|}}{R-C-C-N-R_1}}
$$

In the living cell, however, the synthesis of the peptide bond is a more complex process.

The amino group of amino acids will react with nitrous acid (HNO_2) to liberate N_2. This reaction, which can be quantitative, is important in the estimation of α-amino groups in amino acids, peptides and proteins. The imino acids proline and hydroxyproline do not react, and the ε-amino group of lysine reacts but at a slower rate. The products are N_2 gas, which can be measured manometrically, and the corresponding α-hydroxy acid.

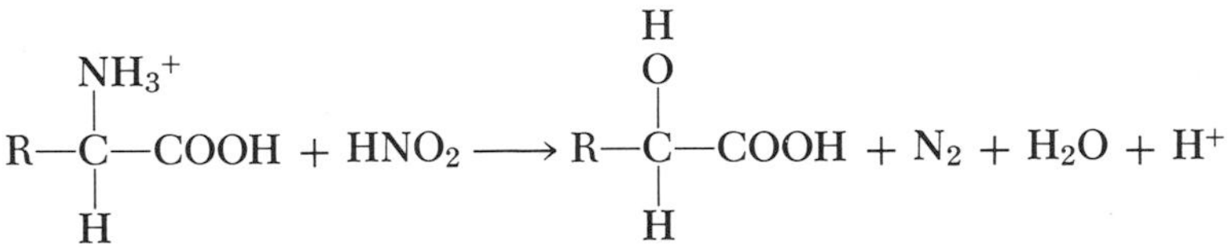

$$R-\underset{\underset{H}{|}}{\overset{\overset{NH_3^+}{|}}{C}}-COOH + HNO_2 \longrightarrow R-\underset{\underset{H}{|}}{\overset{\overset{H}{\overset{|}{O}}}{C}}-COOH + N_2 + H_2O + H^+$$

Another reaction of amino acids which has found much recent use is the reaction with 2,4-dinitrofluorobenzene.

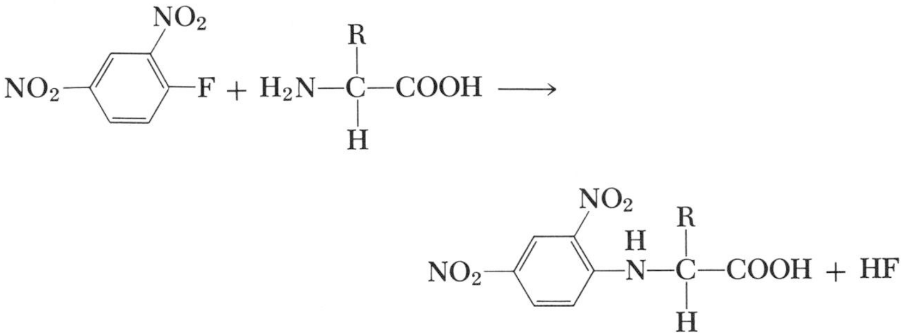

As a result of this reaction the intensely colored dinitrobenzene nucleus is attached to the nitrogen atom of the amino acid to yield a highly colored derivative, the 2,4-dinitrophenyl derivative. 2,4-Dinitrofluorobenzene will react with the free amino group on the N-terminal end of a polypeptide and the ε-amino group of lysine, as well as the amino groups of free amino acids. Thus, by reacting a native protein or intact polypeptide with 2,4-dinitrofluorobenzene and isolating the colored dinitrophenyl derivative, we can determine the terminal amino acid in a polypeptide chain.

A very useful reaction of amino acids is the reaction with ninhydrin or triketohydrindene hydrate. The initial step of this reaction may be represented as an oxidation-reduction reaction leading to the formation of reduced ninhydrin and the α-imino acid:

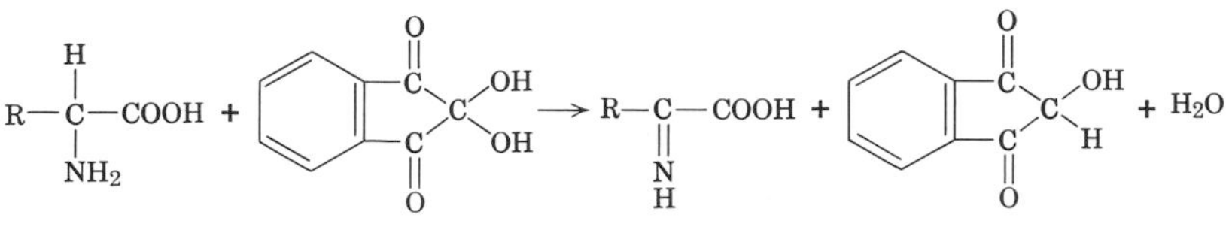

oxidized ninhydrin   α–imino acid   reduced ninhydrin

The α-imino acid then hydrolyzes to form the α-keto acid, which in turn decarboxylates under the conditions of the reaction:

$$R-\underset{\underset{H}{\overset{\parallel}{N}}}{C}-COOH + H_2O \longrightarrow$$

$$NH_3 + R-\underset{\overset{\parallel}{O}}{C}-COOH \longrightarrow R-C\overset{\displaystyle H}{\underset{\displaystyle O}{\diagup}} + CO_2$$

Finally, the NH_3 that has been produced reacts with equimolar quantities of oxidized and reduced ninhydrin to yield a bluish-purple product which is proportional to the amount of amino acid initially present.

oxidized ninhydrin   reduced ninhydrin   blue product

Amino acids are usually detected after chromatography on paper by their reaction with ninhydrin.

Van Slyke has used the ninhydrin reaction for amino acid determination by measuring the CO_2 produced. It is also a useful way to degrade the amino acid and obtain the carbon atom of the carboxyl group as CO_2. Moreover, the aldehyde produced represents all the carbon atoms of the original amino acid except the carboxyl carbon atom. The reaction requires both the amino and the carboxyl group to be free and adjacent to each other.

Other reactions of the amino acids include acylation of the amino group with acid chlorides and acid anhydrides as well as reaction of the amino group with isocyanates to form hydantoins. These reactions are used in the chemical synthesis and determination of the structure of polypeptides.

Analysis of Amino Acid Mixtures

One of the difficult and important problems of biochemistry is to determine the composition and sequence of amino acids in a protein. Not only must the individual amino acids making up the protein be identified, but the amount of each amino acid must be found. The initial step in determining the amino acid composition is usually the hydrolysis of the protein by HCl, after which excess acid is removed. The amino acids in the mixture may then be revealed by various procedures. Older techniques involved the esterification of the carboxyl groups with methanol or ethanol and fractional distillation of their esters. Some amino acids form insoluble salts with silver ions, HCl, picric acid, and other compounds. Thus glutamic acid can be precipitated as its hydrochloride, and its content in protein hydrolysates can be determined.

Some naturally occurring amino acids react quantitatively in specific chemical reactions, and their analysis can be carried out on the hydrolyzed mixture of amino acids. For example, arginine reacts with α-naphthol to yield a red product (the Sakaguchi reaction), and tyrosine, a phenolic amino acid, reacts with a mixture of mercury salts in HNO_3 to give a red complex (the Millon reaction). When other compounds that react similarly with the particular reagents are absent in the hydrolysate these procedures are useful.

Another method for determining a specific amino acid in a mixture of amino acids involves a bacterium that requires the specific amino acid for growth. For example, it is possible to obtain strains of lactic acid bacteria that require L-alanine for growth and the production of lactic acid. If L-alanine is withheld from an otherwise complete growth medium, there is no growth; if L-alanine is supplied in the medium, the amount of growth (and acid production) is proportional to the amount of amino acid supplied. Since the specificity of the response is due to the strict dietary requirement of the organism, the L-alanine content in a mixture of amino acids may be estimated by this procedure.

Two extremely important methods employed routinely in protein chemistry are (1) the use of ion exchange resins, which separate a complex mixture of amino acids into characteristic elution patterns under carefully controlled conditions, and (2) quantitative paper chromatography. All the amino acids derived from the hydrolysis of large proteins may be determined quantitatively by these relatively simple and quick methods. (See Appendix 3.)

Proteins

Proteins consist of a large number of repeating units, the L-amino acids, which are joined one to the other by a *peptide bond* as shown in Figure 4-3. In this figure R is the side chain of the amino acid unit and may be one of twenty possible groups. These groups alternate on each side of the long chain. Two amino acids joined by a peptide bond are called a *dipeptide;* three amino acids joined by two peptide bonds are *tripeptides,* and a large number of amino acids joined together are *polypeptides.* Proteins vary in molecular weight from 10,000 to many millions. Despite this complexity, the amino acid sequences of a small number of proteins have been determined. The English biochemist,

Sanger, received a Nobel Prize in chemistry for determining the precise sequence of amino acids in insulin.   His methods of controlled hydrolysis of proteins to recognizable peptides have been used by others to elucidate the amino acid sequence of ribonuclease and the adrenal corticotrophic hormone, ACTH.

Proteins are divided into two general groups: (1) fibrous and (2) globular proteins.   As the name implies *fibrous proteins* are composed of individual, elongated, filamentous chains which are joined laterally by several types of cross-linkage to form a fairly stable, rather insoluble structure.   Typical examples are keratin, myosin, and collagen.   The *globular proteins,* on the other hand, are somewhat elliptical in shape with a considerable amount of folding of the long polypeptide chain. Biologically active proteins such as antigens and enzymes are of the globular type.

Linus Pauling of the California Institute of Technology received the Nobel Prize in chemistry for his contributions to our knowledge of the fine structure of proteins.   X-ray studies of native proteins and of synthetic polypeptides led Pauling to propose a structure which has the greatest theoretical stability and which incorporates the restrictions of stereochemistry by the use of the necessary bond lengths and bond angles.   This structure is called the α-helix.   The α-helix has a chain of repeating amino acid units wound into a spiral chain which is held together by hydrogen bonds between each carbonyl group and the imido grouping of the third peptide residue further along the chain. The helix contains about 3.6 amino acid residues for each full turn of the spiral.   See Figure 4-4.

Another type of structure found in silk, muscle, and contractile fibers is the β-configuration.   Here two or more peptide chains are tied together laterally by hydrogen bonding.   Wherever hydrogen bonding occurs an orderly or crystalline structure can be observed.

To define a complicated macromolecule such as a protein in descriptive terms, biochemists have assigned four basic structural levels to proteins.

   (a) *Primary Structure:*   The combination of amino acids in a proper

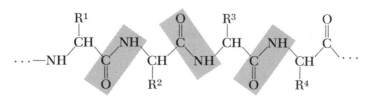

Fig. 4-3.   A polypeptide chain illustrating the basic primary structure of a protein.

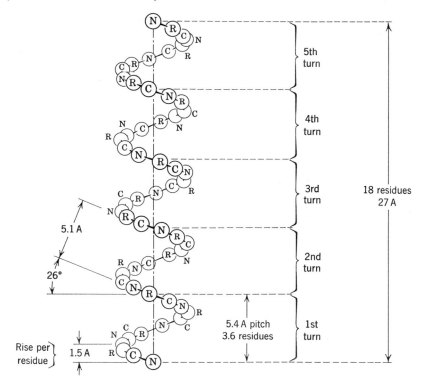

Fig. 4-4. Representation of a polypeptide chain as an α-helical configuration. Here A stands for the Angstrom unit. From L. Pauling and R. B. Corey, *Proc. Intern. Wool Textile Research Conf., B*, 249 (1955), as redrawn in C. B. Anfinsen, *The Molecular Basis of Evolution*, John Wiley and Sons, New York, 1959, p. 101.

sequence through peptide bonds.   No other forces or bonds are implied in this term.   Figure 4-3 illustrates this structure.

(b) *Secondary Structure.*   In this term the right handed α-helical nature of a protein becomes evident.   The spiral is stabilized by hydrogen bonding between the carbonyl and the imido groups of the peptide bonds which appear in a regular sequence along the chain.   See Figure 4-5.

(c) *Tertiary Structure.*   In order to compress the very long spiral chain into a globular form, extensive coiling or folding occurs to give a complex, rigid structure (Figure 4-6).   The stabilization of this structure is also ascribed to the different reactivities associated with the R-groups in the amino acid residues.   These are best depicted in Figure 4-7.

The basic amino acids such as lysine and arginine and the dicarboxylic amino acids aspartic and glutamic are primarily involved in salt linkages. Cysteine is the sole source of sulfhydryl groups which may participate in disulfide bonding.   Van der Waal forces are exerted when like aromatic groups or like aliphatic residues are in close proximity with each other. The tertiary structure is of prime importance in determining the fine structure of a protein and possibly contributes greatly to the unique catalytic properties of biologically active proteins.

(*d*) *Quaternary Structure.*   This defines the degree of polymerization of a protein unit.   Thus the enzyme phosphorylase *a* contains four identical subunits which alone are catalytically inactive but when joined as a tetramer form the active enzyme as shown in Figure 4-8.   This type of structure is called a *homogenous quaternary structure;* if there are dissimilar units as in tobacco mosaic virus, in which ribonucleic acids

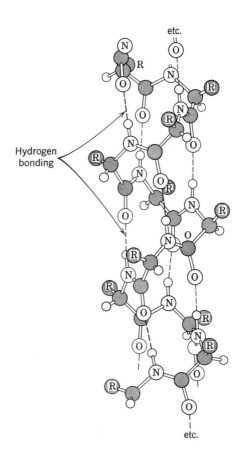

Fig. 4-5.   Stabilization of an α-helical configuration by hydrogen bonding to yield a secondary structure.   All the shaded balls represent carbon atoms or residues (R) of amino acids.   From L. Pauling and R. B. Corey, *Proc. Intern.   Wool Textile Research Conf., B,* 249 (1955), as redrawn in C. B. Anfinsen, *The Molecular Basis of Evolution,* John Wiley and Sons, New York, 1959, p. 101.

Fig. 4-6. Sketch illustrating the complicated folding of a long polypeptide chain stabilized by noncovalent bonds.

and protein units complex to give active virus, a *heterogenous quaternary structure* is obtained.

A protein can then be described on four different levels in terms of its primary, secondary, tertiary, and, if necessary, its quaternary structures.

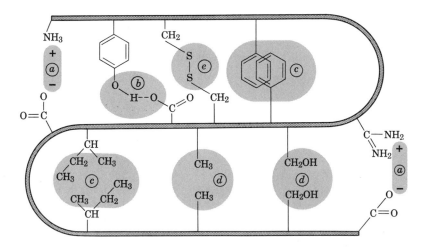

Fig. 4-7. Some types of noncovalent bonds which stabilize protein structure: (*a*) Electrostatic interaction; (*b*) hydrogen bonding between tyrosine residues and carboxylate groups on side chains; (*c*) interaction of nonpolar side chains caused by the mutual repulsion of solvent; (*d*) van der Waals interactions; (*e*) a disulfide linkage, a covalent bond. From C. B. Anfinsen, *The Molecular Basis of Evolution,* John Wiley and Sons, New York, 1959, p. 102.

Fig. 4-8. A tetramer of protein units illustrating the quaternary structure of a complex protein.

A brief discussion concerning the purification and characterization of proteins and the application of ultracentrifugal and electrophoretic procedures is presented in Appendix 3.

REFERENCES

1. J. B. Neilands and P. K. Stumpf, *Outlines of Enzyme Chemistry*, John Wiley and Sons, New York, 2nd edition, 1958.
   Chapter 2 discusses the titration of amino acids in a brief, lucid manner.

2. Joseph S. Fruton and Sofia Simmonds, *General Biochemistry*, John Wiley and Sons, New York, 2nd edition, 1958.
   Chapters 2, 3, 4, and 5 are excellent discussions of the general chemistry of amino acids and proteins.

3. K. U. Linderstrøm-Lang and J. A. Schellman in *The Enzymes*, edited by P. D. Boyer, H. Lardy, and Karl Myrbäck, Academic Press, New York, 2nd edition, 1959, Vol. 1, Chapter 10.
   A thorough treatment of the modern aspects of protein structure by a pioneer in the field.

Five

Nucleic Acids and Their Components

Introduction

The nucleic acids have been the subject of many biochemical investigations almost from the time they were first isolated from cell nuclei about a century ago. Nucleic acids occur in every living cell; they direct the synthesis of proteins, and they are responsible for the transfer of genetic information. Like proteins they are polymers of high molecular weight but their repeating unit is a mononucleotide rather than an amino acid. Nucleotides are a type of compound frequently encountered in biochemistry; several of the common coenzymes involved in intermediary metabolism are nucleotides. In the cell the nucleic acids are conjugated with proteins to form nucleoproteins.

There are two types of nucleic acid. One of these, deoxyribonucleic acid (abbreviated DNA) is a constituent of cell nuclei; the other, ribonucleic acid (RNA) is chiefly located in the cytoplasm outside the nucleus. Both DNA and RNA consist of a long chain of alternating sugar and phosphate residues. In RNA the sugar is D-ribose; the sugar in DNA, as its name implies, is 2-deoxyribose. We show the Haworth formulas for these sugars. Attached to every sugar unit is the third con-

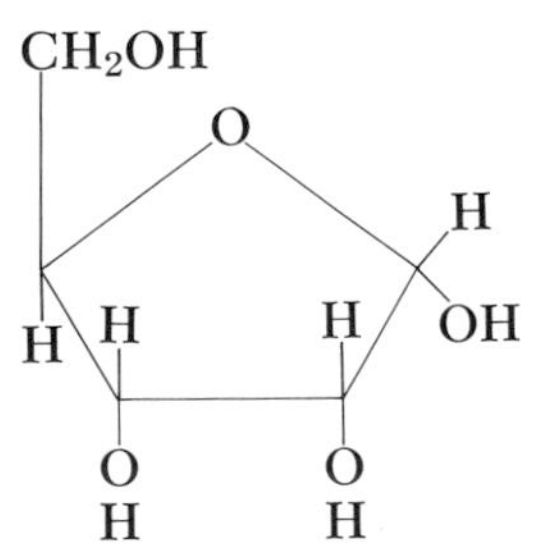

α-D-ribose 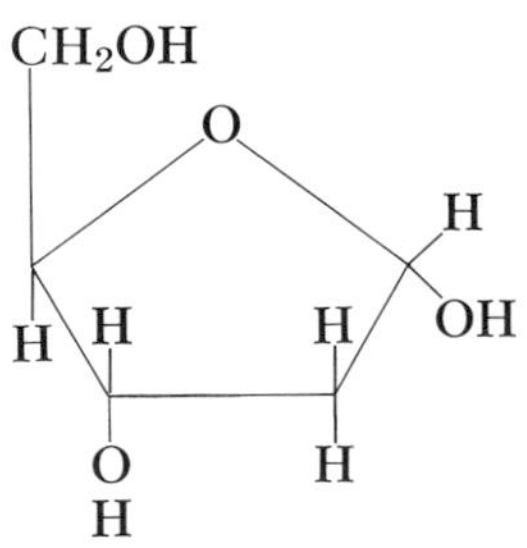   α-2-deoxy-D-ribose

stituent of the nucleic acids, a *nitrogenous base*, which is either a substituted purine or a substituted pyrimidine.

80

Purines and Pyrimidines

Both RNA and DNA contain the two purines adenine and guanine. The structures of these compounds and of purine are given in the diagram, as is the numbering of the atoms in purine. Both RNA and

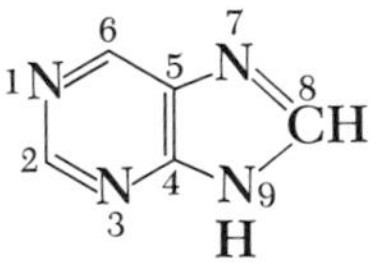

purine 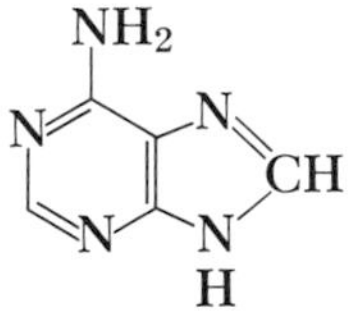   adenine   guanine
                      (6-amino purine)   (2-amino-6-oxypurine)

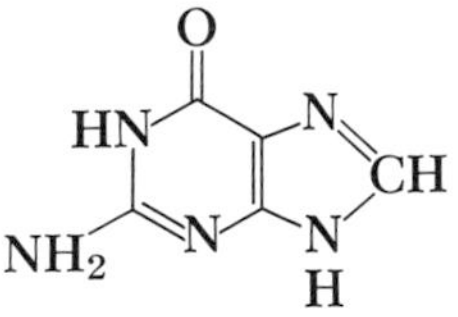

DNA also contain the pyrimidine cytosine. The fourth nitrogenous base found in the two nucleic acids is different, however: RNA contains uracil whereas DNA contains thymine.

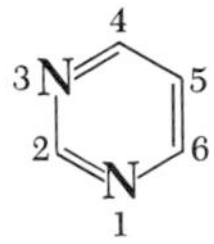

pyrimidine 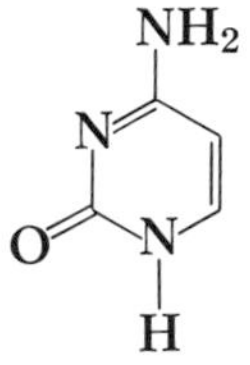   cytosine   uracil   thymine
              (2-oxy-4-amino   (2,4 dioxypyrimidine) (2,4 dioxy-5-methyl
               pyrimidine)   pyrimidine)

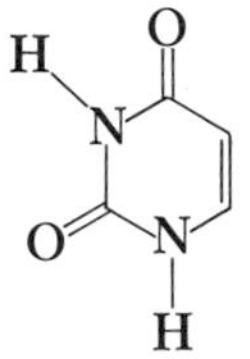

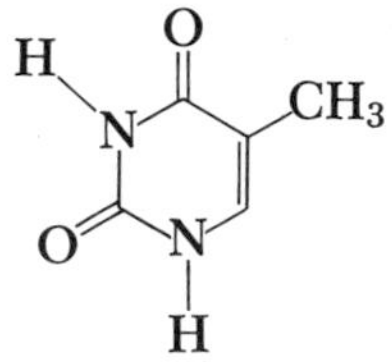

The structure of the oxygen-containing bases has been written in the *keto* (or *lactam*) form. It should be emphasized that there is an equilibrium between the keto and the *enol* (or *lactim*) forms which is dependent on the pH of the environment. It is the lactam form which participates in the glycosidic bond with ribose and deoxyribose (see p. 82) and this form is common at physiological pH.

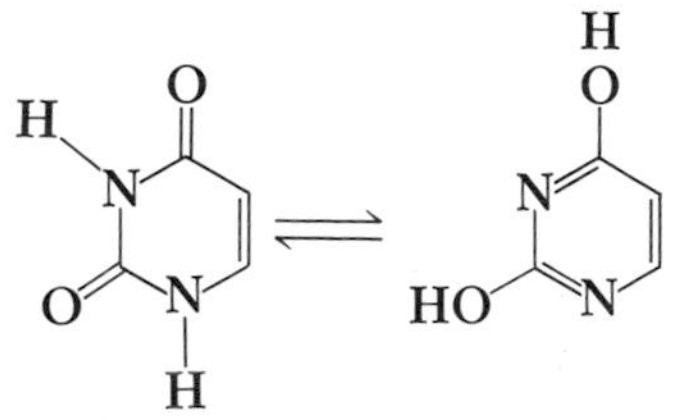

lactam   lactim

In recent years other pyrimidines have been detected in purified samples of DNA; 5-methyl cytosine occurs in the DNA isolated from wheat germ and has also been detected in trace amounts in the DNA from thymus gland and other mammalian sources. Another pyrimidine, 5-hydroxymethyl cytosine, is found instead of cytosine in the DNA of certain bacterial viruses, the T-even coliphages.

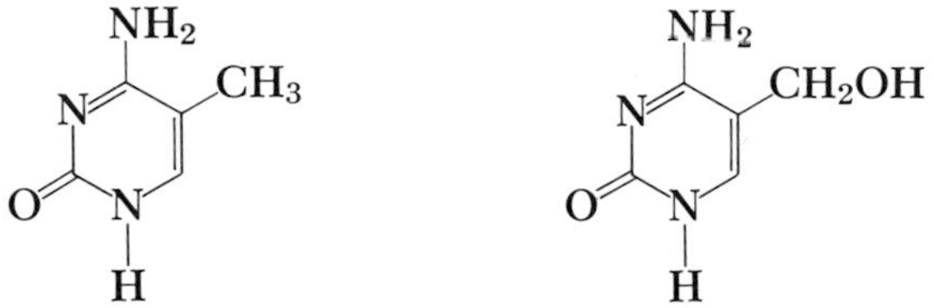

5-methyl cytosine

5-hydroxymethyl cytosine

Nucleosides

The nucleosides are carbohydrate derivatives in which the purines and pyrimidines, found in nucleic acids, are linked to a sugar in a β-N-glycosyl bond. In the naturally occurring nucleosides the sugar is either D-ribose or 2-deoxy-D-ribose. The point of attachment of the sugar to the base is the hydroxyl group on the C-1' carbon atom. The nitrogen atom of the purine which participates in the linkage is N-9. In the pyrimidines it is the N-1 nitrogen atom. In the nucleosides, the carbon atoms of the sugars are designated by prime numbers (i.e., C-1', C-5') while the atoms of the nitrogen bases lack the prime sign.

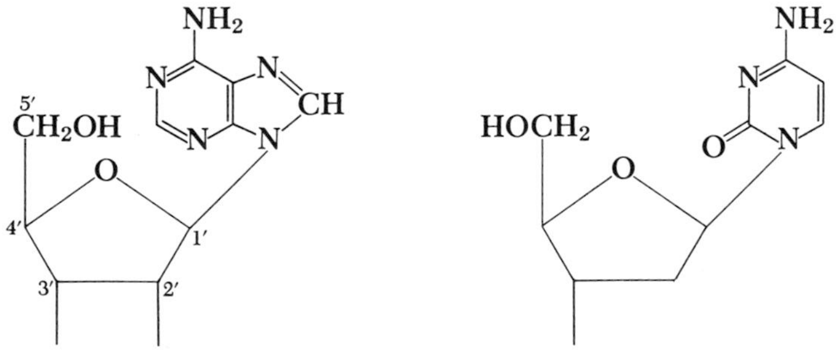

adenine riboside
(adenosine)

cytosine deoxyriboside
(deoxycytidine)

The nomenclature of the nucleosides is frequently confusing to the uninitiated: For this reason the names of some of the naturally occurring nucleosides are found in Table 5-1.

Nucleotides

A nucleotide is a phosphate ester of a nucleoside. The ribose portion of a riboside has three positions where the phosphate could be esterified,

Table 5-1.   *Names of Nucleosides*

Base	Riboside	Deoxyriboside
Adenine	Adenosine	Deoxyadenosine
Guanine	Guanosine	Deoxyguanosine
Uracil	Uridine	Deoxyuridine
Cytosine	Cytidine	Deoxycytidine
Thymine	Thymine riboside	Thymidine

the 2'-hydroxyl, 3'-hydroxyl, and 5'-hydroxyl, whereas the deoxyriboside has only the 3'- and 5' positions available.   As will be shown, all these possible structures exist in nature.   One of the earliest nucleotides to be reported was the 5'-phosphate of inosine, or inosine-5'-monophosphate (IMP), discovered by Liebig in 1847.

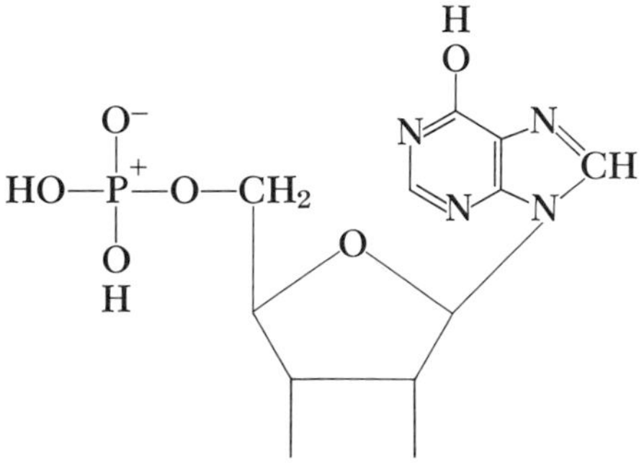

inosine-5'-monophosphate (IMP)
(inosinic acid)

When fresh tissues are homogenized in cold, trichloroacetic acid, the acid filtrate will contain nucleotides in which the 5'-hydroxyl bears the phosphate ester.   During the last half-century these mononucleotides have been systematically identified and studied; the results have shown that several of the compounds or closely related derivatives are substrates or coenzymes for enzymatic reactions encountered in intermediary metabolism.

Hydrolysis by mild acid conditions cleaves the glycosidic bond to yield the purine or pyrimidine base and a phosphorylated sugar; gentle alkaline hydrolysis yields inorganic phosphate and the corresponding nucleoside. This may be represented as in our diagram.

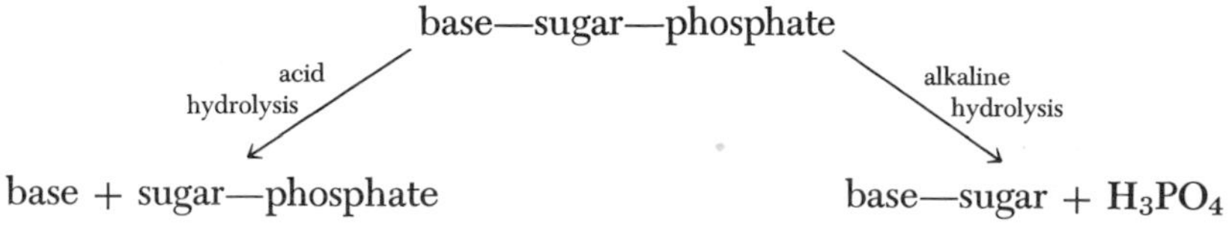

base—sugar—phosphate

acid
hydrolysis

alkaline
hydrolysis

base + sugar—phosphate   base—sugar + H_3PO_4

One of the most important naturally occurring nucleotides is adenosine-5'-monophosphate, also known as muscle adenylic acid because it was first isolated from animal skeletal muscle.[*] Two derivatives of muscle adenylic acid, adenosine-5'-diphosphate (ADP) and adenosine-5'-triphosphate (ATP) play an extremely important role in intermediary metabolism in the conservation and utilization of the energy released during the oxidation of foodstuffs. As we shall see, the physiological

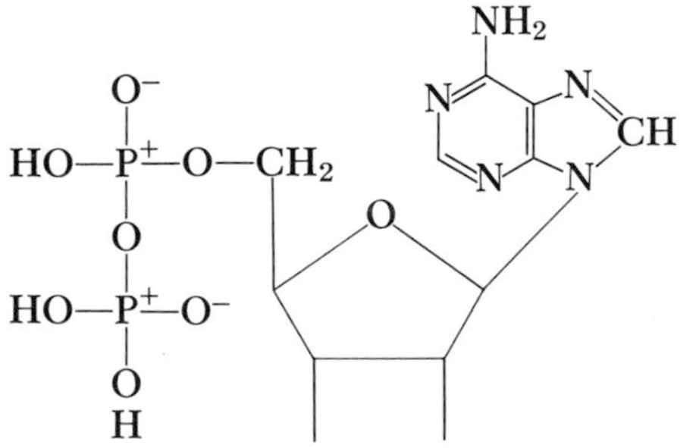

adenosine diphosphate
(ADP)

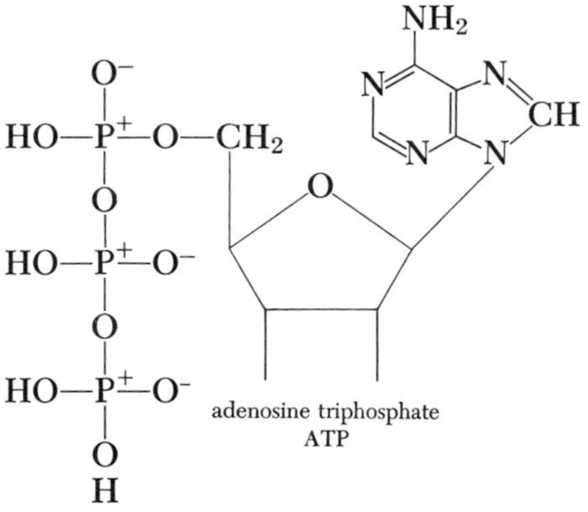

adenosine triphosphate
ATP

significance of these compounds rests in their ability to donate and accept phosphate groups in chemical reactions.

Another example of an important compound with a nucleotide unit as part of its structure will suffice. This compound, known as coenzyme I, diphosphopyridine nucleotide (DPN$^+$), or nicotinamide-adenine dinucleotide (NAD$^+$) (see Chapter 8), functions in oxidation reduction reactions. It consists of nicotinamide mononucleotide linked to adenosine-5'-monophosphate through an acid anhydride bond between the two phosphoric acids.

Table 5-2 lists the names of some of the common nucleotides. Certain of these compounds and their derivative forms will be discussed in detail

[*] This nucleotide can also be called an acid with the name derived from the corresponding nucleoside, that is, 5'-adenylic acid.

in later chapters where their biochemical functions can be appreciated.

In 1918, P. A. Levene obtained a mononucleotide in hydrolysis of the RNA from yeast and characterized it as adenosine-3'-monophosphate.

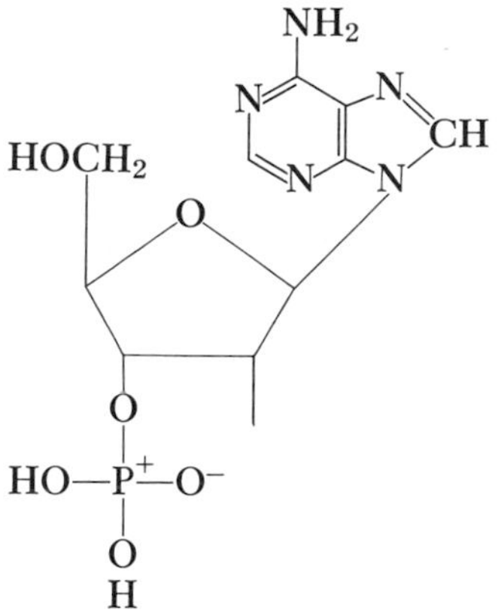

adenosine-3'-monophosphate

This observation was among the first of many in the next few decades relating to the structure of RNA and DNA. Unfortunately, the work went slowly because adequate methods for characterizing the products obtained on hydrolysis of nucleic acids were lacking. In 1949, Waldo Cohn at the Oak Ridge National Laboratories applied *ion exchange chromatography* (see Appendix 3) to the separation of the nucleotide mixtures obtained on hydrolysis of RNA and found that each of the four nucleotides which had formerly been assumed to be 3'-monophosphates also occurred as 2'-monophosphates in the hydrolyzed mixtures. The technique of ion exchange chromatography in the last decade has been extensively applied to the general problem of the linkage in the nucleotides in nucleic acids.

Table 5-2.   Names of Common Nucleotides

Base	Nucletotide Named as an Acid	Nucleotide Named as a Phosphate
	Ribonucleotides	
Adenine	2'-Adenylic acid	Adenosine-2'-monophosphate
Adenine	3'-Adenylic acid	Adenosine-3'-monophosphate
Adenine	5'-Adenylic acid	Adenosine-5'-monophosphate°

Table 5-2.   Names of Common Nucleotides (Continued)

Base	Nucletotide Named as an Acid	Nucleotide Named as a Phosphate
	Ribonucleotides	
Adenine	Cyclic adenylic acid	Adenosine-3'-5'-monophosphate
Guanine	2'-Guanylic acid	Guanosine-2'-monophosphate
Uracil	2'-Uridylic acid	Uridine-2'-monophosphate
Cytosine	2'-Cytidylic acid	Cytidine-2'-monophosphate
Hypoxanthine	2'-Inosinic acid	Inosine-2'-monophosphate
	Deoxyribonucleotides	
Adenine	Deoxyadenylic acid	Deoxyadenosine-5'-monophosphate°
Guanine	Deoxyguanylic acid	Deoxyguanosine-5'-monophosphate°
Thymine	Thymidylic acid	Thymidine-5'-monophosphate°
Cytosine	Deoxycytidylic acid	Deoxycytidine-5'-monophosphate °

° Each of the 5'-monophosphates occurs also as the diphosphate and as the triphosphate.

Hydrolysis of Nucleic Acids

There is abundant evidence to indicate that both DNA and RNA consist of a sequence of nucleotides linked together by phosphoric acid in a *diester* linkage; in a diester, two of the oxygen atoms on a single molecule of H_3PO_4 are bound as esters. The structure of RNA may be represented as shown in the diagram, where the different purine or pyrimidine bases are indicated as "base" and the phosphate group is bound as a diester on the 3'-hydroxyl of one nucleoside and the 5'-hydroxyl of the adjacent nucleoside. The evidence in support of the 3'-hydroxyl and not the 2'-hydroxyl as the group participating in diester formation consists mainly of information on the nature of the products formed on hydrolysis of RNA. In DNA, where there is no 2'-hydroxyl, this group obviously cannot participate in the diester linkage.

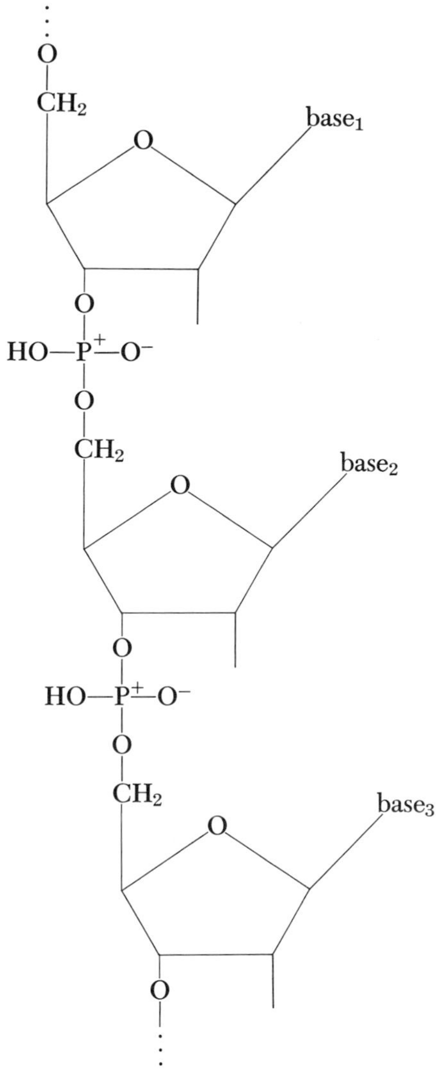

$$\vdots$$
$$O$$
$$\mid$$
$$CH_2 \qquad base_1$$

$$O$$

$$O$$
$$\mid$$
$$HO-\overset{+}{P}-O^-$$
$$\mid$$
$$O$$
$$\mid$$
$$CH_2 \qquad base_2$$

$$O$$

$$O$$
$$\mid$$
$$HO-\overset{\pm}{P}-O^-$$
$$\mid$$
$$O$$
$$\mid$$
$$CH_2 \qquad base_3$$

$$O$$

$$O$$
$$\vdots$$

A greatly simplified means of representing the composition of RNA is:

$$ApGpCpUp$$

In this structure A, G, C, and U represent the nucleosides adenosine, guanosine, cytidine and uridine respectively, and p stands for the phosphate group. The linkage of phosphate to the 3′-hydroxyl group of adenosine is indicated by Ap and the linkage of the phosphate to the 5′-hydroxyl of guanosine is implied by pG. Thus the 5′-"end" of the nucleosides (A, G, U, and C) is at the left of the letters A, G, U, and C, whereas the 3'-"end" is at the right of the letter. With this shorthand we can briefly describe the products obtained on hydrolysis of RNA by different techniques.

Alkaline hydrolysis (0.1 to 1.0N NaOH at room temperature for 24 hours) completely degrades RNA to a mixture of the 2'- and 3'-nucleoside monophosphates. The initial step is to form a cyclic (2',3'-) diester which then undergoes random hydrolysis of either the 2'- or the 3'-bond to yield a mixture of the 3'- and 2'-monophosphates. The

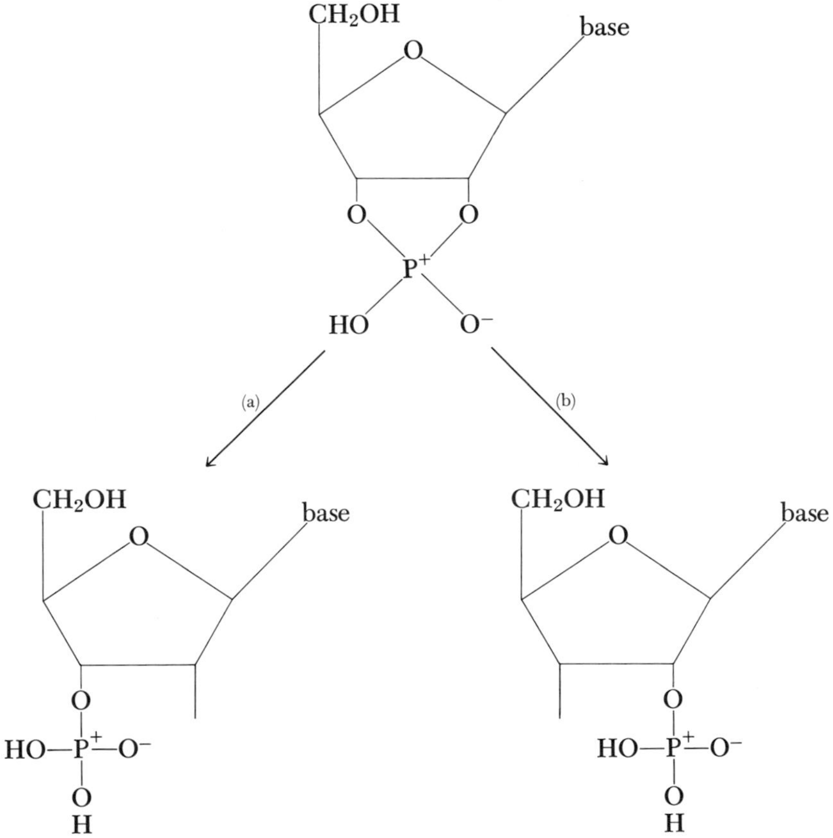

$$CH_2OH \qquad base$$

nucleic acid chain is therefore cleaved as indicated:

$$BpBpBpBpBp \xrightarrow{\text{NaOH}} Bp/Bp/Bp/Bp/Bp \qquad (5\text{-}1)$$

where the diagonal bars represent the point of attack and Bp represents either the 3'-phosphate or the 2'-phosphate.

The action of a crystalline ribonuclease isolated from the pancreas on RNA is similar to that of alkali in that a 2', 3'-diester is transiently formed.

In the presence of the enzyme, however, only the C-2′ phosphate bond (C-2′-P-bond) of the diester is cleaved to yield only the 3′-phosphates of the nucleosides (route (a) in the diagram). The overall reaction catalyzed by ribonuclease is essentially that of reaction 5-1. However, not every C-5′-P-linkage in RNA is attacked by ribonuclease; only those diester bonds in which the C-3′-linkage is to a pyrimidine are cleaved. In this

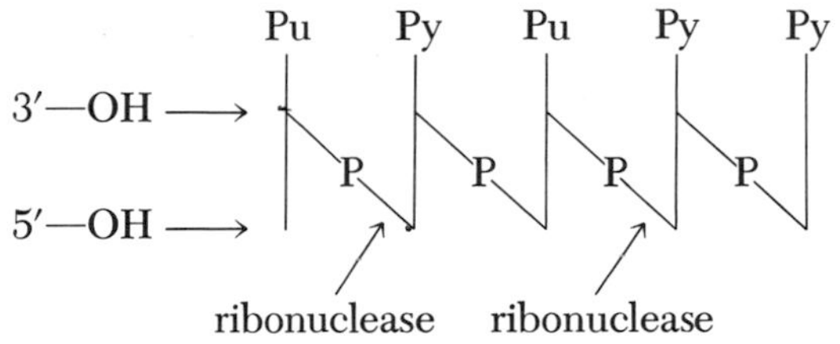

diagram Py and Pu stand for pyrimidine and purine, respectively.

The venoms of various snakes (rattlesnake and Russel's viper) contain a diesterase which splits the C-3′-P-linkage of RNA to yield the 5′-mononucleotides:

$$pBpBpBpBpB \xrightarrow[\text{diesterase}]{\text{snake venom}} pB/pB/pB/pB/pB$$

The actions of both snake venom and pancreatic diesterases are modified somewhat by the nature of the ends of the nucleotide chain, that is, by whether the end nucleotide has the 5′- and 3′-hydroxyl group esterified. The details of these activities are not pertinent to the purpose of our book.

In contrast to RNA, DNA is resistant to hydrolysis by alkali and by the crystalline pancreatic diesterase. There is a DNA-ase in pancreatic tissue, however, which hydrolyses large DNA molecules at C-3′-P-bonds in the interior of the molecule to form smaller oligonucleotides. These

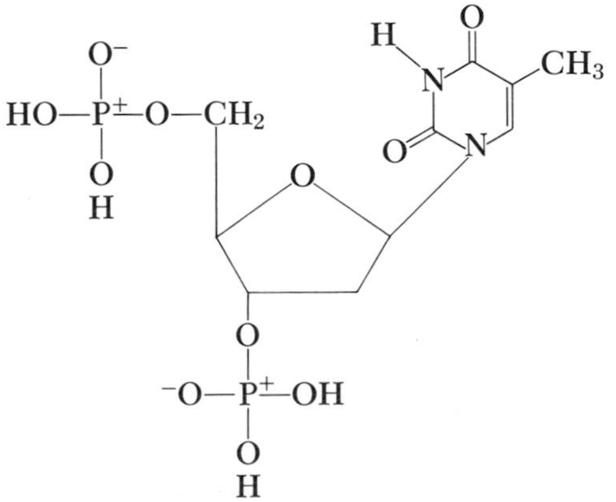

thymidine-3′,5′-diphosphate

smaller polymers can then be hydrolyzed by snake venom diesterase to yield the 5'-deoxyribotides.   Other DNA-ases are known which hydrolyze the C-5'-P-linkage to yield 3'-deoxyribotides.

Acid hydrolysis is of little use in determining the nature of the nucleotide linkage in RNA because the 2'- and 3'-monophosphates are readily interconvertible in mild acid.   The glycosidic bonds between the purines and ribose are also particularly labile to acid hydrolysis.   Mild acid hydrolysis of DNA has yielded 3', 5' diphosphate derivatives of thymidine and deoxycytidine, however, a result that in turn supports the other observations on the diester linkage in the nucleic acids.

Detection, Assay, and Composition of Nucleic Acids

A stain devised by Feulgen is a convenient method of detecting DNA in cells.   The reagent, which consists of a fuchsin dye in sulfurous acid, produces a red color in the presence of DNA but not RNA.   The demonstration that cell nuclei react positively with Feulgen's reagent is the basis for the belief that DNA is confined to the nuclei of cells.   This observation would not preclude the possibility that nuclei also contain RNA; indeed, small amounts of RNA have been reported in cell nuclei. RNA is found predominately in the cytoplasm, however, where it is located for the most part in *ribosomes* (80–90 per cent in liver cells). These are small, beadlike particles clustered on the surfaces of the endoplasmic reticulum, a lacelike network of delicate tubular structures which stretches throughout the cytoplasm.   Ten per cent of the total RNA in cells consists of a highly specialized, soluble compound(s) of molecular weight of approximately 30,000, called soluble RNA, *s*-RNA, or *t*-RNA, which is involved in protein synthesis.   (See Chapter 14 for a discussion of *s*-RNA in protein synthesis.)

The DNA and RNA contents of a tissue may be measured by warming the preparation in dilute alkali.   The RNA is degraded to nucleotides which are soluble in acid while the DNA is unhydrolyzed and is precipitated by acid.   By determining the sugar or phosphate content of the acid-soluble and acid-insoluble fractions, we have a measure of the respective nucleic acid content.

A problem of major importance is the relative concentration of the individual mononucleotides in the nucleic acid.   Originally it was believed that nucleic acids consisted of equal amounts of the four nucleotides, and that a unit consisting of one nucleotide of each of the four bases (that is, a tetranucleotide) was the fundamental unit.   With the development of ion exchange chromatography it was possible to determine the different mononucleotides quantitatively in hydrolyzed samples of nucleic acid, and the results indicated that the original concept was in error. The sum of the purine nucleotides rather equaled the sum of the pyrimidine nucleotides; in several DNA preparations, moreover, the adenine content was equal to the thymine content and the guanine content was equal to that of the cytosine. As a consequence of this quantitative information, Watson and Crick of England proposed a now famous structure for DNA which is in keeping with the analytical data and may explain the major biological role of DNA in transmitting genetic information. It is important to emphasize that the theories on structure of DNA were proposed only when analytical data were obtained from preparations of DNA believed to be only slightly modified from the state in which it occurs in the cell. The early chemical procedures involving treatment with strong alkali or acid clearly led to a degraded sample of nucleic acid which was markedly different from its native structure. By treatment with neutral salt solutions, samples of thymus gland DNA have been obtained which have a molecular weight of several million. Conversely it has been difficult to obtain samples of RNA which are not degraded, and this has hampered research on the precise structure of this important material.

Structure of DNA and RNA

The observation that the ratio of adenine to thymine and that of cytosine to guanine is very close to 1 is of basic importance. Furthermore the adenine and thymine nucleotides can be so paired structurally that a maximum number of two hydrogen bonds can be drawn between these bases, whereas cytosine and guanine can be arranged spatially to permit the formation of three hydrogen bonds.

The final breakthrough came when Wilkens in England observed that DNA from different sources had remarkably similar X-ray diffraction patterns. This suggested a uniform molecular pattern for all DNA. The data also suggested that DNA consisted of two or more polynucleotide chains arranged in a helical structure. With evidence based on (a) the available X-ray data, (b) the data of Chargaff and others on base pairing and equivalence, and (c) titration data that suggested the long nucleotide chains were held together through hydrogen bonding between base residues, Watson and Crick constructed their model of DNA in 1953. (see Figure 5-1). The spatial structure of RNA is not as clearly defined as that of DNA but a similar type of base pairing may probably be envisaged.

In the Watson and Crick model of DNA two parallel chains of polynucleotides are wound into a helix. The chains consist of deoxy-thymine   adenine

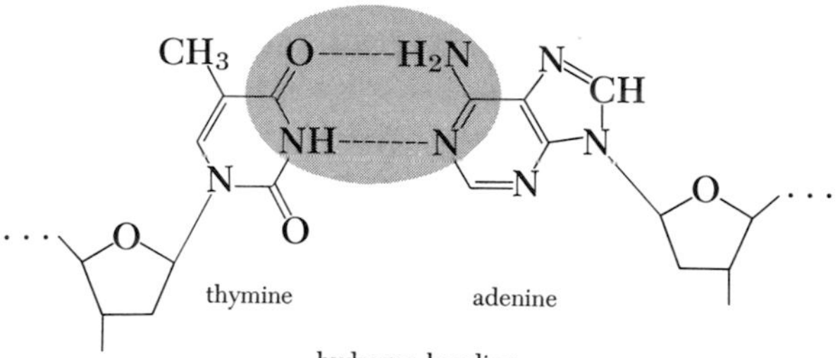

hydrogen bonding
system

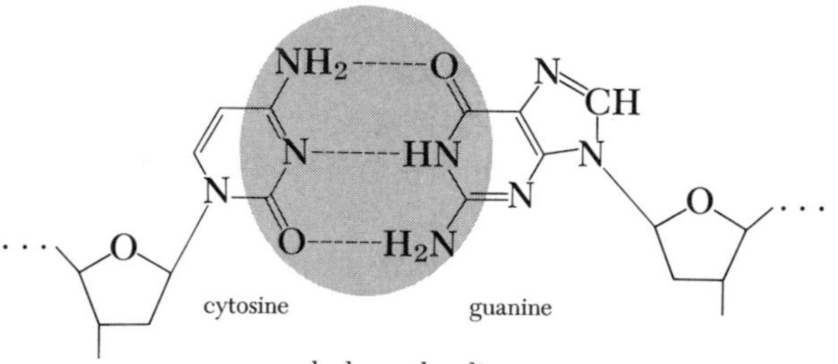

cytosine   guanine

hydrogen bonding
system

ribotide phosphates joined together by phosphate diesters with the bases projecting perpendicularly from the chain into the center axis. For each adenine projecting toward the central axis one thymine must project toward adenine from the second parallel chain and be held by hydrogen bonding to adenine. Cytosine or guanine do not fit in this area and are rejected. Similarly, the specificity of hydrogen bonding between cytosine and guanine dictates their association only with each other. Thus we have a spatial structure of two parallel chains coiled around a common axis and held together by the specific bonding of adenine with thymine, and cytosine with guanine. The unusual property of the helix is that one chain is a precise complement of the other.

Occurrence of Nucleic Acids

At one time it was postulated that the nucleic acid of plants was RNA and that animal species contained only DNA. Today this is recognized as erroneous and the existence of DNA in the nuclei of all plant, animal, and bacterial cells, where it is intimately associated with the nucleoproteins of chromosomes, has already been discussed. The localization of

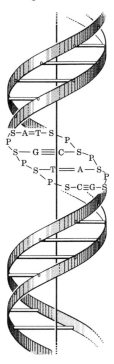

Fig. 5-1. Here P means phosphate diester, S means deoxyribose, A=T is the adenine-thymine pairing, and G≡C is the guanosine-cytosine pairing.

the major fraction of RNA in the extranuclear material has been established. If the individual cell under examination is rich in nuclear components, it may be expected that the DNA content of that cell will be high. Alternatively, if the cell contains little or no nuclear material, RNA will predominate.

Some biological agents contain extremely high concentrations of nucleoproteins and are therefore rich in nucleic acid. Thus the viruses which are small, filterable agents of infection contain large quantities of nucleoprotein. The plant viruses (tobacco mosaic virus, for instance) are almost pure nucleoproteins containing RNA. The bacterial viruses (bacteriophages) on the other hand contain DNA. The molecular weights of the viral nucleic acids are undoubtedly very large. By extremely mild treatment with neutral salts, RNA with a molecular weight of approximately 10^6 has been obtained from tobacco mosaic virus. This structure is readily degraded by dilute alkali to one with a molecular weight of 50,000. These results emphasize the difficulty of obtaining nucleic acids which are unmodified from their native state, and suggest that few if any "native" samples of nucleic acids have been prepared.

REFERENCES

1. Van R. Potter, *Nucleic Acid Outlines, Vol. I, Structure and Metabolism,* Burgess Publishing Company, Minneapolis, 1960.

   An outstanding discussion of a complicated area of biochemistry written in the usual imaginative style of the author.   The student who plans to do graduate work in biochemistry is urged to become thoroughly familiar with this fine book.

2. C. B. Anfinsen, *The Molecular Basis of Evolution,* John Wiley and Sons, New York, 1959.

   Chapter 3 contains an excellent discussion of the chemical structure of DNA and includes the Watson and Crick model.

Part II

Metabolism of
Biological Compounds

Six

Biochemical Energetics

Introduction

Intermediary metabolism is the study of the synthesis (anabolism) and the degradation (catabolism) of the cell constituents of living organisms. In the intact cell both processes go on simultaneously, and energy released from the degradation of some compounds may be utilized in the synthesis of other cellular components. Thus the concept of an *energy cycle* has developed in biochemistry in which foodstuffs, which represent a source of potential chemical energy, are degraded through known enzymatic reactions to produce a few different energy-rich compounds. These compounds can then, in turn, be utilized by other cellular enzymes to synthesize new cellular constituents which again represent a supply of potential energy. In addition, however, these energy-rich compounds may also be utilized by the cell to carry out specific physiological activities such as movement, growth, secretion, absorption, and conductance.

To appreciate the energy relations in biochemistry it is necessary to define and understand a few fundamental terms of *thermodynamics,* a science that relates the energy changes which occur in chemical and physical processes.

The Concept of Free Energy

One thermodynamic concept particularly useful to biochemists is *free energy (F).* We may speak of the *free-energy content* of a substance A but this quantity cannot be measured experimentally. If A is converted to B in a chemical reaction, however,

$$A \rightleftharpoons B \tag{6-1}$$

it is possible to speak of the *change* in *free energy* (ΔF) as A is converted to B. If the free-energy content of the product B (F_B) is less than the free-energy content of the reactant A (F_A), the ΔF will be a negative quantity. That is,

$$\Delta F = F_B - F_A$$
$$= \text{negative quantity when } F_A > F_B$$

For ΔF to be negative means that the reaction occurs with a decrease in free energy. Similarly, if B is converted back to A, the reaction will involve an increase in free energy, that is, ΔF will be positive. Experience has shown that reactions which occur spontaneously do so with a *decrease* in free energy ($-\Delta F$). On the other hand, if the ΔF for a reaction is known to be positive, that reaction will occur only if energy is supplied to the system in some manner to drive the reaction. Reactions having a negative ΔF are termed *exergonic;* those that have a positive ΔF are called *endergonic.*

Experience has also shown that although the ΔF for a given process is negative this fact has no relationship whatever to the rate at which the reaction proceeds. For example, glucose can be oxidized by O_2 to CO_2 and H_2O according to equation 6-2.

$$C_6H_{12}O_6 + 6O_2 \longrightarrow 6CO_2 + 6H_2O \tag{6-2}$$

The ΔF for this reaction is a very large negative quantity, approximately $-686{,}000$ cal/mole of glucose. The large $-\Delta F$ has no relationship to the rate of the reaction, however. Oxidation of glucose may occur in a matter of a few seconds in the presence of a catalyst in a bomb calorimeter. Reaction 6-2 also goes on in most living organisms at rates varying from minutes to several hours. Glucose can nevertheless be kept in a bottle on the shelf for years in the presence of air without undergoing oxidation.

The free-energy change of a reaction can be related to other thermodynamic properties of A and B by the expression

$$\Delta F = \Delta H - T\,\Delta S \tag{6-3}$$

In this expression ΔH is the *change in heat content* that occurs as the reaction proceeds at constant pressure, ΔS is the change in *entropy,* a term which refers to the degree of orderliness in a molecule, and T is the absolute temperature at which the reaction occurs. The absolute heat H and entropy S contents of substances A and B are difficult to measure, but it is possible to measure the changes in these quantities as they are interconverted (reaction 6-1). The ΔH for a reaction may be measured in a calorimeter, a device for measuring quantitatively the heat produced at constant pressure. To describe the measurement of ΔS and the absolute entropy content of chemical substances is beyond the scope of this book.

Determination of ΔF

For reaction 6-1 it is possible to derive the expression

$$\Delta F = \Delta F^\circ + RT \ln \frac{[B]}{[A]} \qquad (6\text{-}4)$$

where ΔF° is the *standard change in free energy*, soon to be defined, R is the universal gas constant, T is the absolute temperature, and [B] and [A] are the concentrations of A and B in moles per liter. Precisely, [B] and [A] should be replaced by the activities of A and B, a_A and a_B. As with pH, however, this corrrection is not usually made, because the activity coefficients are seldom known for the concentrations of compounds existing in the cell.

From equation 6-4 the ΔF for a reaction is a function of the concentrations of reactant and product as well as the standard free-energy change ΔF°. It is possible to evaluate ΔF° if we consider the ΔF at equilibrium. At equilibrium there is no net conversion of A to B, and hence the change in free energy ΔF is 0. Similarly the ratio of [B] to [A] is the ratio at equilibrium or the equilibrium constant K_{eq}. Substituting these quantities in equation (6-4),

$$0 = \Delta F^\circ + RT \ln K_{eq}$$
$$\boxed{\Delta F^\circ = -RT \ln K_{eq}} \qquad (6\text{-}5)$$

When the constants are evaluated ($R = 1.987$ cal/mole/deg, $25°C = 298° T$, and $\ln x = 2.303 \log_{10} x$), the equation becomes

$$\Delta F^\circ = -(1.987)(298)(2.303) \log_{10} K_{eq}$$
$$\boxed{= -1363 \log_{10} K_{eq}} \qquad (6\text{-}6)$$
$$\text{at } 25°C$$

This equation relating the ΔF° to K_{eq} is an extremely useful way to determine the ΔF° for a specific reaction. If the concentration of both reactants and products at equilibrium can be measured, the K_{eq} and in turn the ΔF° of the reaction can be calculated. Of course, if the K_{eq} is extremely large or extremely small, this method of measuring ΔF° is of little value because the equilibrium concentration of the reactants and products respectively will be too small to measure. The ΔF° for each of a series of K_{eq} ranging from 0.001 to 10^3 is calculated in Table 6-1.

From inspection of Table 6-1 it is clear that reactions which have a K_{eq} greater than 1 proceed with a decrease in free energy. Thus for reaction 6-1, if the $K_{eq} = 1000$ (that is, if B/A is 1000), the tendency is for the reaction to proceed in the direction of the formation of B. If we start with 1001 parts of A, equilibrium will be reached only when

Table 6-1.   Relation between K_{eq} and $\Delta F°$

K_{eq}	$\log_{10}K_{eq}$	$\Delta F° = -1363 \log_{10}K_{eq}$
0.001	−3	4089 cal
0.01	−2	2726 cal
0.1	−1	1363 cal
1.0	0	0
10	1	−1363 cal
100	2	−2726 cal
1000	3	−4089 cal

1000 parts (or 99.9 per cent) of A have been converted to B.   If reaction 6-1 has a K_{eq} of 10^{-3} (that is, if B/A = 0.001), equilibrium will be attained when only 1 part or 0.1 per cent of A has been converted to B.

It is also possible to evaluate $\Delta F°$ for the situation where both the reactants and products are present at unit concentrations.   When [A] = [B] = 1 molal, equation 6-4 becomes

$$\Delta F = \Delta F° + RT \ln \frac{1}{1}$$

$$= \Delta F°$$

Thus $\Delta F°$ may be defined as the change in free energy when reactants and products are present in unit concentration, or more broadly, in their "standard state."   The standard state for solutes in solution is unit molal; for gases, 1 atm; for solvents such as water, unit activity.   If water is a reactant or a product of a reaction, its concentration in the standard state is taken as unity in the expression for the ΔF (equation 6-4).   If a gas is either formed or produced, its standard state concentration is taken as 1 atm.   If a hydrogen ion is produced or utilized in a reaction its concentration will be taken at 1 molal or pH = 0.

Since in the cell few if any reactions occur at pH 0 but rather at pH 7.0, the standard free-energy change $\Delta F°$ is frequently corrected for the difference in pH.   Conversely, the equilibrium of a reaction may be measured at some pH other than 0.   The standard free-energy change $\Delta F°$ at any pH other than 0 is designated as $\Delta F'$ and the pH for a given $\Delta F'$ should be indicated.   Of course if a proton is neither formed nor utilized in the reaction, $\Delta F'$ will be independent of pH and $\Delta F°$ will equal $\Delta F'$.

An example will demonstrate the use of these terms.   In the presence of the enzyme phosphoglucomutase, glucose-1-phosphate is converted to glucose-6-phosphate.   Starting with 0.020M glucose-1-phosphate at 25°C, it is observed that the concentration of this compound decreases to 0.001M while the concentration of glucose-6-phosphate increases to 0.019M. The K_{eq} of the reaction is 0.019 divided by 0.001, or 19. Therefore

$$\Delta F^\circ = -RT \ln K_{eq}$$
$$= -1363 \log_{10} K_{eq}$$
$$= -1363 \log_{10} 19$$
$$= (-1363)(1.28)$$
$$= -1745 \text{ cal}$$

The ΔF° for this reaction will be independent of pH since acid is neither produced nor used up in the reaction. This amount of free-energy decrease (-1745 cal) will occur when 1 mole of glucose-1-phosphate is converted to 1 mole of glucose-6-phosphate under such conditions that the *concentration of each compound is maintained at 1 molal,* a situation quite different from the experimental situation just described for measuring the K_{eq}. Indeed these conditions of *unit molality* are difficult to maintain either in the test tube or in the cell. It should be pointed out, however, that the concentration of a particular substance (for example, glucose-6-phosphate) may frequently be maintained relatively constant at some concentration over a time interval, since it may be produced in one reaction while it is being used up in another. This condition of *steady-state* equilibrium undoubtedly exists in many biological systems and requires that thermodynamics be applied to the steady-state condition rather than to the equilibrium condition for which thermodynamics was first developed. A second complication is that the thermodynamic quantities discussed in this chapter apply only to reactions occurring in homogeneous systems, whereas much metabolism occurs in heterogeneous systems involving more than one phase. As a result most of the values reported in the literature cannot be considered more than 10 per cent accurate. Nevertheless the concept of the standard free-energy change has found many fruitful applications in intermediary metabolism.

ΔF and Oxidation Reduction

The ΔF of a reaction which involves an oxidation-reduction process may be related to the difference in oxidation-reduction potentials (ΔE_0) of the reactants. A detailed discussion of electromotive force is beyond the scope of this book, but some appreciation of the term *oxidation-reduction potential* is necessary.

A reducing agent may be defined as a substance that tends to furnish an electron and be oxidized;

$$Fe^{2+} \xrightarrow{\text{oxidized}} Fe^{3+} + 1 \text{ electron}$$

Similarly Fe^{3+} is an oxidizing agent because it can accept electrons and be reduced.

$$Fe^{3+} + 1 \text{ electron} \longrightarrow Fe^{2+}$$

Other substances such as H_2 gas and organic compounds such as succinic acid can serve as reducing agents and be oxidized:

$$\tfrac{1}{2}H_2 \longrightarrow H^+ + \text{electron}$$

$$
\begin{array}{c}
\text{COOH} \\
| \\
\text{CH}_2 \\
| \\
\text{CH}_2 \\
| \\
\text{COOH}
\end{array}
\longrightarrow
\begin{array}{c}
\text{H} \quad \text{COOH} \\
\diagdown \ / \\
\text{C} \\
\| \\
\text{C} \\
/ \ \diagdown \\
\text{HOOC} \quad \text{H}
\end{array}
+ 2H^+ + 2 \text{ electrons}
$$

From right to left these reactions represent reductions. Clearly the tendency or potentiality for each of these agents to furnish or accept electrons will be due to the specific properties of that compound, and hence it is necessary to have some standard for comparison. That standard is H_2, which has been arbitrarily given the oxidation-reduction potential E_0 of 0.000 v at pH 0. Since a proton is produced when H_2 is oxidized, the potential will vary with pH and at pH 7.0 the oxidation-reduction potential E_0' of H_2 may be calculated to be -0.420 v. With this as a standard it is possible to determine the potential of any other compound capable of oxidation reduction with reference to hydrogen. A list of such potentials, which includes several coenzymes and substrates to be discussed in subsequent chapters, is found in Table 6-2. The point to be stressed here is that hydrogen, which is a very good reducing agent, has the lowest value for E_0' of any of the substances listed at pH 7.0. Thus Fe^{2+} iron, whose Fe^{2+}/Fe^{3+} pair has an E_0' of 0.771 at pH 7.0, is not a good reducing agent. Instead it follows that Fe^{3+} will be a strong oxidizing agent and would be easily reduced by H_2 or, theoretically, by the reduced form of any other compound on this chart with a more negative E_0'.

It is possible to derive the expression $\Delta F' = -n\mathscr{F}\Delta E_0'$ where n is the number of electrons transferred in an oxidation-reduction reaction, $\mathscr{F}$ is Faraday's constant (23,063 cal/v equiv.) and $\Delta E_0'$ is the difference in potential between the oxidizing and reducing agents. In the case of equation 6-7, which describes the reaction between H_2 and Fe^{3+},

$$\tfrac{1}{2}H_2 + Fe^{3+} \longrightarrow H^+ + Fe^{2+} \tag{6-7}$$

$\Delta E_0'$ will equal the E_0' for Fe^{2+}/Fe^{3+} minus the E_0' for $\frac{1}{2}H_2/H^+$ or $0.771 - (-0.420) = 1.291$ v. Hence

$$\Delta F' = (-1)(23{,}063)(1.291)$$
$$= -29{,}800 \text{ cal}$$

Because this figure is a large negative quantity the reaction is feasible thermodynamically. Whether the reaction will occur at a detectable rate is not indicated by the information at hand.

In a similar manner the $\Delta F'$ may be calculated for the oxidation of NADH by molecular O_2, a common reaction in living tissues:

$$NADH + H^+ + \tfrac{1}{2}O_2 \longrightarrow NAD^+ + H_2O$$

In this reaction $n = 2$, and $\Delta E_0' = 0.816 - (-0.320)$ or 1.136 v, and

$$\Delta F' = -n\mathfrak{F}\Delta E_0'$$
$$= (-2)(23{,}063)(1.135)$$
$$= -52{,}350 \text{ cal}$$

We re-emphasize that the fact that the $\Delta F'$ is a large negative quantity has no bearing on whether NADH is rapidly oxidized. As a matter of fact, NADH is stable in the presence of O_2 and will react only in the presence of appropriate enzymes.

Table 6-2.   Oxidation-Reduction Potentials

Compound	E_0' at pH 7.0
$\frac{1}{2}H_2/H^+$	-0.420
$NADH/NAD^+$	-0.320
Leucoriboflavin/riboflavin	-0.20
Lactate/pyruvate	-0.19
Malate/oxalacetate	-0.166
Yellow enzyme, reduced/oxidized	-0.122
Cytochrome a, reduced/oxidized	0.29
Cytochrome b, reduced/oxidized	-0.04
Cytochrome c, reduced/oxidized	0.25
Succinate/fumarate	0.031
Fe^{2+}/Fe^{3+}	0.771
Water/oxygen	0.816

Coupling of Reactions

In the cell the energy released or made available in an exergonic reaction is utilized to drive other endergonic reactions and thereby made to do work.   The only way this can occur is by common reactants in a process known as the *coupling of reactions*.   As an example, consider reactions 6-8 and 6-9.

$$A \rightleftharpoons B \qquad K_{eq} = 0.1 \qquad \Delta F^\circ = +1363 \text{ cal} \qquad (6\text{-}8)$$

$$B \rightleftharpoons C \qquad K_{eq} = 1000 \qquad \Delta F^\circ = -4089 \text{ cal} \qquad (6\text{-}9)$$

In the first reaction, which is endergonic, the ratio of [B]/[A] will be 1/10 at equilibrium.   For the second reaction, the ratio of [C]/[B] will be 1000/1.   Therefore at equilibrium there will be 10 parts of A for every 1000 parts of C.   The overall reaction can be obtained by adding 6-8 and 6-9; the equilibrium constant for the overall reaction will be 100, and reaction is exergonic:

$$A \rightleftharpoons C, \qquad K_{eq} = \frac{[C]}{[A]} = 100, \qquad \Delta F^\circ = -2726 \text{ cal}$$

In this process we could start with 1011 parts of A.   If equilibrium is attained according to the first reaction, approximately 9 per cent or about 91 parts of B will be formed.   As soon as the concentration of B builds up, however, about 99.9 per cent of B will in turn be converted to C in keeping with the equilibrium requirement for reaction 6-9.   At final equilibrium 10 parts of A, 1 part of B, and 1000 parts of C will exist; this corresponds to converting 99 per cent of the A initially present to C.   In this process B has been the common reactant through which an endergonic process has been "driven" by the exergonic reaction.   It should be apparent that this process has not been accomplished by any mysterious transfer of some form of energy but simply follows from a consideration of the equilibria for these reactions.   In the cell coupled reactions are likely to occur when the concentration of a reactant is increased or when the concentration of a product is decreased.

Energy-Rich Compounds

In all nature one compound repeatedly functions as a common reactant linking endergonic processes to others that are exergonic.   This compound, adenosine triphosphate (ATP), is one of a group of "energy-rich" or "high-energy" compounds whose structure will now be considered.   They are called "high-energy" compounds because when they undergo hydrolytic reactions they exhibit a large decrease in free energy.   They are in general unstable to acid, to alkali, and to heat.   In subsequent chapters their synthesis and utilization will be described in detail.

It is informative to compare the $\Delta F'$ of hydrolysis of ATP with that of other phosphate compounds. The hydrolysis of the terminal phosphate of ATP may be written as shown. The $\Delta F'$ at pH 7 has been estimated

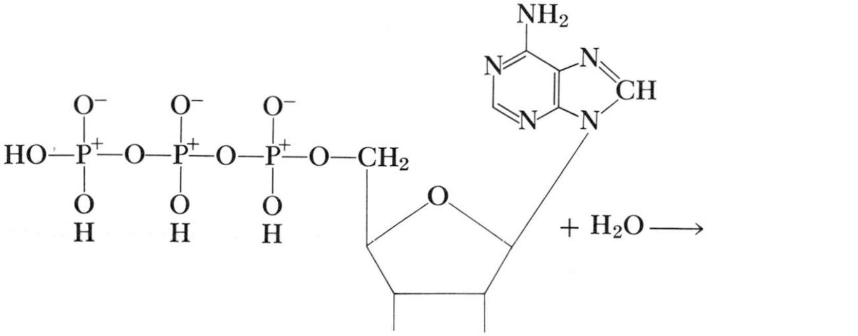

adenosine-5'-triphosphate
(ATP)

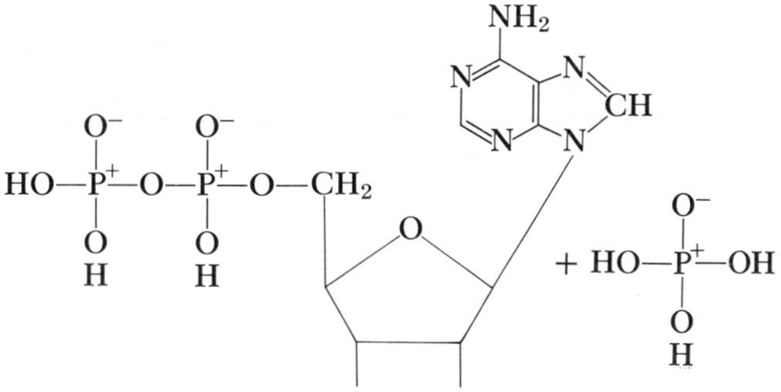

adenosine-5'-diphosphate
(ADP)

$$\Delta F' = -8000 \text{ cal (pH 7.0)}$$

to be -8000 cal/mole. This is in contrast to the hydrolysis of glucose-6-phosphate. That hydrolysis results in a much smaller decrease in free energy.

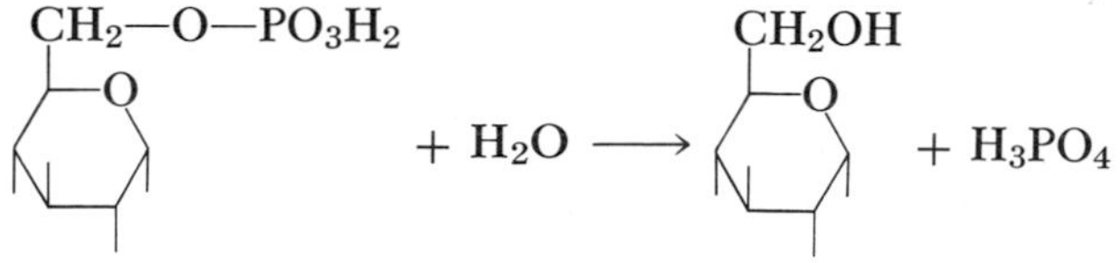

$$\Delta F' = -3300 \text{ cal (pH 7.0)}$$

We may properly ask why this large difference in the free energy of hydrolysis exists. In the case of ATP, the structure under consideration

is a pyrophosphate bond, the general structure of which may be
represented:

$$\underset{\underset{H}{\overset{|}{O}}}{\overset{\overset{O^-}{|}}{R-O-\overset{+}{P}}}-O-\underset{\underset{H}{\overset{|}{O}}}{\overset{\overset{O^-}{|}}{\overset{+}{P}}}-O-\underset{\underset{H}{\overset{|}{O}}}{\overset{\overset{O^-}{|}}{\overset{+}{P}}}-OH$$

This structure is the most accurate representation of the phosphate
groups of ATP where R represents the adenosine moiety. In this structure the electronegative character of the oxygen atom is recognized and
a residual positive charge induced on the phosphorous atom is indicated.
Energy is required to overcome the electrostatic repulsion of like
charges on the adjacent phosphorous atoms and this energy is liberated
when hydrolysis occurs.

A second factor contributing to the free energy of hydrolysis is the
greater stability of the products (ADP and inorganic phosphate) in contrast to that of ATP itself. A clue to this stability is found in the number of resonance forms which may be written for reactants and products.
The inorganic phosphate formed after hydrolysis possesses a number of
resonance structures.

$$\underset{\overset{||}{O}}{\overset{\overset{O^-}{|}}{HO-\overset{+}{P}}}-O^- \qquad\qquad \underset{\overset{|}{O^-}}{\overset{\overset{O^-}{|}}{HO-\overset{+}{P}}}=O \qquad\qquad \underset{\overset{|}{O^-}}{\overset{\overset{O}{||}}{HO-\overset{+}{P}}}-O^-$$

The number of resonance forms for ATP is obviously less because two
of the oxygens participate in the pyrophosphate bond structures of the
nucleoside triphosphate. A consequence of this effect, known as "opposing resonance," is that greater stability resides in the compounds for
which a larger number of resonance forms may be written. (See Appendix 2 for a definition of resonance.)

In glucose-6-phosphate the phosphorous atom is not adjacent to
another positively charged atom; the arguments for a large decrease in
free energy on hydrolysis therefore do not exist with this compound

$$\underset{\underset{H}{\overset{|}{O}}}{\overset{\overset{O^-}{|}}{R-CH_2-O-\overset{+}{P}}}-OH$$

where R is the remainder of the glucose molecule. In addition, since
the opportunity for resonance structures in the phosphate esters is ap-

preciable in contrast to the pyrophosphate compounds, the esters represent a more stable form which exhibits a smaller decrease of free energy on hydrolysis. Other calculations have shown that the driving force in the hydrolysis of a low-energy phosphate ester is related to the high concentration of H_2O (55 molar) which participates in these reactions.

The hydrolysis of ADP to AMP and inorganic phosphate also exhibits a similarly large decrease in free energy. On the other hand, the hy-

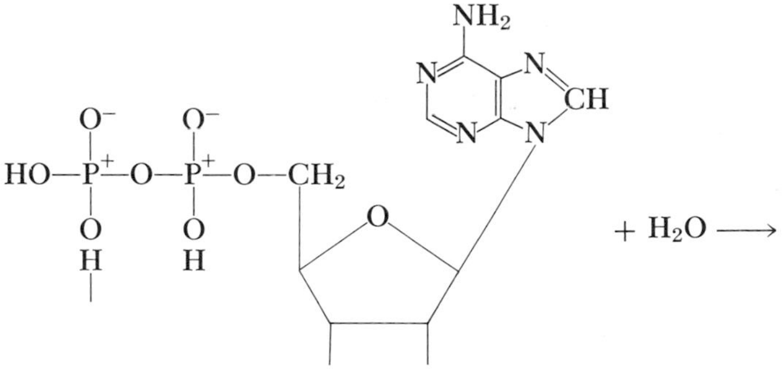

adenosine-5'-diphosphate
(ADP)

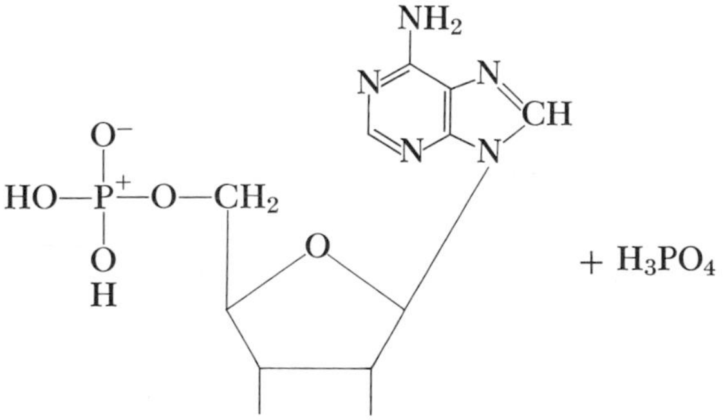

$+ H_2O \longrightarrow$

adenosine-5'-phosphate
(AMP)

$+ H_3PO_4$

$$\Delta F' = -6500 \text{ cal (pH 7.0)}$$

drolysis of the third phosphate, which is bound in an ester linkage to the ribose, occurs with the smaller $\Delta F'$ characteristic of phosphate esters. (See page 108.)

In the past it has been common practice in biochemistry to refer to high-energy and low-energy phosphate bonds. Lipmann introduced the symbol ~ph to indicate a high-energy phosphate structure. This practice has resulted in the tendency to think of the energy as concentrated in the single chemical bond. This is erroneous, because the free energy

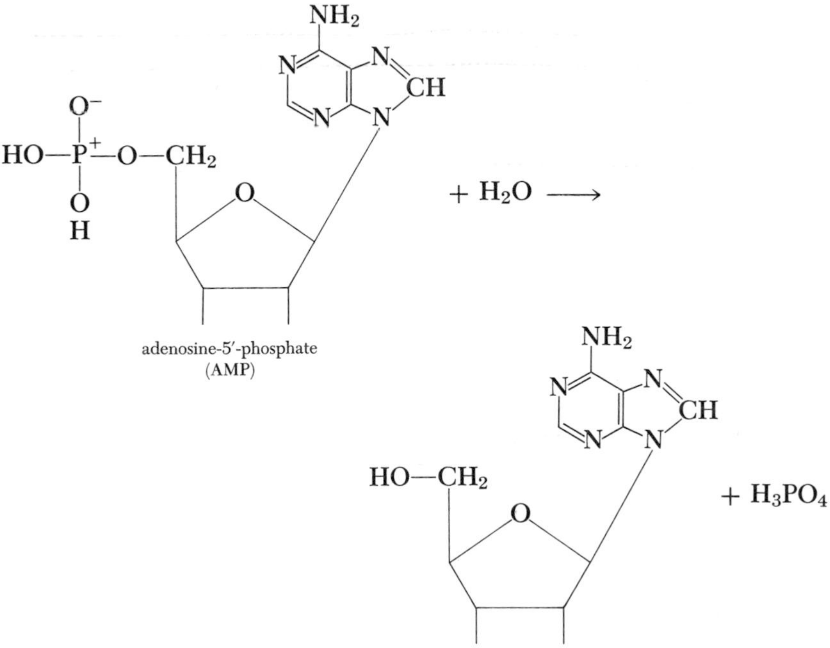

adenosine-5'-phosphate
(AMP)

$+ H_2O \longrightarrow$

adenosine

$+ H_3PO_4$

$$\Delta F' = -2200 \text{ cal (pH 7.0)}$$

change ΔF depends on the structure of the compound hydrolyzed and the products of hydrolysis. Moreover, the ΔF refers to the specific chemical reaction involved, namely, the *hydrolysis* of the compound. Thus it is more common now to refer to *energy-rich compounds* or *high-energy compounds.*

There are other types of energy-rich compounds which contain phosphate; acyl phosphates, guanidinium phosphates, and enolic phosphates. Typical of the acyl phosphate group is acetyl phosphate; its hydrolysis may be written:

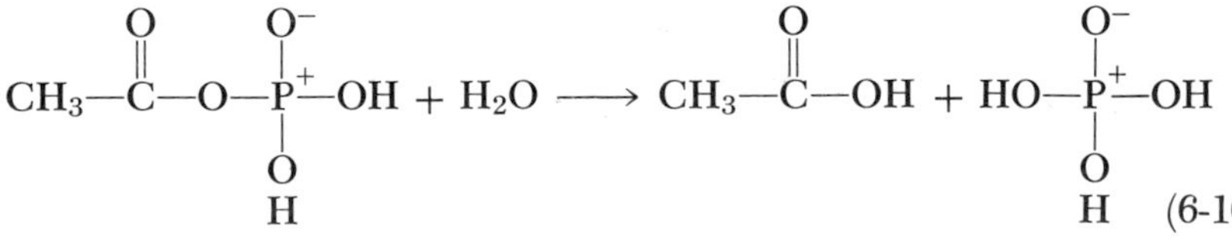

acetyl phosphate

$$\Delta F' = -10,000 \text{ cal (pH 7.0)}$$

At pH 7.0, $\Delta F'$ is approximately $-10,000$ cal/mole. Again the electronegative character of the oxygen atom results in residual negative charges on the oxygen atoms and induced positive charges on the carboxyl carbon and phosphate atoms.   Structures I and II are permissible resonance forms.   Structure III, where positive charges are placed

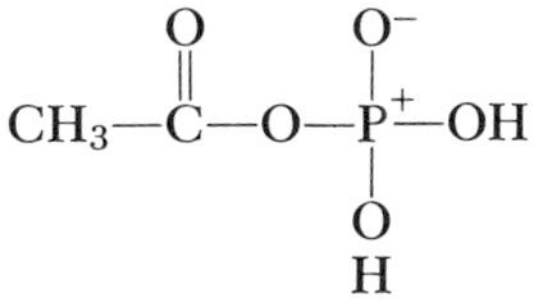

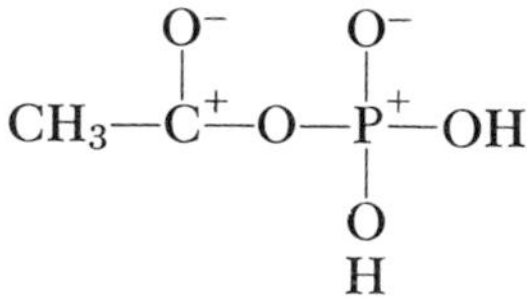

on adjacent atoms, is not permissible, and only structures I and II contribute to the resonance stability of the acyl phosphate.   The products of hydrolysis are more stable by virtue of the resonance forms IV, V, and VI that may be written for the carboxyl anion.   In addition, the

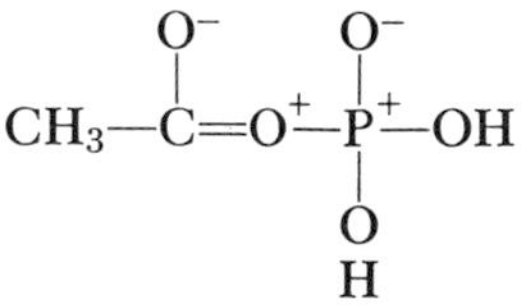

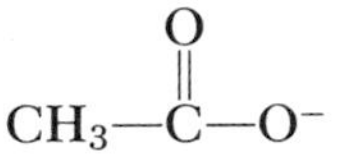

other product of the reaction, inorganic phosphate, has numerous resonance structures which contribute to its stability.   The electrostatic repulsion of like charges in structure II, which is a permissible resonance form, also contributes to the instability of the acyl phosphate and results in a larger negative value for the $\Delta F'$ of hydrolysis of acetyl phosphate.

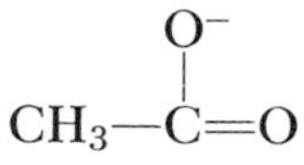

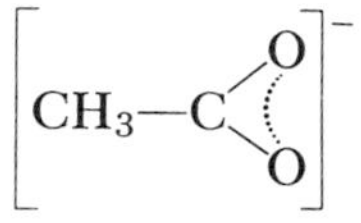

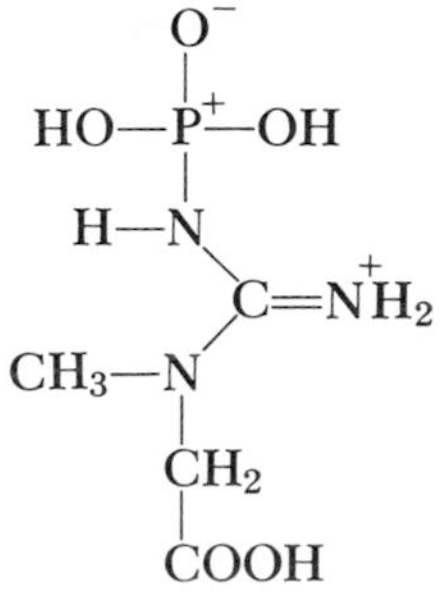

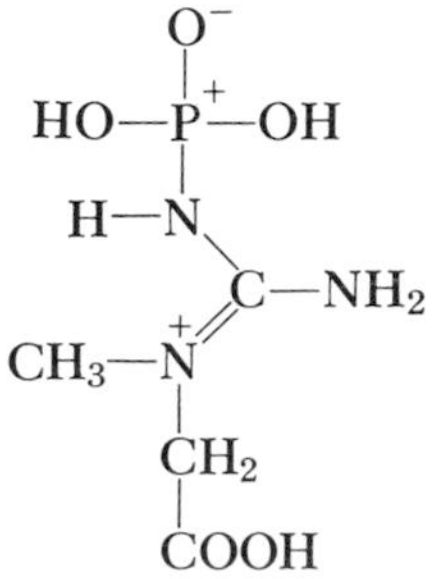

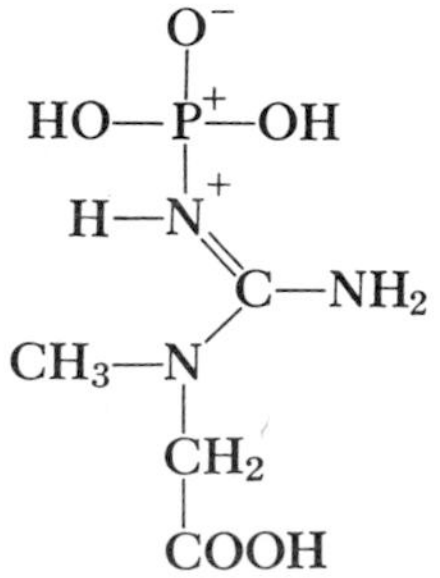

   A third type of energy-rich phosphate compound is the guanidinium phosphate represented by creatine phosphate ($\Delta F'$ of hydrolysis = $-10{,}500$ cal, pH 7.0).   As in the case of the pyrophosphates and acyl phosphates, creatine phosphate is unstable by virtue of opposing resonance.   The structures of creatine phosphate that may be written are VII and VIII.   Structure IX, in which two like charges are placed on adjacent atoms, is not possible, and the stability of creatine phosphate is less for that reason.   In the case of the products structures X, XI, and XII may be written for creatine itself as well as the usual number for inorganic phosphate written previously.

$$
\begin{array}{ccc}
\underset{\substack{| \\ CH_3-N}}{\overset{\substack{H_2N \\ \diagdown \\ C=\overset{+}{N}H_2}}{}} & \underset{\substack{| \\ CH_3-\overset{+}{N}}}{\overset{\substack{H_2N \\ \diagdown \\ \diagup C-NH_2}}{}} & \underset{\substack{| \\ CH_3-N}}{\overset{\substack{\overset{+}{H_2N} \\ \diagdown \\ C-NH_2}}{}} \\
\underset{COOH}{\overset{|}{CH_2}} & \underset{COOH}{\overset{|}{CH_2}} & \underset{COOH}{\overset{|}{CH_2}} \\
X & XI & XII
\end{array}
$$

A fourth type of energy-rich phosphate compound is represented by phosphoenol pyruvic acid, the hydrolysis of which is written:

$$
\underset{\substack{\text{phosphoenol pyruvic} \\ \text{acid}}}{\overset{\substack{COOH \\ | \\ C-O-PO_3H_2 \\ || \\ CH_2}}{}} + H_2O \longrightarrow \underset{\text{pyruvic acid}}{\overset{\substack{COOH \\ | \\ C=O \\ | \\ CH_3}}{}} + H_3PO_4 \quad (6\text{-}11)
$$

$$\Delta F' = -12{,}800 \text{ cal (pH 7.0)}$$

The $\Delta F'$ of hydrolysis is about $-13{,}000$ cal/mole.   This compound has a high energy of hydrolysis because the pyruvic acid is held by the phosphate group in the much less stable *enolic* form.   In the reaction just given, the enol form of pyruvic acid may be considered as an intermediate which will immediately ketonize to form the much more stable keto acid.

$$
\underset{\substack{\text{phosphoenol} \\ \text{pyruvic acid}}}{\overset{\substack{COOH \\ | \\ C-O-PO_3H_2 \\ || \\ CH_2}}{}} + H_2O \longrightarrow H_3PO_4 + \underset{\substack{\text{pyruvic acid} \\ \text{(enol)}}}{\overset{\substack{COOH \\ | \\ C-OH \\ || \\ CH_2}}{}} \longrightarrow \underset{\substack{\text{pyruvic acid} \\ \text{(keto)}}}{\overset{\substack{COOH \\ | \\ C=O \\ | \\ CH_3}}{}} \quad (6\text{-}12)
$$

The $\Delta F'$ for the enol-to-keto tautomerization is estimated to be from -5500 to -9000 cal and thus contributes to the high $\Delta F'$ of hydrolysis of the enolic phosphate.

The *thioester* constitutes a fifth type of high-energy compound. Typical of this group is acetyl-CoA, whose structure and hydrolysis is represented in equation 6-13.

$$
\underset{}{\overset{\substack{O \\ || \\ CH_3-C-S-CoA}}{}} + H_2O \longrightarrow \overset{\substack{O \\ || \\ CH_3-C-OH}}{} + HS-CoA \quad (6\text{-}13)
$$

$$\Delta F' = -8200 \text{ cal (pH 7.0)}$$

The $\Delta F'$ of hydrolysis of this compound is about -8000 cal/mole.

In considering the reasons for the relative instability of the thioester, the factor of opposing resonance is of major importance. Structures XIII and XIV are possible resonance forms that may be written, but XV is not permissible. This is due to the fact that the sulfur atom has little tendency to form double bonds (see Chapter 13).

$$CH_3-\overset{\overset{\displaystyle O}{\|}}{C}-S-CoA \qquad CH_3-\overset{\overset{\displaystyle O^-}{|}}{\underset{}{C^{\pm}}}-S-CoA \qquad CH_3-\overset{\overset{\displaystyle O^-}{|}}{C}=S^{\pm}-CoA$$

XIII   XIV   XV

On hydrolysis the three resonance forms IV, V, and VI previously written for the acetyl anion are possible. In addition, the free energy of ionization of the acid groups produced on hydrolysis undoubtedly contributes to the $\Delta F'$ of hydrolysis for the thioester.

In the preceding discussion of the hydrolysis of energy-rich compounds the ionization of the hydrolysis products has not been taken into consideration. For example, the hydrolysis of acetyl phosphate results in the formation of two new acid groups which can ionize to form protons.

$$CH_3-\overset{\overset{\displaystyle O}{\|}}{C}-O-\overset{\overset{\displaystyle O^-}{|}}{\underset{\underset{\displaystyle H}{|}}{\underset{O}{P^{\pm}}}}-OH + H_2O \longrightarrow CH_3-\overset{\overset{\displaystyle O}{\|}}{C}-OH + HO-\overset{\overset{\displaystyle O^-}{|}}{\underset{\underset{\displaystyle H}{|}}{\underset{O}{P^{\pm}}}}-OH$$

$$(6\text{-}14)$$

If reaction 6-14 occurs at pH 0, the standard state for H^+, none of the dissociable acid groups will be ionized. In the cell the pH will usually be near 7.0, however, at which value the primary and secondary hydrogens on the phosphoric acid as well as the hydrogen on the acetic acid will be dissociated. At pH 7.0, therefore, reaction 6-14 is more accurately written as

$$CH_3-\overset{\overset{\displaystyle O}{\|}}{C}-O-\overset{\overset{\displaystyle O^-}{|}}{\underset{\underset{\displaystyle O_-}{|}}{P^{\pm}}}-O^- + H_2O \longrightarrow HO-\overset{\overset{\displaystyle O^-}{|}}{\underset{\underset{\displaystyle O^-}{|}}{P^{\pm}}}-O^- + CH_3-\overset{\overset{\displaystyle O}{\|}}{C}-OH \xrightarrow{\text{dissociates}} CH_3-\overset{\overset{\displaystyle O}{\|}}{C}-O^- + H^+$$

The acetic acid formed will immediately ionize to form acetate anions; this process occurs with a significant decrease in free energy ($\Delta F' = -3200$ cal) and indeed contributes to the $\Delta F'$ of hydrolysis of acetyl phosphate. Similar arguments are valid for any of the energy-rich compounds where a product with a dissociable proton is formed. It should be pointed out that the tertiary hydrogen ($pK_3 = 12.7$) of H_3PO_4 which is formed on hydrolysis will not be ionized at pH 7.0 and therefore its ionization need not be taken into consideration.

In subsequent chapters the role of these energy-rich compounds will be discussed in detail. At that time it will be seen that they play an essential part in coupling the production of energy from foodstuffs to the utilization of that energy by the cell for its multifold activities.

REFERENCES

1. A. B. Pardee and L. L. Ingraham in *Metabolic Pathways*, edited by D. M. Greenberg, Academic Press, New York, 2nd edition, 1960, Vol. 1, Chapter 1.

2. J. B. Neilands and P. K. Stumpf, *Outlines of Enzyme Chemistry*, John Wiley and Sons, New York, 2nd edition, 1958, Chapter 13.

   Two references which provide a firm introduction to the subject of energy relations in metabolism.

3. M. J. Johnson in *The Enzymes*, Vol. III, edited by P. D. Boyer, H. Lardy, and K. Myrbäck, Academic Press, New York, 1960, Chapter 21.

   An extraordinarily lucid article on the subject of enzymic equilibria and thermo-dynamics.

4. F. M. Huennekens and H. R. Whitely in *Comparative Biochemistry*, Vol. I, edited by M. Florkin and H. S. Mason, Academic Press, New York, 1960, Chapter 4.

5. M. R. Atkinson and R. K. Morton in *Comparative Biochemistry*, Vol. II, edited by M. Florkin and H. S. Mason, Academic Press, New York, 1960, Chapter 1

   These articles contain valuable thermodynamic data for the phosphate compounds commonly encountered in biochemistry.

Seven

Enzymes

Introduction

One of the unique characteristics of a living cell is its ability to permit complex reactions to proceed rapidly at the temperature of the surrounding environment. In the absence of the cell these reactions would proceed too slowly. The complex metabolic machinery so fundamental to a cell could not exist under such sluggish conditions. The principal agents which participate in the remarkable transformations in the cell belong to a group of proteins named enzymes.

An enzyme is a protein that is synthesized in a living cell and catalyzes or speeds up a thermodynamically possible reaction so that the rate of the reaction is compatible with the biochemical process essential for the maintenance of a cell. The enzyme in no way modifies the equilibrium constant or the ΔF of a reaction. The enzyme works at extremely small concentrations, completely out of proportion to the change it catalyzes. The protein nature of the enzyme confers on the enzyme the property of specificity; that is, one enzyme does not speed up all reactions, but rather thousands of different enzymes are required to catalyze the thousands of different reactions that occur in the cell. Being a protein, an enzyme loses its catalytic properties if subjected to agents like heat, strong acids or bases, organic solvents, or other materials which denature the protein.

Let us now describe the properties of the enzymically catalyzed reaction.

Effect of Enzyme and Substrate Concentration

The rate of any enzyme-catalyzed reaction depends directly on the concentration of the enzyme. Figure 7-1 depicts the relation between the rate of a reaction and increasing enzyme concentration in the presence of an excess of the compound which is being transformed (also called the substrate).

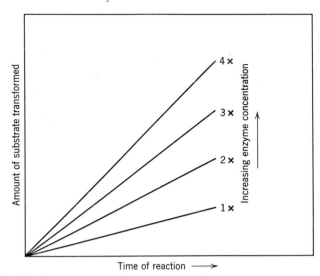

Fig. 7-1. Effect of enzyme concentration on reaction rate, assuming that substrate concentration is in saturating amounts.

With a fixed concentration of enzyme and with increasing substrate concentration, a second important relationship is observed. A typical curve is shown in Figure 7-2. Let us discuss the implications of this curve in more detail.

With fixed enzyme concentration, an increase of substrate will result at first in a very rapid rise in velocity or reaction rate. As the substrate concentration continues to increase, however, the rate of reaction begins to slow down until, with a large substrate concentration, no further change in velocity is observed. The velocity of the reaction obtained at this high substrate concentration is defined as the *maximum velocity* (V) of the enzyme-catalyzed reaction under the specified conditions.

The substrate concentration required to yield half the maximum velocity (V/2) can be readily determined from Figure 7-2 and is an important constant in enzyme chemistry. It defines the Michaelis constant or K_m. Under carefully defined conditions of temperature, pH, and ionic strength of the buffer, this constant K_m *approximates* the dissociation constant of an enzyme-substrate complex. The reciprocal of K_m, or $1/K_m$, approximates the affinity of an enzyme for its substrate. Thus a K_m of 0.1 mole/l of substrate would indicate that the active site of an enzyme is half saturated when its substrate is present at that concentration. The enzyme therefore has a *low* affinity for its substrate. On the other hand, a K_m of 0.0001 mole/l indicates that the enzyme has a *high* affinity, since it is half saturated at this low substrate concentration. Enzymes that require a high substrate concentration to attain reasonable rates of reaction may operate in the living cell at low rates unless a localized high concentration of substrate can be organized.

Some biochemists have reasoned that those substrates having extremely low K_m's with a specific enzyme are therefore the natural substrates and those with a high K_m are unnatural. This is fallacious reasoning and should not be considered as correct.

The K_m is of considerable importance since it provides a valuable clue to the mode of action of an enzyme catalyzing a reaction. It should be noted that at low substrate concentration the relation of velocity to substrate is almost linear and obeys first-order kinetics; that is, the rate of the reaction A $\longrightarrow$ B is directly proportional to the substrate concentration [A]:

$$v = k'[A] \qquad \text{low [substrate]}$$

where v is the observed velocity of the reaction at concentration A and k' is the specific rate constant. At high substrate concentration, however, the velocity of the reaction is maximum and is independent of substrate [A]; hence it obeys zero-order kinetics:

$$V = k' \qquad \text{saturating [substrate]}$$

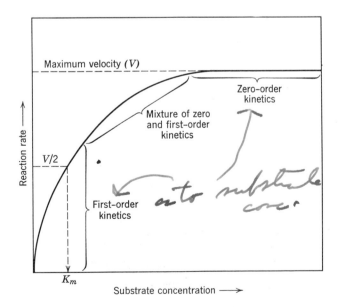

Fig. 7-2. Effect of substrate concentration on reaction rate, assuming that enzyme concentration is constant.

Michaelis and others in the early part of this century reasoned correctly that an enzyme-catalyzed reaction at varying substrate concentrations is diphasic; that is, at low substrate concentrations the active sites on the enzyme are not saturated by substrate and thus the enzyme is not working at full capacity. As the number of substrate molecules increases, the sites are covered to a greater degree until at saturation no more sites are available and the enzyme is working at full capacity. This relationship is shown in Figure 7-3. The mathematical treatment of this type of reaction is examined in detail in several references cited at the end of this chapter. Suffice it to say that equation 7-1 fully describes what has been said in the preceding paragraphs:

$$v = \frac{V[S]}{K_m + [S]} \tag{7-1}$$

where v = observed reaction rate at given substrate concentration [S]

K_m = Michaelis constant, moles/liter

V = maximum reaction rate at saturating concentration of substrate

Note that if we permit [S] to be very large, equation 7-1 reduces to

$$v = V$$

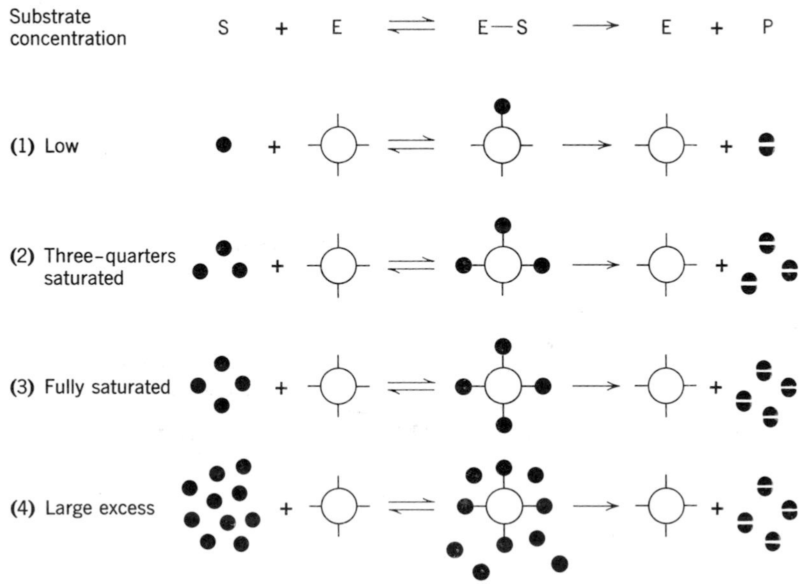

Fig. 7-3. Diagrammatic demonstration of effect of substrate concentration on saturation of active sites on enzyme surface. Note that for a unit time interval cases 3 and 4 give the same amount of P despite the large excess of substrate in case 4.

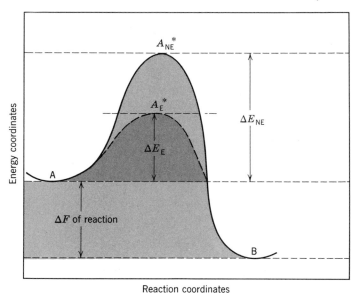

Fig. 7-4. A diagram showing the energy barriers of a reaction $A \rightarrow B$. A_{NE}° indicates the activated complex in a nonenzymic reaction and A_E° the activated complex in an enzyme-catalyzed reaction. A is the initial substrate and B the product. ΔE_{NE} is the energy of activation for nonenzymic and ΔE_E for the enzymic reaction. ΔF is the difference in free energy in $A \rightarrow B$.

If we select $v = \frac{1}{2}V$, equation 7-1 can be written as:

$$\frac{V}{2} = \frac{V[S]}{K_m + [S]}$$

$$K_m + [S] = 2[S]$$

$$K_m = [S]$$

in agreement with the experimental curve depicted in Figure 7-2.

The second important feature of an enzyme catalyzed reaction is that from the thermodynamic point of view an enzyme is a catalytic agent which speeds up a reaction by lowering the activation energy. It does so by increasing the number of molecules that are activated and therefore reactive. This can be depicted in Figure 7-4. Note here that the enzymic reaction has a lower E (activation energy), and therefore a larger proportion of molecules will be in the activated state susceptible to reaction. Also note that regardless of the route of reaction both the catalyzed and noncatalyzed reaction have the same ΔF of reaction. Thus we see that an enzyme does not alter the ΔF or equilibrium constant of a reaction but lowers the activation energy that molecule A must attain before it can undergo change.

Effect of Temperature

Since chemical reactions are affected by temperature, an enzyme-catalyzed reaction will also be sensitive to temperature changes. Because of the protein nature of an enzyme, however, thermal denaturation of the enzyme protein with increasing temperatures will decrease the effective concentration of an enzyme and consequently decrease the reaction rate. Up to perhaps 45°C the predominant effect will be an increase in reaction rate as predicted by chemical kinetic theory. Above 45°C an opposing factor, namely thermal denaturation, will become increasingly important, however, until at 55°C rapid denaturation will destroy the catalytic function of the enzyme protein. The usual temperature-enzyme reaction relationship is depicted in Figure 7-5.

Effect of pH

Since enzymes are proteins, pH changes will profoundly affect the ionic character of the amino and carboxylic acid groups on the protein surface and will therefore markedly affect the catalytic nature of an enzyme. In addition to the purely ionic effects, low or high pH values can cause considerable denaturation and hence inactivation of the enzyme protein. These effects are probably the main determinants of a typical enzyme activity-pH relation. Thus a bell-shaped curve obtains with a relatively small plateau and with sharply decreasing rates on either side as indicated in Figure 7-6. The plateau is usually called the *optimal* pH point.

In enzyme studies it becomes extremely important to determine early in the investigation the optimal pH and its plateau range. The

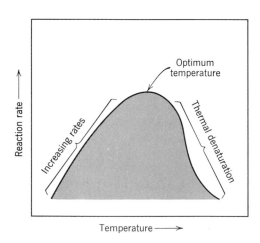

Fig. 7-5. Effect of temperature on reaction rate of an enzyme-catalyzed reaction.

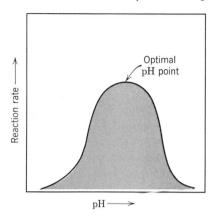

Fig. 7-6.   Effect of pH on an enzyme-catalyzed reaction.

reaction mixture must then be carefully controlled with buffers of suitable buffering capacity.

In the milieu of the cell the control of the pH in various parts of the cell becomes important since a marked shift in enzyme rates will result if pH stability is not maintained.   This would result in major disturbances in the closely geared catabolic and anabolic systems of the cell. Obviously, then, it would be of great value in understanding the regulation of cellular metabolism if we had better knowledge of how pH is controlled or modified in the cellular geography.

Activation

Many enzymes are simple proteins and need no additional factor to exhibit full activity.   Some of these proteins exist as *proenzymes* or *zymogens,* which are inactive, however.   Trypsinogen, pepsinogen, and chymotrypsinogen are zymogens that have been isolated and carefully studied.   To transform the zymogen to an active enzyme an inhibitory or a blocking peptide must be removed.   When trypsinogen is converted to trypsin by enterokinase or trypsin, for example, there is a loss of a polypeptide consisting of valine, aspartic acid, and lysine and a change in the conformation of the protein.

$$\text{trypsinogen} \xrightarrow{\text{trypsin}} \text{trypsin} + \text{val (asp)}_4 \text{ lysine}$$

Another type of activation depends on maintaining the integrity of sulfhydryl ($-SH$) groups in the enzyme protein.   These groups may maintain or perhaps constitute part of the active center of the enzyme. If they are oxidized to the disulfide ($-S-S-$) form, the enzyme becomes inactive.   Thus the proteolytic enzyme papain is inert after exposure to oxygen; when a suitable reductant is added to convert

—S—S to —SH, papain becomes fully activated (providing the enzyme is protected from oxygen). It can also be shown chemically that as the —S—S— groups are converted to —SH groups the enzyme becomes activated. Similar observations have been made with a large number of enzymes including triosephosphate dehydrogenase and pyruvic carboxylase.

A third type of activation requires the participation of still another factor in addition to the protein molecule. The general term *cofactor* encompasses this activation. Cofactors may however be divided rather loosely into three groups which include (a) prosthetic groups, (b) coenzymes, and (c) metal activators.

A prosthetic group is usually considered to be a cofactor *firmly bound* to the enzyme protein. Thus, for example, the porphyrin moiety of the haemoprotein peroxidase and the firmly associated flavin adenin dinucleotide in succinic dehydrogenase are prosthetic groups.

A coenzyme is a small, heat-stable, organic molecule which *readily dissociates* off an enzyme protein and in fact can be dialyzed away from the protein. Thus NAD^+, $NADP^+$, tetrahydrofolic acid, and thiamin pyrophosphate are examples of coenzymes.

The metal activator group is represented by the requirement of a large number of enzymes for metallic mono- or divalent cations such as K^+, Mn^{2+}, Mg^{2+}, Ca^{2+}, or Zn^{2+}. These may be either loosely or firmly bound to an enzyme protein, presumably by chelation with phenolic, amino, phosphoryl, or carboxyl groups. On the other hand Fe^{2+} ion bound to a porphyrin moiety and Co^{2+} bound to the vitamin B_{12} complex would be included in the group in which porphyrin and vitamin B_{12} belong.

There is much evidence now that the molecular explanation for the nutritional needs for vitamins or trace metals are related to the participation of vitamin derivatives as cofactors for complex or conjugated enzymes (as indicated in Chapter 8). The mechanisms by which these cofactors participate in enzymically catalyzed reactions are treated fully in Chapter 8 and elsewhere in this book.

Specificity

As we have already mentioned, one important characteristic of an enzyme is its substrate specificity; that is, because of the conformation of the complex protein molecule, the uniqueness of its active site, and the structural configuration of the substrate molecule, an enzyme will discriminate or select only a limited number of compounds for attack.

An enzyme will usually exhibit *group specificity;* that is, a general group of compounds may serve as substrates. Thus a series of aldohexoses may be phosphorylated by a kinase and ATP. If the enzyme will only attack one single substrate, for example, glucose and no other monosaccharide, it is said to have an *absolute group specificity*. It may have a *relative group specificity* if it attacks a homologous series of aldohexoses.

Another important aspect of enzyme specificity is the enzyme's stereospecificity towards substrates. As has been mentioned in Chapters 2 and 4 an enzyme may have optical specificity for a D or L-optical isomer. Thus L-amino acid oxidase attacks only the L-amino acids whereas D-amino acid oxidases only react with the D-amino acid isomers.

$$\text{L-amino acids} \xrightarrow[\substack{\text{L-amino acid} \\ \text{oxidase}}]{O_2} \alpha\text{-keto acids} + NH_3 + H_2O_2$$

$$\text{D-amino acids} \xrightarrow[\substack{\text{D-amino acid} \\ \text{oxidase}}]{O_2} \alpha\text{-keto acids} + NH_3 + H_2O_2$$

Although enzymes exhibit optical specificity, a small group of enzymes, the racemases, catalyzes an equilibrium between the L- and D-isomer and functions through an intermediate complex with pyridoxal phosphate. Thus alanine racemase catalyzes the reaction

$$\text{L-alanine} \rightleftharpoons \text{D-alanine}$$

Still other enzymes have specificities toward geometric or *cis-trans* isomers. Thus fumarase will readily add water across the double-bond system of the *trans* isomer fumaric acid but is completely inactive toward the *cis* isomer maleic acid.

In some enzyme-catalyzed reactions the substrate is symmetrical from the point of view of organic chemistry. Glycerol and citric acid can be considered in this category since they have a plane of symmetry.

general case:

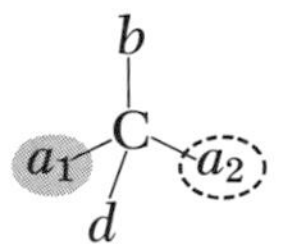

where $a_1 = a_2$

specific cases:

glycerol

citric acid

Fig. 7-7. Apparent symmetrical substrates which are attacked only in the shaded area and not in the dotted area.

It has been shown, however, that these compounds behave asymmetrically when serving as substrates for enzymes. That is, $C_{a_1a_2bd}$, though symmetrical, is preferentially attacked at a_1 but not at a_2, although both groups are identical. The shaded area in glycerol and in citric acid is preferentially attacked whereas the dotted area remains unattacked by specific enzymes. This puzzling observation was resolved when Ogston in England in 1948 made the important deduction that although a substrate may appear *symmetrical* the enzyme-substrate relationship is *asymmetrical*. The substrate will have a definite spatial relationship to the enzyme with at least three points of specific interaction between enzyme and substrate. The following specific requirements must be fulfilled:

(1) A substrate molecule must be associated with the enzyme in a specific orientation. Attachment between substrate and enzyme must be at not less than three sites.

(2) The reactivities of the three enzymic sites must be different or asymmetric.

(3) The compound must have only two identical groups (a_1 and a_2) affected by the enzyme and two dissimilar groups (b and d) all associated with a central carbon atom C.

Figure 7-8 brings out these salient features.

Inhibition

Although an important number of compounds have the ability to combine with certain enzymes, they do not serve as substrates and

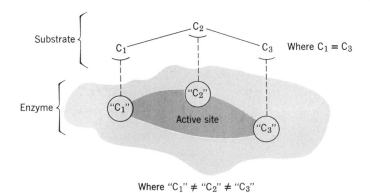

Fig. 7-8. Diagrammatic representation of the positioning of a substrate with its active site on an enzyme surface.

therefore block catalysis by that enzyme. These compounds are called *inhibitors* and are classified into two categories, competitive and noncompetitive inhibitors.

Competitive Inhibition. When a compound competes with a substrate or coenzyme for the active site on the enzyme protein and thereby reduces the catalytic activity of that enzyme, the compound is considered to be a competitive inhibitor. Thus succinic dehydrogenase readily oxidizes succinic acid to fumaric acid. If increasing concentrations of malonic acid, which closely resembles succinic acid in structure, are added, however, succinic dehydrogenase activity falls markedly.

$$
\begin{array}{cc}
\begin{array}{c}
\text{COOH} \\ | \\ \text{CH}_2 \\ | \\ \text{CH}_2 \\ | \\ \text{COOH}
\end{array}
&
\begin{array}{c}
\text{COOH} \\ | \\ \text{CH}_2 \\ | \\ \text{COOH}
\end{array}
\\
\text{succinic acid} & \text{malonic acid}
\end{array}
$$

This inhibition can now be reversed by increasing in turn the concentration of the substrate succinic acid. The amount of inhibition in this type of inhibition is related to (a) inhibitor concentration, (b) substrate concentration, and (c) relative affinities of inhibitor and substrate. The inhibitory effect is reversible.

Noncompetitive Inhibition. The type of inhibition that cannot be reversed by increasing substrate concentration is called noncompetitive inhibition. The inhibitor combines rather strongly with a site on the enzyme surface and *cannot be displaced* by increasing substrate concentration. The amount of inhibition in this type of inhibition is related to (a) inhibitor concentration and (b) inhibitor affinity for the enzyme. Note that substrate concentration has no effect on this system.

A good example is the reaction of iodoacetamide on triose phosphate dehydrogenase, a sulfhydryl enzyme:

$$\text{enzyme—SH} + \text{ICH}_2\text{CONH}_2 \longrightarrow \text{enzyme—S—CH}_2\text{CONH}_2 + \text{HI}$$

A considerable body of information supports the rationale in medicine that many drugs function because of a specific inhibitory effect on a critical enzyme in a tissue. Thus penicillin appears to block cell wall construction in micro-organisms and the highly dangerous nerve poison diisopropylphosphofluoridate strongly inhibits acetylcholine esterase, the enzyme intimately associated with nerve function.

Specific inhibitors have played an important role in the elucidation of metabolic pathways in tissues. The results must be interpreted with extreme care, however, since there are very few if any inhibitors that are specific for one enzyme. For example, malonic acid for many years was thought to be metabolically inert and was therefore added in large quantities to tissue slices to inhibit succinic dehydrogenase. We now know, however, that malonic acid can be converted to malonyl-CoA which in turn can be decarboxylated to yield acetyl-CoA and CO_2. Thus in a system containing a high malonate concentration several events take place: (a) succinic dehydrogenase is blocked, (b) ATP and CoA are redirected to the activation of malonic acid, and (c) acetyl-CoA, derived from the decarboxylation of malonyl-CoA, is flooding the various pathways which utilize this compound. The experimental results are in reality complex in interpretation rather than simple.

Nomenclature and Classification

We propose to introduce here the main recommendations developed in 1961 by the Commission on Enzymes of the International Union of Biochemistry for naming and classifying the hundreds of enzymes now known. In this edition we shall nevertheless retain the trivial names of the enzymes rather than use the systematic names suggested by the Commission. We feel justified in doing this since it will be several years before the new rules for systematic names are universally adopted. In any future editions the systematic names will be introduced.

Since a chemical reaction catalyzed by an enzyme is the specific property that distinguishes one enzyme from another, six main divisions are employed in the classification of enzymes (as suggested by the Commission).

I. OXIDOREDUCTASES

These are enzymes which catalyze oxidoreduction reactions. Dehydrogenases, oxidases (where O_2 acts as acceptor) and oxygenases (where O_2 is partly incorporated into the molecule), and peroxidases (where H_2O_2 serves as an acceptor) are the trivial names of the many enzymes found in this class of enzymes. Malic dehydrogenase would be given the systematic name of malate-$(NADP^+)$-oxidoreductase.

II. TRANSFERASES

These are a group of enzymes that catalyze group transfers. Transaminases, kinases, and transacetylases are typical enzymes of this group identified under their trivial names. The systematic name of acetate kinase (trivial name), for example, which catalyzes the reaction

$$\text{ATP} + \text{CH}_3\text{COOH} \rightleftharpoons \text{ADP} + \text{CH}_3\underset{\underset{\text{O}}{\|}}{\text{C}}\text{—OPO}_3\text{H}_2$$

is ATP-acetate phosphotransferase.

III. HYDROLASES

The hydrolases compose a long list of enzymes. They have as their primary function the hydrolysis of a variety of compounds by water. These enzymes would be named on the pattern of "substrate hydrolases." Thus a lipase (trivial name) would be considered correctly as "glycerol ester hydrolase." Other well-known enzymes in this group are phosphatases, peptidases, and amidases.

IV. LYASES

These form a group of enzymes that reversibly catalyze the removal of groups from substrates nonhydrolytically. Thus fumarase (systematic name L-malate hydrolyase) catalyzes the removal of water from malate in a reversible manner to yield fumarate. A decarboxylase (carboxy-lyase) would also be included in the group as would aldolase (ketose-1-phosphate aldehyde-lyase).

V. ISOMERASES

These include a rather large variety of enzymes catalyzing different types of isomerization. These are further subdivided into:

(a) *Racemases*

L-alanine $\rightleftharpoons$ D-alanine

L-β-hydroxy acids $\rightleftharpoons$ D-β-hydroxy acids

(b) *Epimerases*

D-ribulose-5-phosphate $\rightleftharpoons$ D-xylulose-5-phosphate

(c) *Cis-Trans Isomerase*

all-*trans* retinene $\rightleftharpoons$ all-*cis* retinene

(d) *Intramolecular Ketol Isomerases*

D-glyceraldehyde-3-phosphate $\rightleftharpoons$ dihydroxyacetone phosphate

(e) *Intramolecular Transferases or Mutases*

methylmalonyl CoA $\rightleftharpoons$ succinyl-CoA

VI. LIGASES

This class includes enzymes catalyzing the linking together of two molecules, coupled with the breaking of a pyrophosphate bond. A triphosphate nucleotide such as ATP presumably participates in the reaction.

Thus

$$X + Y + ATP \rightleftharpoons X—Y + AMP + P—P$$

The systematic name is X:Y ligase (AMP); an example of such a ligase would be:

$$\text{acetate} + \text{CoA-SH} + ATP \rightleftharpoons \text{acetyl-CoA} + AMP + P—P$$

This enzyme is usually called acetic thiokinase but the systematic name would be acetate:CoA-SH-ligase (AMP).

Although this discussion on classification of enzymes has been greatly simplified, the student should examine the extensive report of the Commission to appreciate the gigantic task at hand.   To illustrate the complexity we simply list the six major classes and the number of enzymes definitely classified under each group as of 1961.

General Class	Number in Each Class
I. Oxidoreductases	187
II. Transferases	171
III. Hydrolases	181
IV. Lyases	88
V. Isomerases	37
VI. Ligases	41

In order to become familiar with the purification techniques commonly employed in enzyme chemistry the student should read Sections 7 and 8 in Appendix 3.

REFERENCES

1. J. B. Neilands and P. K. Stumpf, *Outlines of Enzyme Chemistry*, John Wiley and Sons, New York, 2nd edition, 1958.
2. Malcolm Dixon and Edwin C. Webb, *Enzymes*, Academic Press, New York, 1958.
   These two textbooks are of value to the student.
3. Paul D. Boyer, Henry Lardy, and Karl Myrbäck, *The Enzymes*, Academic Press, New York, 2nd edition, 1959.   Several volumes.
   A very important series of volumes covering all aspects of enzyme chemistry.   An excellent source of information for the practicing biochemist.
4. *Report of the Commission of Enzymes of the International Union of Biochemistry, 1961*, Pergamon Press, London, 1961.
   A pertinent discussion of the nomenclature and classification of enzymes, coenzymes, and related topics.

Eight

Vitamins and Coenzymes

Historical Introduction

The term *vitamin* refers to an essential dietary factor which is required by an organism in small amounts and whose absence results in deficiency diseases. The description of the deficiency symptoms and the amounts required for their alleviation is properly the subject of nutrition. In this book the emphasis will be placed instead on the relation that exists between vitamins and coenzymes. As will be described, many coenzymes contain a vitamin as part of their structure; this relation is undoubtedly responsible for creating an "essential" role for the vitamin. The research which established this relation is one of the most rewarding in biochemistry because it has constituted a model for the investigation of almost all the other vitamin-coenzyme relationships.

In 1932 the German biochemist Otto Warburg published the first of a series of classic papers dealing with two important coenzymes. Warburg was investigating an enzyme system in yeast which catalyzed the oxidation of glucose-6-phosphate to 6-phosphogluconic acid. The reaction required the presence of two different proteins obtainable from yeast and a coenzyme (or coferment, as it was earlier called) which could be isolated from erythrocytes. Two separate reactions were involved; the first was the oxidation of the sugar phosphate and the simultaneous reduction of the coenzyme from red blood cells. The

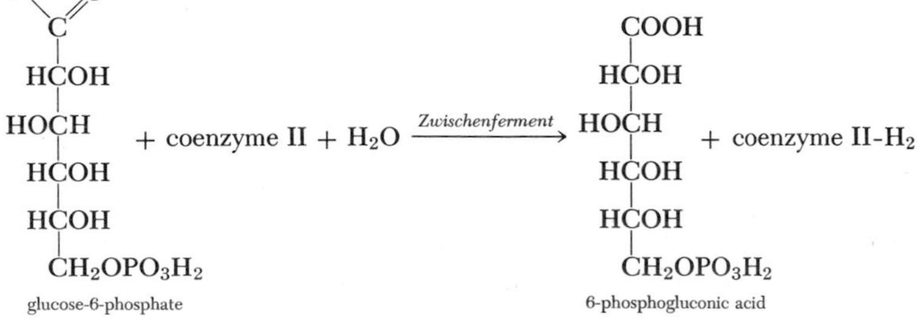

$$
\begin{array}{l}
\text{H}\diagdown\diagup\text{O} \\
\quad\text{C} \\
\text{HCOH} \\
\text{HOCH} \\
\text{HCOH} \\
\text{HCOH} \\
\quad\text{CH}_2\text{OPO}_3\text{H}_2
\end{array}
+ \text{coenzyme II} + \text{H}_2\text{O} \xrightarrow{\textit{Zwischenferment}}
\begin{array}{l}
\text{COOH} \\
\text{HCOH} \\
\text{HOCH} \\
\text{HCOH} \\
\text{HCOH} \\
\quad\text{CH}_2\text{OPO}_3\text{H}_2
\end{array}
+ \text{coenzyme II-H}_2
\qquad (8\text{-}1)
$$

glucose-6-phosphate   6-phosphogluconic acid

enzyme (a dehydrogenase) required as a catalyst for this reaction was called *Zwischenferment*. The coenzyme was subsequently known as coenzyme II because of its similarity to another coenzyme, coenzyme I, which many years earlier had been shown by Harden and Young to be involved in the anaerobic fermentation of carbohydrates. Coenzyme I was recognized to be closely related to muscle adenylic acid AMP since the latter compound was formed on enzymatic hydrolysis of coenzyme I.

Work in Warburg's laboratory in 1935 revealed that coenzyme II contained another nitrogenous base, nicotinamide, in addition to adenine. Shortly thereafter it was possible with this knowledge to write the structures of both coenzyme I and coenzyme II (see p. 130).

Warburg had discovered that the reduced coenzyme II-H$_2$ could be reoxidized by molecular oxygen provided a second protein was present. Since this protein was yellow in color when purified extensively from brewer's yeast, Warburg called it the yellow enzyme. It provided the link for the oxidation of organic substrates to molecular oxygen, the ultimate oxidizing agent in aerobic organisms. By treatment with ammonium sulfate in acid in the cold the protein component of the yellow enzyme was precipitated as a white solid, leaving the yellow color in solution. In Copenhagen in 1934, Theorell also accomplished the separation of the yellow coenzyme from the protein component by dialysis in acid with the concomitant loss of enzymatic activity. When the coenzyme was added back to the protein component the enzymatic activity was restored. This was the first demonstration of the reversible separation of an enzyme into its prosthetic group (coenzyme) and a pure protein component (apoenzyme).

Examining the action of this "old yellow enzyme," as it subsequently came to be known, Warburg showed that the catalyst became colorless in the presence of glucose-6-phosphate, *Zwischenferment,* and coenzyme II. The German biochemist subsequently established that this colorlessness was due to the reduction of the coenzyme component of the old yellow enzyme by coenzyme II-H$_2$. This reaction occurred at a significant rate only when the coenzyme was firmly associated with the protein component of the old yellow enzyme.

coenzyme II-H$_2$ + old yellow enzyme $\longrightarrow$
 (oxidized)

 yellow

coenzyme II + old yellow enzyme   (8-2)
 (reduced)

 colorless

When exposed to air the reduced enzyme-coenzyme complex was reoxidized, and O$_2$ in turn was reduced to H$_2$O$_2$.

old yellow enzyme   + O$_2$ $\longrightarrow$ old yellow enzyme   + H$_2$O$_2$
 (reduced)   (oxidized)

The Swiss chemists Kuhn and Karrer had determined, simultaneously with these enzyme studies, the chemical structure of the vitamin ribo-flavin, which occurred as a yellow pigment in egg yolk and milk. The vitamin (p. 135) became colorless on reduction with zinc in acid and regained its yellow color on reoxidation. With this information avail-able, other properties of the coenzyme and vitamin were compared and it was soon established that the coenzyme of the old yellow enzyme was the monophosphate of the vitamin (p. 136). Thus the coenzyme role of riboflavin was established simultaneously with its description as an essential nutrient, and this was the first demonstration of the vitamin-coenzyme relation.

The overall reaction, therefore, which accounted for the oxidation of glucose-6-phosphate to phosphogluconic acid by O_2, was

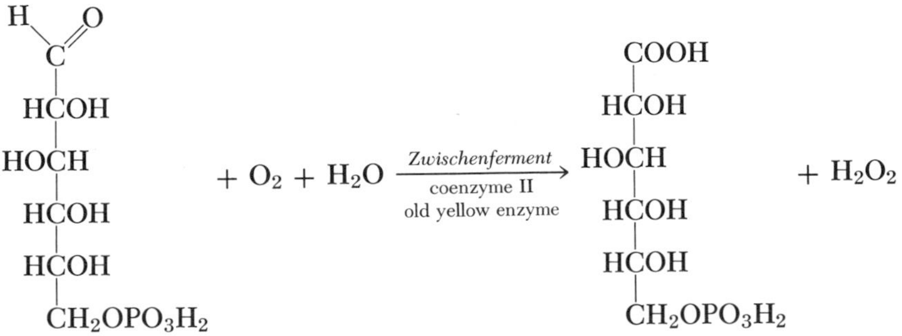

$$
\begin{array}{l}
\overset{H}{}\overset{\diagdown}{}\overset{O}{} \\
\overset{}{C} \\
HCOH \\
HOCH \\
HCOH \\
HCOH \\
CH_2OPO_3H_2
\end{array}
+ O_2 + H_2O \xrightarrow[\substack{\text{coenzyme II} \\ \text{old yellow enzyme}}]{\textit{Zwischenferment}}
\begin{array}{l}
COOH \\
HCOH \\
HOCH \\
HCOH \\
HCOH \\
CH_2OPO_3H_2
\end{array}
+ H_2O_2
$$

In this system the coenzyme II functions catalytically by being alter-nately reduced and oxidized. The flavin component of the old yellow enzyme functions catalytically in the same way.

Vitamins with Coenzyme Functions

Nicotinamide; Nicotinic Acid

Structure: The term *niacin* is the official name of the vitamin which is nicotinic acid or nicotinamide.

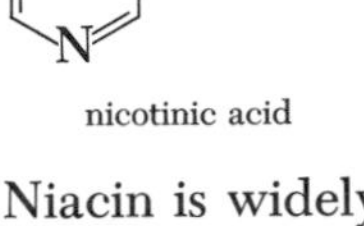

nicotinic acid 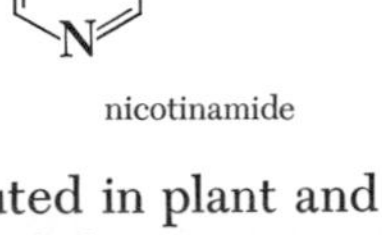   nicotinamide

Occurrence: Niacin is widely distributed in plant and animal tissues; meat products are an excellent source of the vitamin. The coenzyme forms of the vitamin are the pyridine nucleotide coenzymes known as nicotinamide-adenine dinucleotide (NAD^+) or coenzyme I, and nicotinamide-adenine   dinucleotide   phosphate   (NADP$^+$)   or   coenzyme   II.

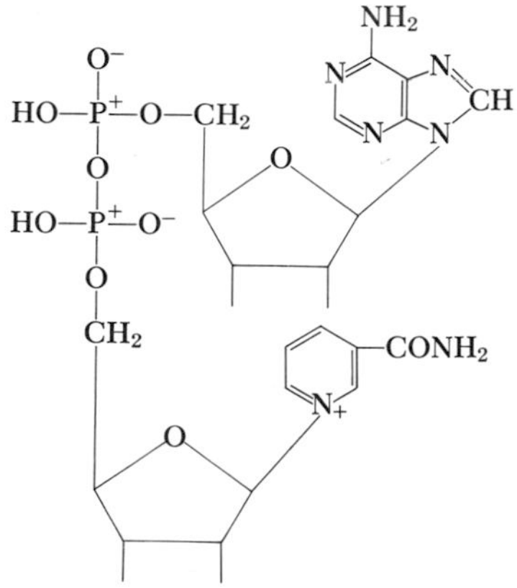

nicotinamide-adenine dinucleotide (NAD$^+$)
DPN$^+$ or coenzyme I

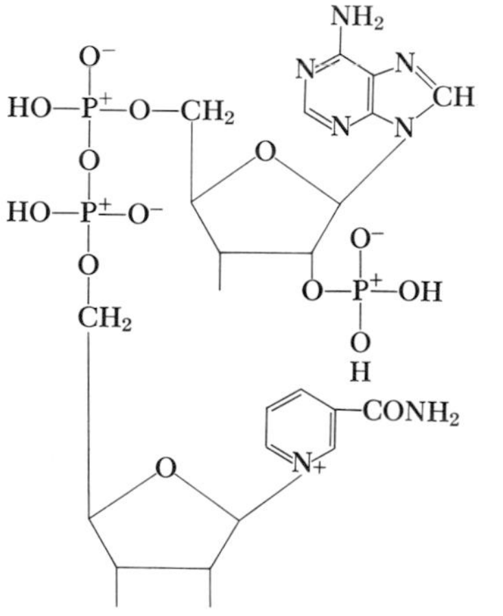

nicotinamide-adenine dinucleotide phosphate
(NADP$^+$)
TPN$^+$ or coenzyme II

These names for NAD$^+$ and NADP$^+$ are relatively new, having been proposed in 1961 by the Commission on Enzymes of the International Union of Biochemistry.   Much of the current literature refers to these coenzymes as diphosphopyridine nucleotide (DPN$^+$) for coenzyme I or NAD$^+$, and triphosphopyridine nucleotide (TPN$^+$) for coenzyme II or NADP$^+$.   DPN$^+$ and TPN$^+$ were names originally proposed by Warburg. The term *pyridine nucleotide* was used to refer to both NAD$^+$ and NADP$^+$.   This terminology will still be used in this text.

Although the structure and physiological role of these coenzymes were fairly evident by 1935, nicotinic acid was not recognized as a vitamin until 1937, when Elvehjem at the University of Wisconsin established its essential nature.   A deficiency of niacin causes pellagra in man and black tongue in dogs.   The coenzymes NAD$^+$ and NADP$^+$ are ubiquitous in nature, presumably because of their fundamental role in biological oxidations.

Biochemical Function: The pyridine nucleotides are coenzymes for enzymes known as dehydrogenases which catalyze oxidation-reduction reactions.   Thus in the reaction catalyzed by *Zwischenferment* (8-1) the glucose-6-phosphate is oxidized and NADP$^+$ (coenzyme II) is simultaneously reduced.

Similarly the alcohol dehydrogenase of yeast catalyzes the oxidation of ethanol with the concomitant reduction of NAD$^+$.

$$CH_3CH_2OH + NAD^+ \rightleftharpoons CH_3CHO + NADH + H^+ \qquad (8\text{-}3)$$

The apparent equilibrium constant of this reaction may be written

$$K_{app} = \frac{[CH_3CHO][NADH]}{[CH_3CH_2OH][NAD^+]}$$

When determined experimentally, K_{app} was approximately 10^{-4} at pH 7.0 and 10^{-2} at pH 9.0. The equilibrium constant is therefore obviously related to the pH; this is because an H^+ is a product of the reaction when alcohol is oxidized. Clearly the reaction from left to right will be favored by a low H^+ concentration or high pH, while by the Law of Mass Action the equilibrium would be displaced to the left at high H^+ concentration or low pH.

In order to understand the production of an equivalent of H^+ ion in this reaction we shall consider the reduction of NAD^+ (or $NADP^+$) in detail. An examination of the reactions catalyzed by pyridine nucleotide dehydrogenases shows that the reaction involves the removal of the equivalent of two hydrogen atoms from the substrate. This occurs when ethanol is oxidized to acetaldehyde. The overall process might occur by the removal of two hydrogen atoms (with their electrons), two electrons and two protons H^+ in separate steps, or a hydride ion (a hydrogen atom with an additional electron, H^-) and a proton H^+.

The reduced form of NAD^+ ($NADP^+$) has the formula shown, where R

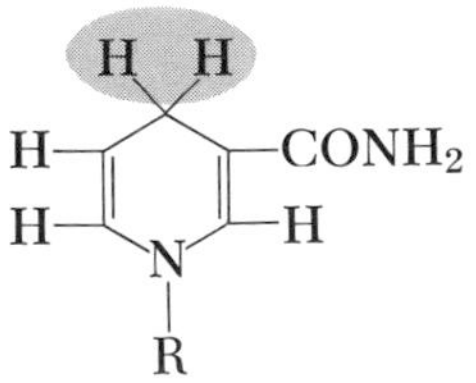

reduced pyridine nucleotide
NADH or NADPH

equals the remainder of the NAD^+ (or $NADP^+$) molecule.

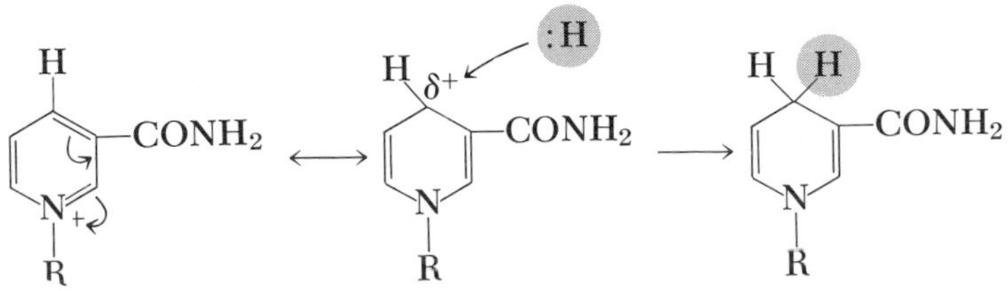

The structure shown is produced when the equivalent of one proton and two electrons have entered the pyridine ring. This may occur in a single step by the addition of a hydride ion to the oxidized pyridine nucleotide at position 4, where the added hydrogen is known to enter the ring. This can be more readily pictured if we write a resonance form of oxidized NAD^+ in which the carbon at position 4 possesses the positive charge usually placed on the nitrogen atom. The proton, required to balance the reaction when a hydride ion is removed from the substrate, is released in solution.

It is important to emphasize the two general modes of action of the pyridine nucleotide enzymes. The dehydrogenases that require NAD+ and NADP+ catalyze the oxidation of alcohols (primary and secondary), aldehydes, α- and β-hydroxy carboxylic acids and α-amino acids (Table 8-1). These reactions are frequently readily reversible. In other instances, the value of the equilibrium constant may determine that under physiological conditions the reaction proceeds in only one direction, which, however, may result in either the reduction or oxidation of the pyridine nucleotide. Because of this, the pyridine nucleotides may readily accept electrons directly from a reduced substrate and donate them directly to an oxidized substrate in a sequence called a coupled reaction. Thus the reduction of acetaldehyde to ethanol (in the pres-

Table 8-1.   Some Reactions Catalyzed by Pyridine Nucleotide Enzymes

Enzyme	Substrate	Product	Coenzyme
Alcohol dehydrogenase	Ethanol	Acetaldehyde	NAD+
Isocitric dehydrogenase	Isocitrate	α-Ketoglutarate $+CO_2$	NAD+
α-Glycerolphosphate dehydrogenase	L-α-Glycerol-phosphate	Dihydroxyacetone phosphate	NAD+
Lactic dehydrogenase	Lactate	Pyruvate	NAD+
Malic enzyme	L-Malate	Pyruvate $+CO_2$	NADP+
Glyceraldehyde-3-phosphate dehydrogenase	Glyceraldehyde-3-phosphate $+ H_3PO_4$	1,3-Diphospho-glyceric Acid	NAD+
Glucose-6-phosphate dehydrogenase	Glucose-6-phosphate	6-Phospho-gluconic Acid	NADP+
Glutamic dehydrogenase	L-Glutamic acid	α-Ketoglutarate $+NH_3$	NAD+ and NADP+
Glutathione reductase	Oxidized glutathione	Reduced Glutathione	NADPH
Quinone reductase	p-Benzoquinone	Hydroquinone	NADH and NADPH
Nitrate reductase	Nitrate	Nitrite	NADPH

ence of alcohol dehydrogenase) is linked to the oxidation of glyceralde-hyde-3-phosphate (in the presence of triosephosphate dehydrogenase).

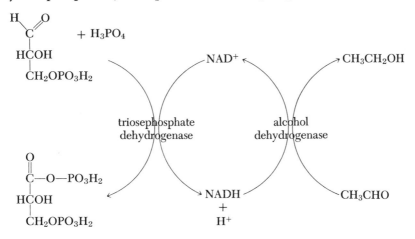

The other manner in which the pyridine nucleotides function is in the reduction of the flavin coenzymes. Since the flavin coenzymes are the prosthetic groups of enzymes which accomplish the oxidation or reduction of organic substrates, this reduction provides a link for a reaction between pyridine nucleotides and these substrates. As an example we may cite the reduction of the disulfide compound oxidized gluta-thione by glutathione reductase. The overall reaction may be written

$$NADH + H^+ + GSSG \longrightarrow NAD^+ + 2\,GSH$$

$$\underset{\substack{oxidized \\ glutathione}}{} \qquad \underset{\substack{reduced \\ glutathione}}{}$$

where G stands for the tripeptide moiety of the glutathione molecule. The glutathione reductases are enzymes that contain flavin adenine dinucleotide (FAD) as a prosthetic group. In the presence of NADH the flavin is first reduced, and the resulting FADH$_2$ in turn accomplishes the reduction of GSSG.

$$NADH + H^+ + FAD \longrightarrow NAD^+ + FAD\text{-}H_2$$
$$FAD\text{-}H_2 + GSSG \longrightarrow FAD + 2GSH$$

The flavin coenzyme, although written as a separate compound, is firmly associated with the protein of the reductase. Other compounds are reduced by the reduced pyridine nucleotides in the presence of enzymes containing FAD and flavin mononucleotide (FMN) as pros-thetic groups; these include nitrate ion (nitrate reductase) and cyto-chrome c (cytochrome c reductase).

The pyridine nucleotides and their dehydrogenases have been a favorite subject for the study of the kinetics and the mechanisms of enzyme action.   Several of the dehydrogenases are available in the form of highly purified, crystalline proteins.   In addition, there is a convenient method for distinguishing the reduced pyridine nucleotide from its oxidized form.   The method is based on the observation by Warburg that the reduced coenzymes strongly absorb light at 340 mμ and that the oxidized coenzymes do not.   The absorption spectra of the oxidized and reduced pyridine nucleotides are shown in Figure 8-1; the molar absorbancy a_m for the two coenzymes is identical.   By measuring the change in the absorption of light at 340 mμ during the course of a reaction, it is possible to follow the reduction or oxidation of the coenzyme. An example of such measurements is given in Figure 8-2, where the reduction of NAD$^+$ in the presence of ethanol and alcohol dehydrogenase is shown.

In Figure 8-2 the absorbancy at 340 mμ is plotted as a function of time.   After equilibrium is obtained and no further reduction of NAD$^+$ occurs acetaldehyde is added.   In adding a product of the reaction, the equilibrium of reaction 8-3 is displaced to the left and some of the reduced NADH is reoxidized, as indicated by a decrease in the absorption of light at 340 mμ.   If additional alcohol is added now the equilibrium is again adjusted, this time from left to right, and NAD$^+$ reduction results, as shown by the increase in light absorption at 340 mμ (see also Appendix 3).

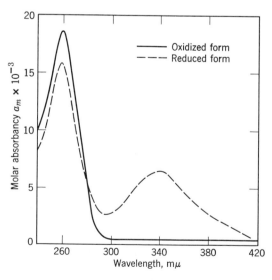

Fig. 8-1.   Absorption spectra of oxidized and reduced nicotinamide-adenine dinucleotides.

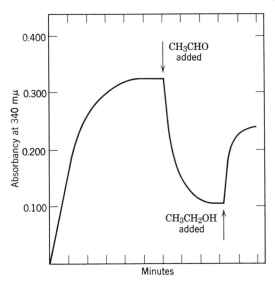

Fig. 8-2.   The reduction and reoxidation of NAD^+ in the presence of ethanol, acetaldehyde, and alcohol dehydrogenase.

Riboflavin

Structure: Riboflavin (vitamin B_2) consists of the sugar alcohol D-ribitol attached to a substituted isoalloxazine ring.

riboflavin

Occurrence: The vitamin was detected as a growth factor for rats. It is obtained commercially from the culture medium of certain micro-organisms which produce it in good yield. One of the most important chemical properties of riboflavin is its change from a yellow to a color-less form on reduction and its reoxidation to the yellow form by expo-sure to air. The structures of the oxidized and reduced forms of the vitamin have been established as shown.

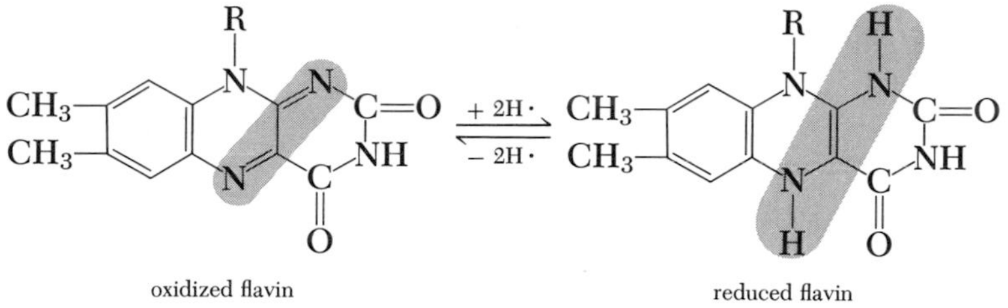

oxidized flavin

reduced flavin

R = remainder of FMN or
FAD molecule

As indicated in the diagram, the reduction consists of the addition of two hydrogen atoms (two electrons + two protons) in a one-four addition reaction to form the reduced or leuco-riboflavin.

The vitamin occurs in nature almost exclusively as a constituent of the two flavin coenzymes flavin mononucleotide (FMN) and flavin adenine dinucleotide (FAD). Although the flavin coenzymes were

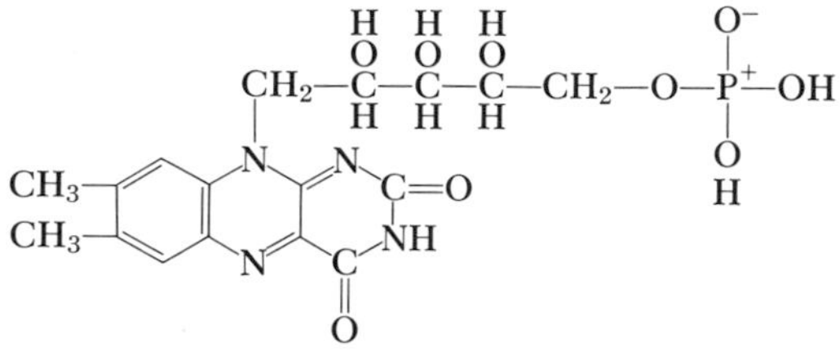

flavin mononucleotide (FMN)
riboflavin monophosphate

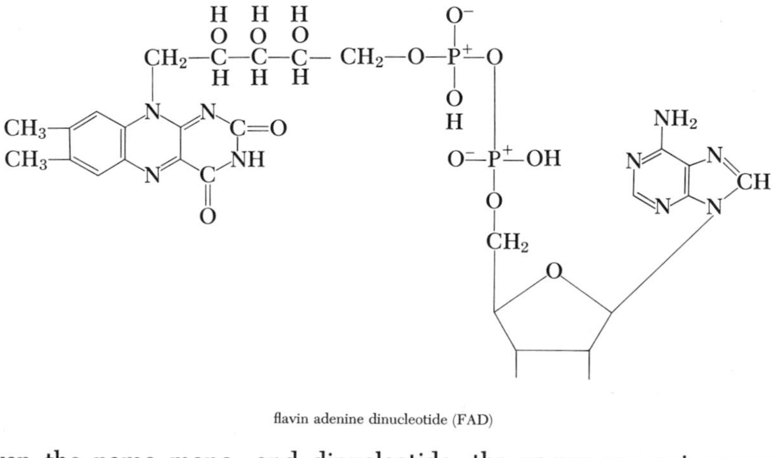

flavin adenine dinucleotide (FAD)

given the name mono- and dinucleotide, the names are not accurate chemically speaking, since the compound attached to the flavin moiety is the sugar alcohol ribitol and not the aldose sugar ribose.

Table 8-2.   Some Reactions Catalyzed by Flavoproteins

Enzyme	Electron Donor	Product	Coenzyme	Electron Acceptor
D-Amino acid oxidase	D-Amino acids	α-Ketoacids $+NH_3$	FAD	O_2
Glycolic acid oxidase	Glycollate	Glyoxylate	FMN	O_2
NAD$^+$-cytochrome c reductase	NADH	NAD$^+$	FAD	Cytochrome C_{ox}
Aldehyde oxidase	Aldehydes	Carboxylic acids	FAD	O_2
Succinic dehydrogenase	Succinate	Fumarate	FAD	Oxidized dyes
Nitrate reductase	NADPH	NADP$^+$	FAD	Nitrate
Nitrite reductase	NADPH	NADP$^+$	FAD	Nitrite
Xanthine oxidase	Xanthine	Uric acid	FAD	O_2
Lipoyl dehydrogenase	Reduced lipoic acid	Oxidized lipoic acid	FAD	NAD$^+$

Biochemical Function: The role of FMN as a coenzyme for the old yellow enzyme of Warburg has been mentioned. FAD was first demonstrated as a coenzyme for D-amino acid oxidase. These enzymes belong to a group of proteins termed *flavoproteins* which catalyze oxidation-reduction reactions (Table 8-2). In contrast to the pyridine nucleotide dehydrogenases, the prosthetic coenzymes FAD and FMN are firmly associated with the protein component and are carried along during the purification of the enzyme. In fact, the flavin coenzymes are usually only separated from the apoenzyme by acid treatment in the cold or, perhaps, by boiling. The latter technique destroys the protein nature of the apoenzyme and the separation is therefore irreversible. The separation by acid in the cold is reversible and the mixing of flavin coenzyme to the apoenzyme restores activity.

It is difficult to generalize on the types of chemical reaction in which flavoproteins participate. Certainly they function in accepting hydrogen atoms from reduced pyridine nucleotides. Another oxidative reaction commonly occurring in intermediary metabolism involves the removal of two hydrogen atoms on adjacent carbon atoms to form a double bond. These reactions seem to involve flavin coenzymes and enzymes. Thus the enzyme succinic dehydrogenase, which catalyzes the oxidation of succinate to fumarate, contains FAD as a prosthetic group.

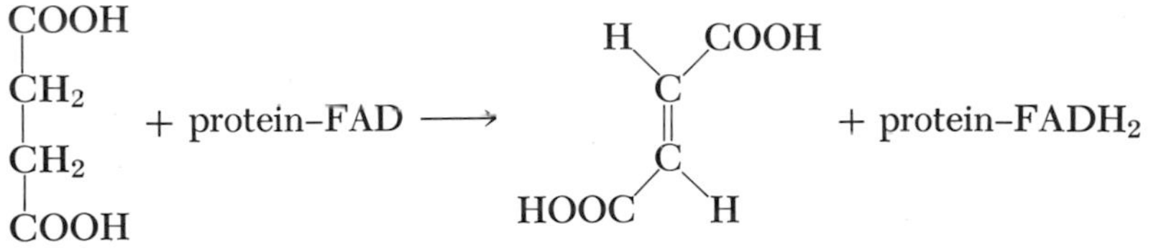

$$
\begin{array}{c}
\text{COOH} \\
| \\
\text{CH}_2 \\
| \\
\text{CH}_2 \\
| \\
\text{COOH}
\end{array}
+ \text{protein–FAD} \longrightarrow
\qquad
\begin{array}{c}
\text{H}\quad\text{COOH} \\
\diagdown\diagup \\
\text{C} \\
\| \\
\text{C} \\
\diagup\diagdown \\
\text{HOOC}\quad\text{H}
\end{array}
+ \text{protein–FADH}_2
$$

succinate   fumarate

Some of the flavoproteins listed in Table 8-2 are more complex in that they contain a metal such as molybdenum or iron in addition to the riboflavin derivative. The metals also appear to function by virtue of their ability to be alternately oxidized and reduced, although this may not be their only function.

Various lines of evidence have indicated that the reduction of the flavin coenzyme occurs in two separate steps, each involving the addition of a single electron. If the reaction occurs by the addition of one electron (with its proton) at a time, a semi-reduced compound known as a semiquinone will be an intermediate. The reaction may be represented as in the diagram. The semiquinone form of the riboflavin co-

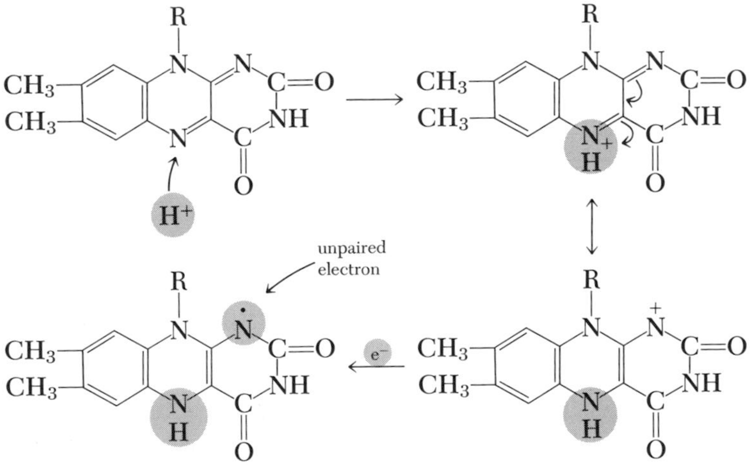

semiquinone

enzymes may be expected to be reasonably stable because of the possible existence of different resonance forms. In addition, the occurrence of a metal such as molybdenum or iron would be expected to stabilize the semiquinone; such structures possess an unpaired electron which could be shared with the unpaired electrons commonly encountered in metal ions.

Lipoic Acid

Structure:

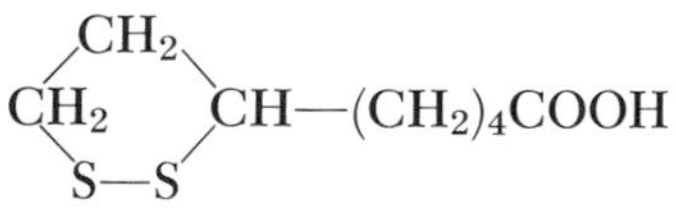

$$\underset{\text{lipoic acid (1,2-dithiolane-3-valeric acid)}}{\underset{S-S}{\overset{CH_2}{\underset{CH_2}{\diagup}}\diagdown}{CH-(CH_2)_4COOH}}$$

Occurrence: Lipoic acid, a microbial growth factor, occurs in liver and in yeast. Bound to protein, lipoic acid is released by acid, base, or proteolytic hydrolysis. Lipoic acid is relatively stable in the solid state. When heated or exposed to light it rapidly polymerizes in solution, however. Careful hydrolysis of lipoyl protein complexes releases lipoic acid bound to lysine as ε-N-lipoyl-L-lysine. This structure has a striking

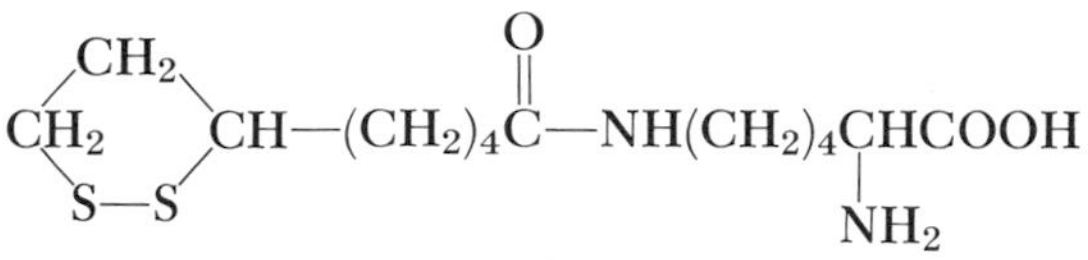

$$\underset{\text{ε-N-lipoyl-L-lysine}}{\underset{S-S}{\overset{CH_2}{\underset{CH_2}{\diagup}}\diagdown}{CH-(CH_2)_4\overset{\overset{O}{\|}}{C}-NH(CH_2)_4\underset{\underset{NH_2}{|}}{CH}COOH}}$$

resemblance to biocytin (ε-N-biotinyl-L-lysine) isolated as a hydrolysis product of biotin-protein complexes.

Biochemical Function: Lipoyl enzymes function as important catalysts in the generation of an acyl group, acyl transfer, and electron transport. Thus pyruvic oxidase and α-ketoglutaric acid oxidase are large lipoyl protein complexes which catalyze the oxidation of α-keto acids to acyl moieties; the oxidation mechanism involves lipoic acid. Thiamin pyrophosphate and coenzyme A are intimately related in the total picture of lipoyl enzyme activity, probably by the sequence we show. The acyl-

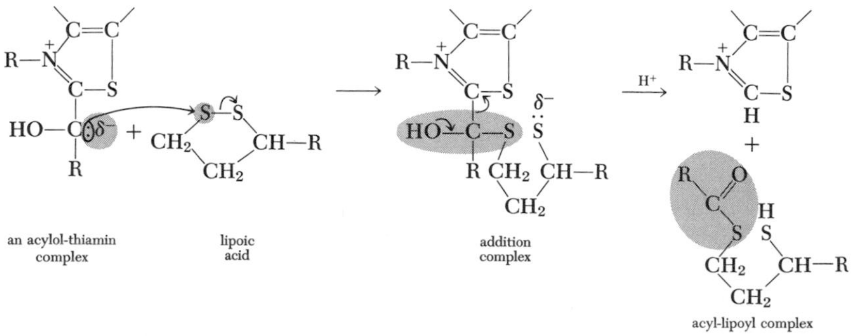

| an acylol-thiamin complex | lipoic acid | addition complex | acyl-lipoyl complex |

lipoyl complex then reacts with coenzyme A in an acyl transfer, and the reduced lipoic acid is reoxidized by a FAD-lipoyl dehydrogenase to lipoic acid.

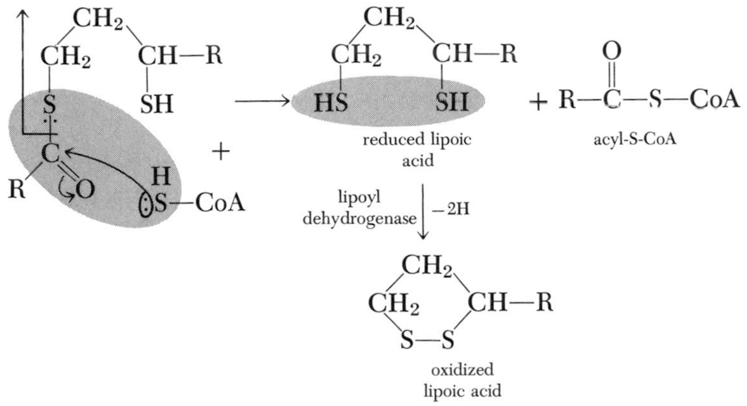

$$\begin{array}{c}
\text{CH}_2 \\
\text{CH}_2 \quad \text{CH}-\text{R} \\
\text{S} \quad \text{SH} \\
\text{C} \\
\text{R} \quad \text{O} \qquad \text{H} \\
\qquad \text{S}-\text{CoA}
\end{array}
\quad + \quad
\begin{array}{c}
\text{CH}_2 \\
\text{CH}_2 \quad \text{CH}-\text{R} \\
\text{HS} \qquad \text{SH}
\end{array}
\quad + \quad
\begin{array}{c}
\text{O} \\
\| \\
\text{R}-\text{C}-\text{S}-\text{CoA}
\end{array}$$

reduced lipoic   acyl-S-CoA
acid

lipoyl
dehydrogenase $\Big|$ $-2H$

$$\begin{array}{c}
\text{CH}_2 \\
\text{CH}_2 \quad \text{CH}-\text{R} \\
\text{S}-\text{S}
\end{array}$$

oxidized
lipoic acid

Biotin

Structure:

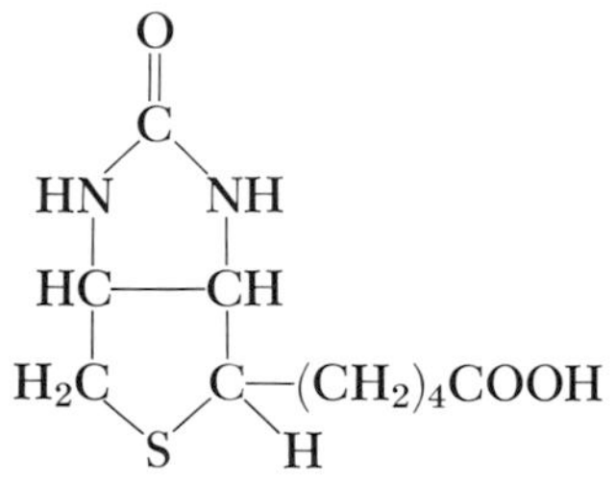

$$\begin{array}{c}
\text{O} \\
\| \\
\text{C} \\
\text{HN} \qquad \text{NH} \\
\text{HC}-\text{CH} \\
\text{H}_2\text{C} \qquad \text{C}-(\text{CH}_2)_4\text{COOH} \\
\text{S} \qquad \text{H}
\end{array}$$

Occurrence: The essential nature of biotin was established by its ability to serve as a growth factor for yeast and certain bacteria, as well as a recognition that it was the "anti-egg white injury factor." The latter term refers to the observation that a nutritional deficiency may be induced in animals by feeding them large amounts of avian egg white. Egg white contains a basic protein known as avidin which has a remarkably high affinity for biotin or its simple derivatives. At 25°C the binding constant is about 10^{21}. Avidin is therefore an extremely effective inhibitor of biotin-requiring systems and is employed by the biochemist to test for possible reactions in which biotin may participate.

Biotin is widely distributed in nature with yeast and liver as excellent sources. The vitamin occurs mainly in combined forms bound to protein through the ε-N-lysine moiety. Biocytin, ε-N-biotinyl-L-lysine, has been isolated as a hydrolysis product from biotin-containing proteins.

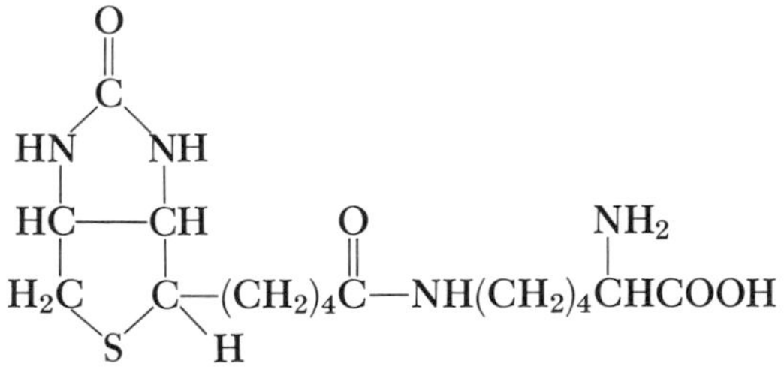

Because of their linkage with proteins through covalent peptide bonds, neither biotin nor lipoic acid is dissociated by dialysis, a technique commonly used to remove readily dissociable groups such as the nicotinamide nucleotides. As a result no enzymes have been described that can be reactivated by the simple expedient of adding biotin to the apoenzyme. A biotin-containing enzyme will be inhibited by the addition of avidin to the reaction, however.

Biochemical Function: Biotin bound to its specific enzyme-protein is intimately associated with carboxylation reactions. There are three well-described carboxylations catalyzed by different enzymes in which biotin participates. All three reactions employ biotin as the actual car-

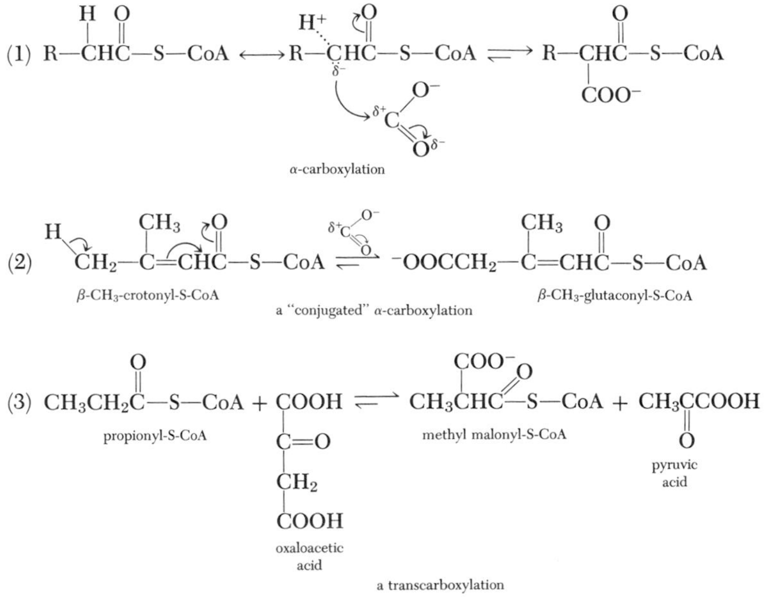

α-carboxylation

β-CH₃-crotonyl-S-CoA   a "conjugated" α-carboxylation   β-CH₃-glutaconyl-S-CoA

propionyl-S-CoA   methyl malonyl-S-CoA   pyruvic acid

oxaloacetic acid

a transcarboxylation

rier of CO_2. In order that CO_2 can carboxylate the α-carbon atom in reactions 1 and 2, ATP and magnesium must be present. In reaction 3 no cofactors need be added. The concerted reaction we shall give probably describes the CO_2-activation step.

(a)

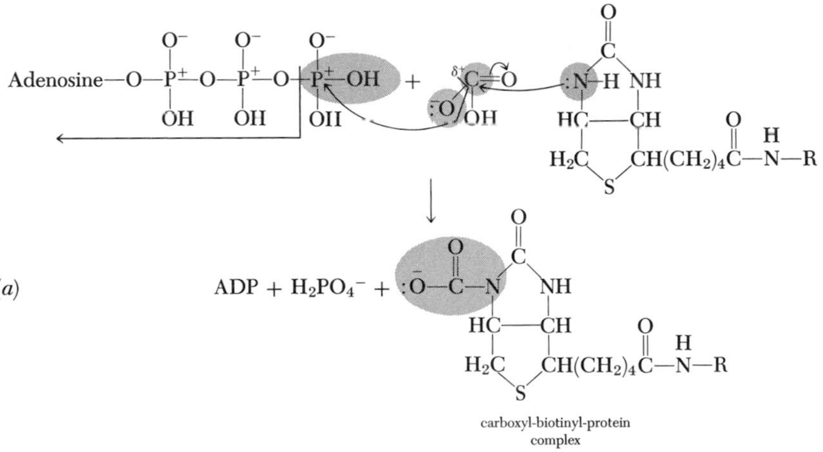

$$ADP + H_2PO_4^- + :\overset{-}{O}-C-N \quad NH$$

carboxyl-biotinyl-protein
complex

(b)

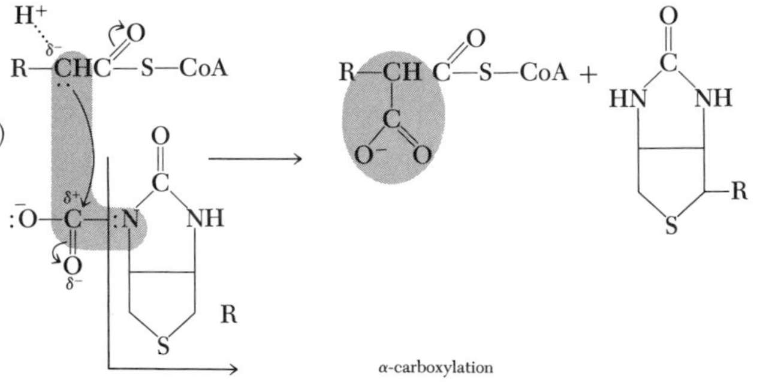

α-carboxylation

There is good evidence that the carboxyl-biotinyl-protein complex is the actual carboxylating unit that donates the CO_2.

Thiamin

Structure: Thiamin, or vitamin B_1, is usually isolated as the free vitamin.

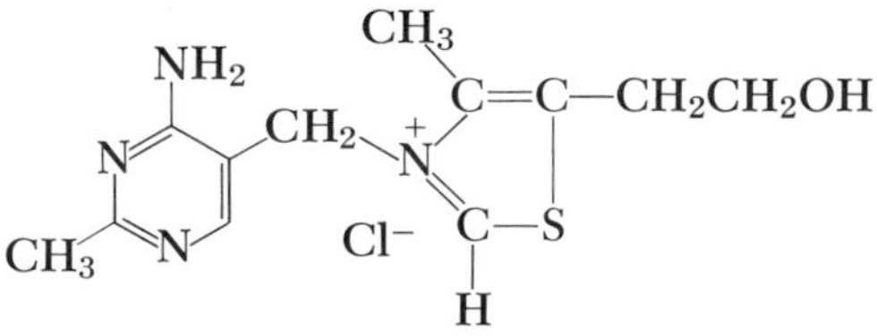

Occurrence: Thiamin occurs free in nature in relatively high concentrations in the cereal grains. In animal tissues and in yeast it occurs chiefly as its coenzyme thiamin pyrophosphate, whose structure was established by Lohman in 1937.

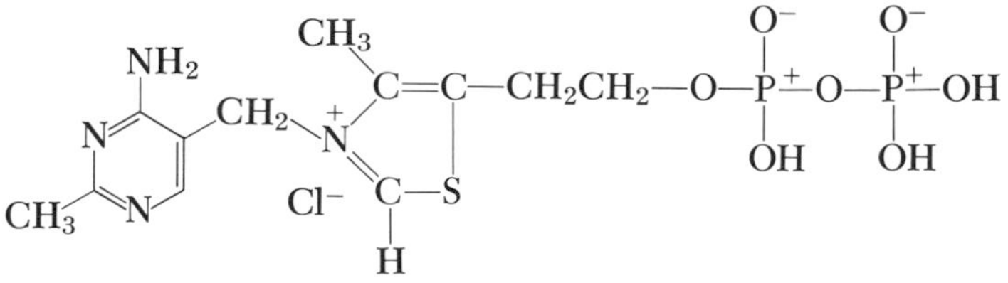

A lack of vitamin B_1 results in the deficiency disease known as beri-beri, which is common in the Far East. It is due to the practice of using polished rice from which the outer, thiamin-rich layers of the seed have been removed. Thiamin may also be present in marginal concentrations in the diet of many peoples.

Biochemical Function: Thiamin pyrophosphate participates as a coenzyme in the following systems:

(1) α-Keto acid decarboxylases
(2) α-Keto acid oxidases
(3) Transketolase
(4) Phosphoketolase

In all these reactions the common site of action is C-2 of the thiazole ring. The hydrogen atom at this position readily dissociates as a proton with the formation of a carbanion. The carbanion is believed to partic-

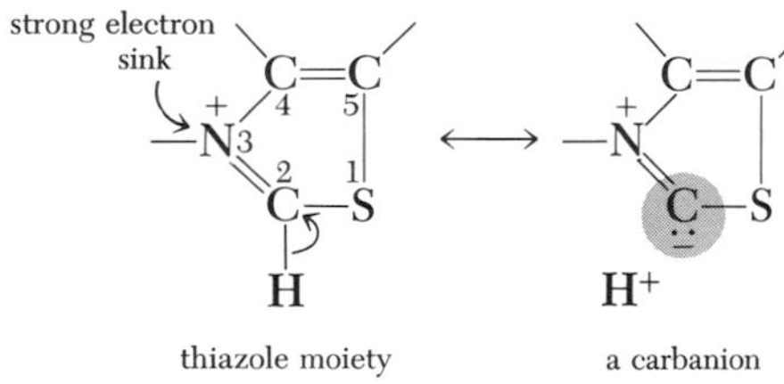

thiazole moiety   a carbanion

ipate in the decarboxylation of α-keto acids as shown in the next diagram. The adduct formed after the appropriate rearrangement of electrons undergoes decarboxylation, and acetaldehyde dissociates with the regeneration of the carbanion.

The reaction mechanism for α-keto acid oxidation is discussed in Chapter 11 and in the section on lipoic acid in this chapter. Slightly modified mechanisms have been proposed for the reactions catalyzed by transketolase and phosphoketolase, again employing the thiazole carbanion as the attacking species. The student is encouraged to develop mechanisms to explain the action of these two enzymes. As a hint for

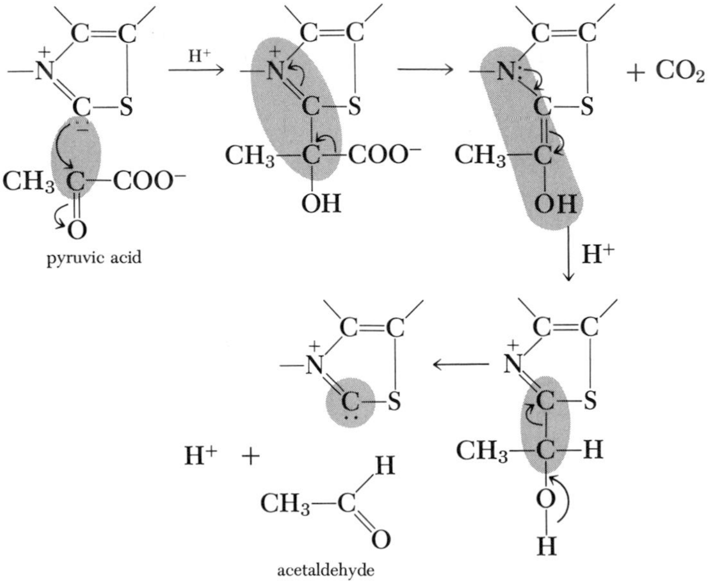

pyruvic acid

$+ CO_2$

H^+

acetaldehyde

the phosphoketolase mechanism, it is of interest that the intermediate is extremely labile to nucleophiles such as water, which can attack this compound with ease to form R—COOH and regenerate the thiazole base.

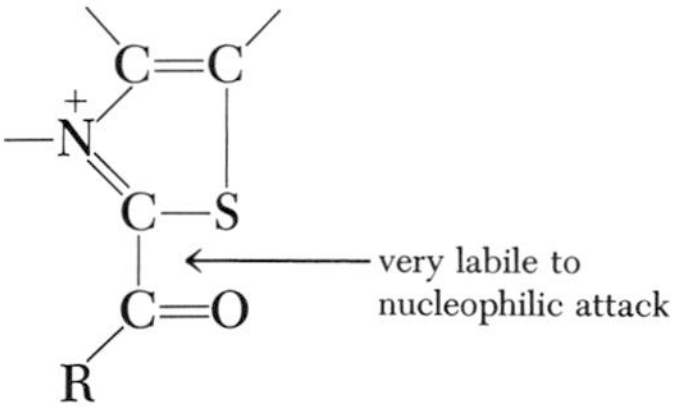

very labile to
nucleophilic attack

Vitamin B₆

Structure: Three compounds belong to the vitamin group known as B₆. They are *pyridoxal, pyridoxine,* and *pyridoxamine.*

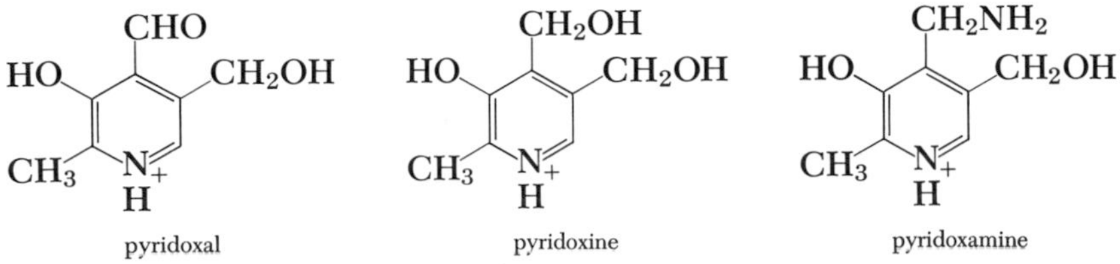

pyridoxal

pyridoxine

pyridoxamine

Occurrence: The three forms of vitamin B$_6$ are widely distributed in animal and plant sources; cereal grains are especially rich sources of the vitamin. Pyridoxal and pyridoxamine also occur in nature as their phosphate derivatives which are the coenzyme forms of the vitamin.

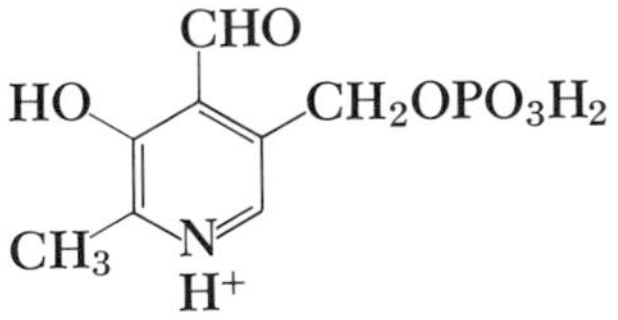

pyridoxal
phosphate

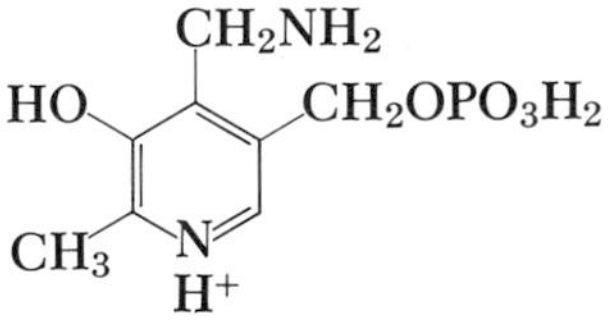

pyridoxamine
phosphate

All three forms of the vitamin are effective in preventing vitamin B$_6$ deficiency symptoms which, in rats, occur initially as a severe dermatitis. Extreme deficiency in animals causes convulsions similar to those of epilepsy and indicates a profound disturbance in the central nervous system. The different forms of vitamin B$_6$ also serve as growth factors for many bacteria.

Biochemical Function: Pyridoxal phosphate is a versatile vitamin derivative which participates in the catalysis of several important reactions of amino acid metabolism, namely transamination, decarboxylation, and racemization.

transamination:

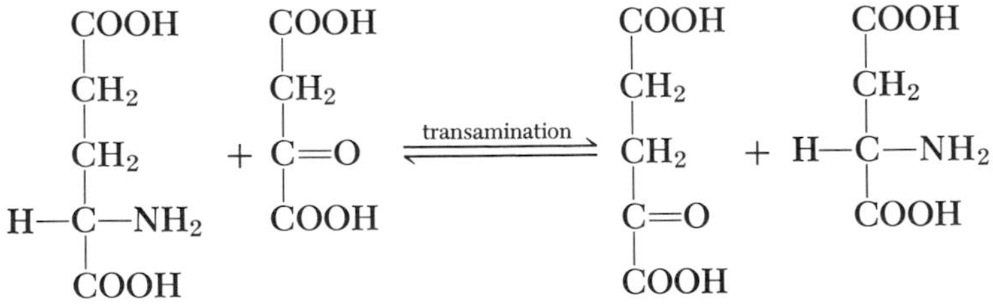

| glutamic acid | oxalacetic acid | | α-ketoglutaric acid | aspartic acid |

$\begin{pmatrix} \text{donor amino} \\ \text{acid} \end{pmatrix}$ $\begin{pmatrix} \text{acceptor} \\ \text{keto acid} \end{pmatrix}$ $\begin{pmatrix} \text{product} \\ \text{keto acid} \end{pmatrix}$ $\begin{pmatrix} \text{product} \\ \text{amino acid} \end{pmatrix}$

decarboxylation:

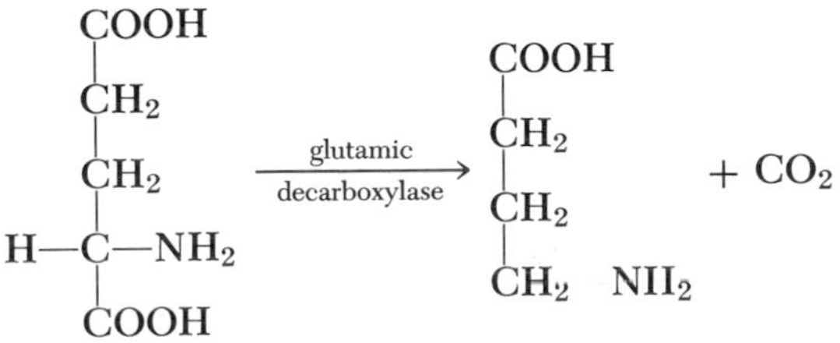

glutamic acid

γ-amino butyric acid

racemization:

$$\text{L-glutamic acid} \rightleftharpoons \text{D-glutamic acid}$$

Each reaction is catalyzed by a different, specific enzyme, but in each case pyridoxal phosphate functions as a coenzyme.

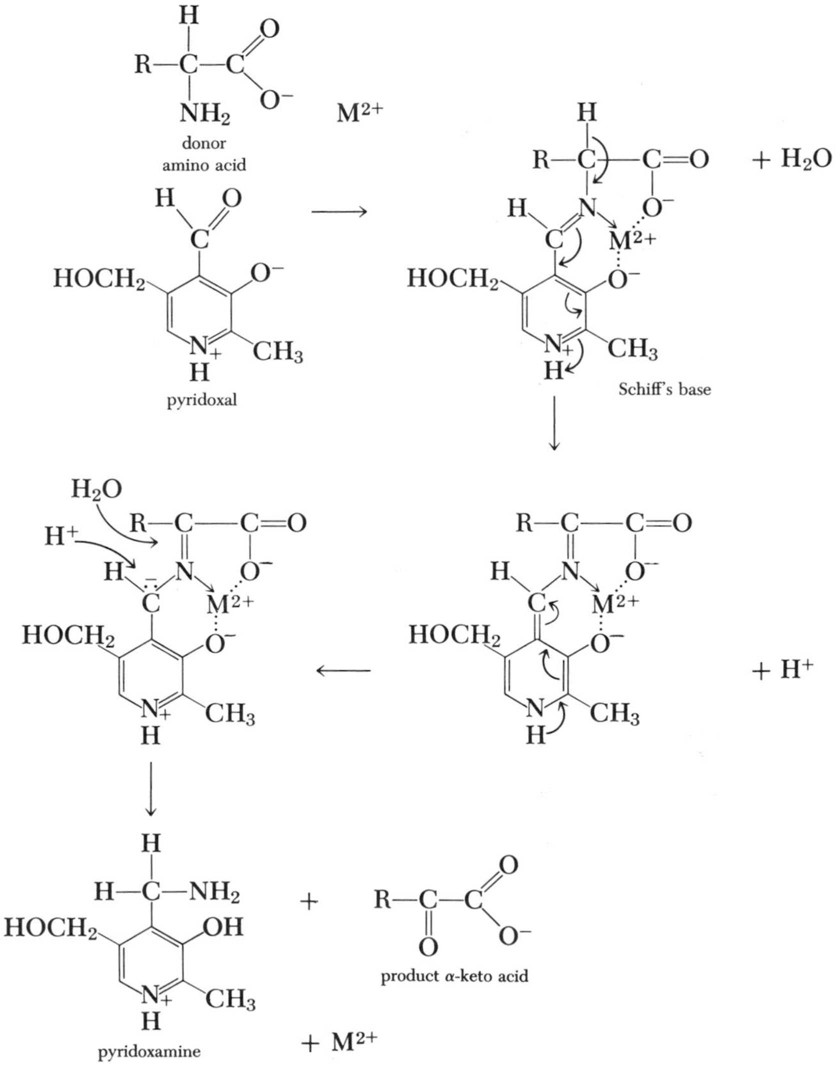

Snell of the University of California and his associates Metzler and Ikawa have examined the role of vitamin B_6 in model systems that include pyridoxal, amino acids, and metal ions; these mixtures are capable of carrying out many of the reactions observed in the presence of enzymes. Their studies have led the California workers to propose a general mechanism that can account for the reactions which require pyridoxal phosphate. According to this mechanism a *Schiff's base* is formed between the amino acid and the aldehyde moiety of pyridoxal. Then, by judicious displacement of different electrons, we can account for different reactions. The mechanism for transamination is given as an example (page 146).

In this sequence the initial step involves the dissociation of the α-hydrogen atom. Subsequently a negative charge is developed in the side-chain carbon atom of pyridoxal. In the model system which requires a metal ion but no enzyme, the metal is believed to aid in forming the Schiff's base by stabilizing a six-membered planar ring.

In transamination the amino group of the donor amino acid is transferred to pyridoxal phosphate to form pyridoxamine phosphate and the keto acid produced by transamination. In an analagous series of reactions pyridoxamine phosphate then reacts with the acceptor keto acid to produce the product amino acid and regenerate pyridoxal phosphate.

Approximately twenty other specific reactions of amino acids involving pyridoxal phosphate have been discovered, one of which is the interconversion of serine and glycine. Of unusual interest is the fact that pyridoxal phosphate is found bound to lysine in animal and plant phosphorylases. If the coenzyme is removed from the protein, phosphorylase activity disappears but can be restored by adding pyridoxal phosphate. The precise role of pyridoxal phosphate in this system is unknown.

Folic Acid

Structure:

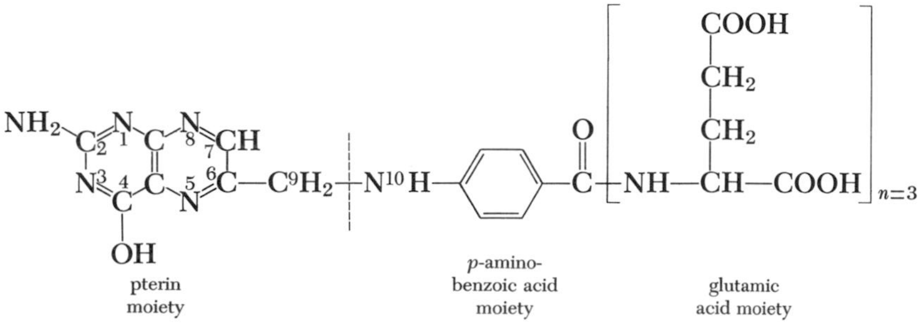

folic acid (pteroyl-L-glutamic acid, [F])

Occurrence: Folic acid and its derivatives, which are chiefly the tri- and heptaglutamyl peptides, are widespread in nature. The vitamin cures nutritional anemia in chicks and serves as a specific growth factor in a number of micro-organisms. Since extremely small amounts are needed by experimental animals, it is very difficult to produce folic acid-deficiencies. Intestinal bacteria provide the small amounts necessary for growth. Derivatives of folic acid play an important but yet unknown role in the formation of normal erythrocytes.

Biochemical Function: Although folic acid is the vitamin, its reduction products are the actual coenzyme forms. An enzyme, *folic reductase,* reduces folic acid to dihydrofolic acid (FH_2); this compound is reduced in turn by *dihydrofolic reductase* to tetrahydrofolic acid (FH_4).

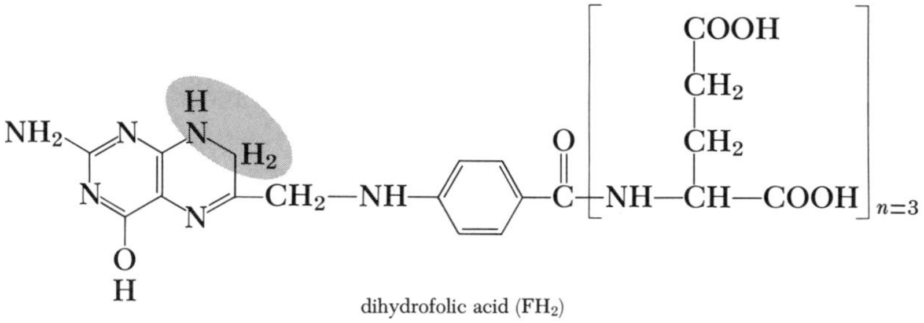

dihydrofolic acid (FH_2)

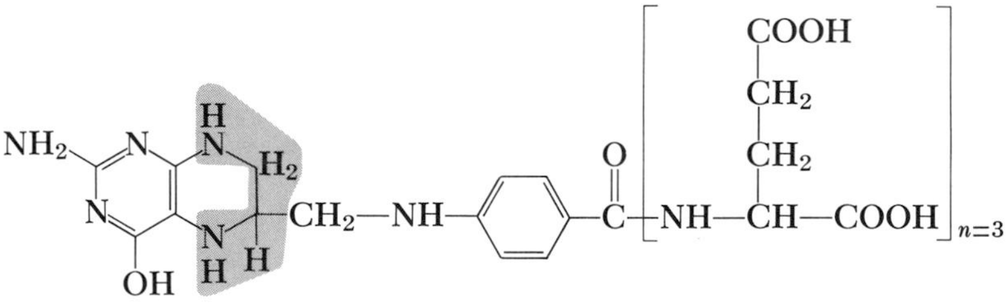

tetrahydrofolic acid (FH_4)

The reducing agent in both reactions is NADPH.

$$\text{folic} + \text{NADPH} + \text{H}^+ \xrightarrow[\text{reductase}]{\text{folic}} FH_2 + \text{NADP}^+$$

$$FH_2 + \text{NADPH} + \text{H}^+ \xrightarrow[\text{reductase}]{\text{dihydrofolic}} FH_4 + \text{NADP}^+$$

The central role of FH_4 is that of a carrier for a C_1 or a formate unit. The formate unit is used in the biosynthesis of purines, serine, and glycine. The chemistry of this formate unit is complex but involves initially the activation of formic acid.

$$FH_4 + ATP + HCOOH \longrightarrow \text{formyl } N^{10}FH_4 + ADP + Pi$$

Formyl $N^{10}FH_4$ (the structure shown in the diagram) undergoes

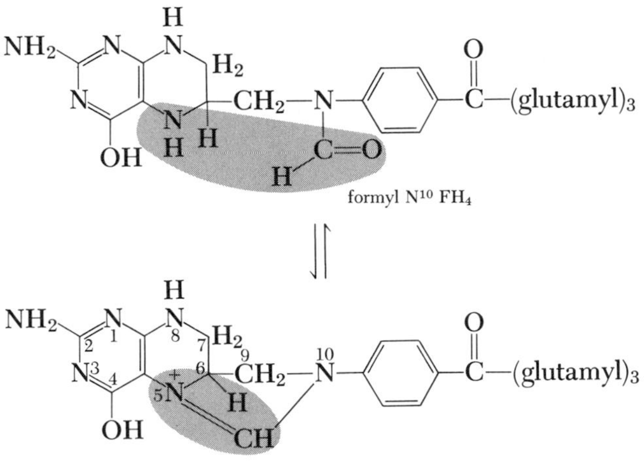

formyl N^{10} FH$_4$

methenyl N^{5-10} FH$_4$

ring closure to methenyl $N^{5-10}FH_4$ which then is reduced by NADPH in the presence of a specific dehydrogenase.

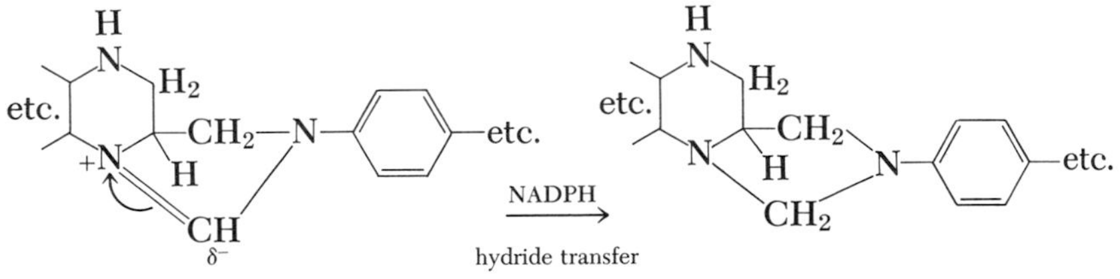

methenyl N^{5-10} FH$_4$ hydride transfer   methylene N^{5-10} FH$_4$

Methylene $N^{5-10}FH_4$, in the presence of pyridoxal phosphate, serine hydroxyl-methylase, and glycine, forms serine. Thus the reduction of formate to $-CH_2OH$ is complex. Of interest is the observation that not one but two derivatives of important vitamins, folic acid and pyridoxal phosphate, are required cofactors for the utilization of formate to form serine; this is an excellent example of the intermeshing of vitamins in the tissue economy.

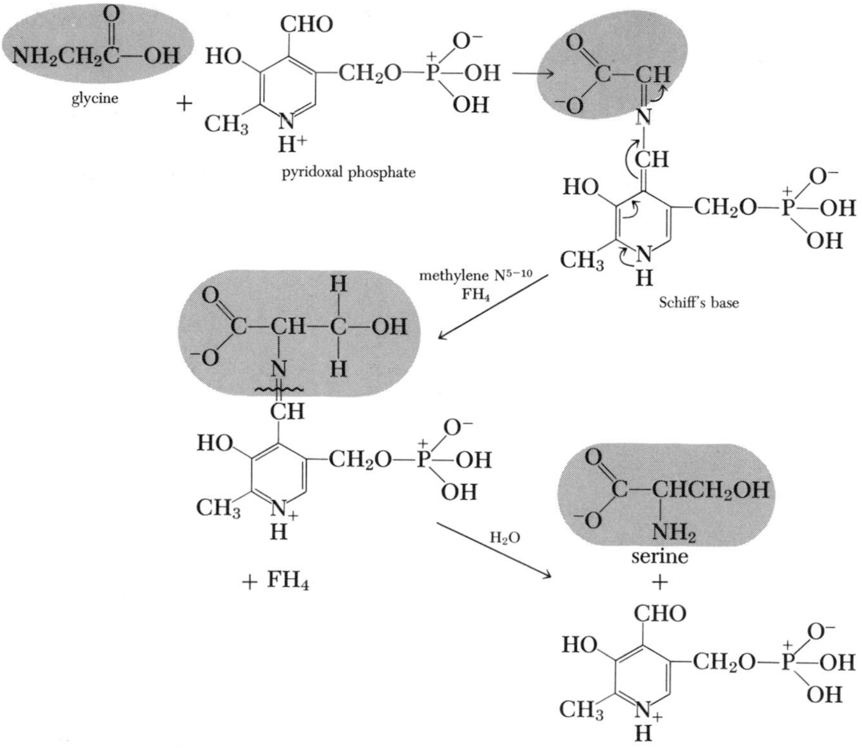

FH$_4$ is also involved in a most interesting and important reaction by which it functions both as a source of hydrogen atoms and as a source of carbon for CH$_3$ synthesis. In this reaction dihydrofolic acid (FH$_2$) is a product.

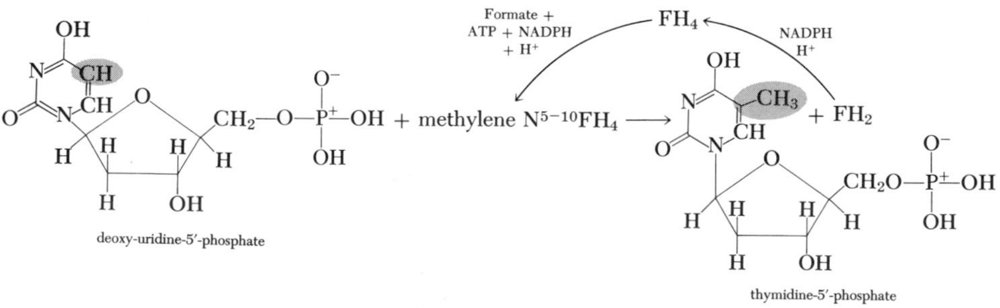

A summary of the metabolism of C$_1$ units as related to folic acid reactivites follows:

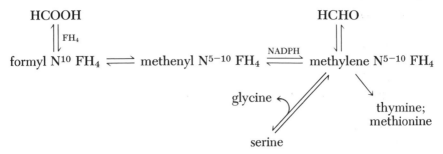

$$\text{formyl } N^{10} \text{ FH}_4 \rightleftharpoons \text{methenyl } N^{5-10} \text{ FH}_4 \xrightleftharpoons{\text{NADPH}} \text{methylene } N^{5-10} \text{ FH}_4$$

Vitamin B₁₂

Structure: Vitamin B_{12} as it is isolated from liver is a cyanocobalamin whose structure is shown in the accompanying diagram.

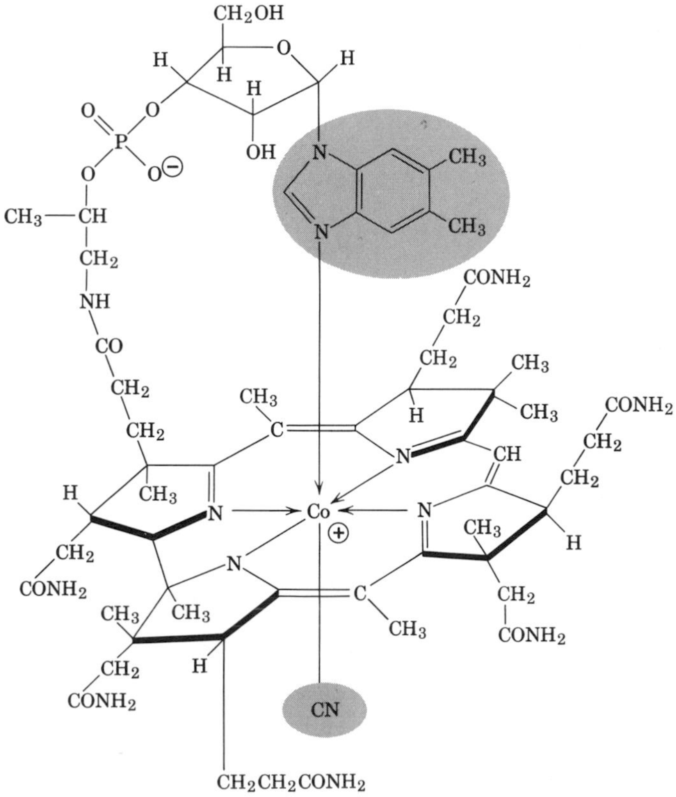

Liver extracts also contain a hydroxocobalamin (vitamin B_{12b}) in which the cyanide is replaced by a hydroxyl group, however. Still other vitamin B_{12}-like compounds in which the dimethylbenzimidazole moiety is replaced by other nitrogenous bases have been isolated from bacteria. In pseudo-vitamin B_{12} the nitrogenous base is adenine; in another form of the vitamin, the base is benzimidazole.

Occurrence: Vitamin B_{12}, which has been found only in animals and micro-organisms and not in plants, has recently been shown by H. A. Barker of the University of California to occur as part of a coenzyme known as coenzyme B_{12}. The structure of this compound is shown in our sketch. In the coenzyme the position occupied by either a cyanide

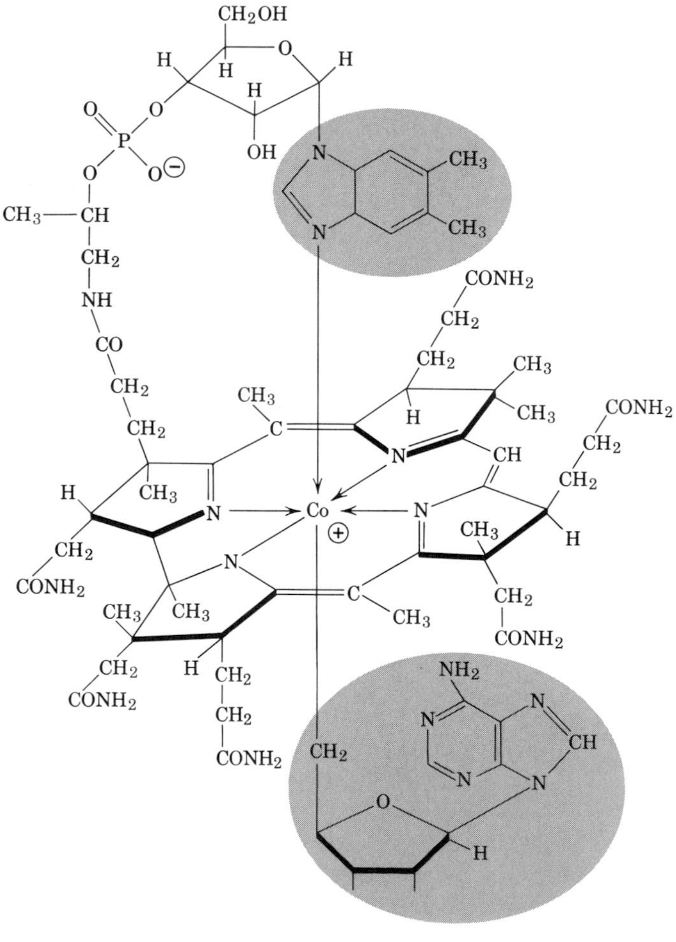

or a hydroxyl ion in the vitamin is bonded directly to the 5'-carbon atom of the ribose of adenosine.

The coenzyme is relatively unstable and in the presence of light or cyanide is decomposed, respectively, to the hydroxocobalamine or cyanocobalamine form known as the vitamin. Hence the very distinct possibility exists that vitamin B_{12} occurs in nature chiefly as coenzyme B_{12}.

Since pseudo-vitamin B_{12} occurs with adenine rather than 5,6-dimethylbenzimidazole as the base attached to ribose, there also exists a coenzyme form of pseudo-vitamin B_{12}. A coenzyme form of the vitamin which contains benzimidazole also occurs.

Vitamin B_{12} was first recognized as an agent useful in the prevention and treatment of pernicious anemia. Previously termed the antipernicious anemia factor, it is also a growth factor for several bacteria, a protozoan, *Euglena*, and may be involved in symbiotic nitrogen fixation.

Biochemical Function: This extremely important vitamin has recently been brought into sharp focus on an enzyme level. Though the precise mechanism is not known, it participates in two types of reactions, (1) the isomerization of dicarboxylic acids and (2) the conversion of vincinal dihydroxy compounds to the deoxy, monohydroxyl grouping. Three examples can be cited.

methylmalonyl-CoA isomerase:

$$
\begin{array}{ccc}
\underset{1}{C}\!\!\diagup^{\displaystyle O}\!\!-S\!-\!CoA & & \underset{1}{C}\!\!\diagup^{\displaystyle O}\!\!-S\!-\!CoA \\
| & \rightleftharpoons & | \\
\underset{3}{C}H\!-\!\underset{2}{C}H_3 & & \underset{2}{C}H_2 \\
| & & | \\
\underset{4}{C}OOH & & \underset{3}{C}H_2 \\
& & | \\
& & \underset{4}{C}OOH
\end{array}
$$

β-methyl aspartic isomerase:

$$
\begin{array}{ccc}
\underset{1}{C}OO^- & & \underset{1}{C}OO^- \\
| & & | \\
\underset{2}{C}HNH_3^+ & \rightleftharpoons & \underset{2}{C}HNH_3^+ \\
| & & | \\
\underset{4}{C}HCH_3 & & \underset{3}{C}H_2 \\
| & & | \\
\underset{5}{C}OOH & & \underset{4}{C}H_2 \\
& & | \\
& & \underset{5}{C}OOH
\end{array}
$$

the conversion of propylene glycol to propionaldehyde:

$$
CH_3\,CHOH\,CH_2OH \;\rightleftharpoons\; CH_3\,CH_2\,CHO
$$

propylene glycol   propionaldehyde

The third reaction is of great interest since it is a model system for the conversion of ribonucleotides to deoxyribonucleotides. Thus it has been known for some time that thymidine (a deoxynucleotide) replaces vitamin B_{12} as a growth factor in *Lactobacillus leichmanii*. Vitamin B_{12} is required, however, to incorporate radioactive guanosylriboside into the deoxyribosyl moiety of DNA, which suggests that:

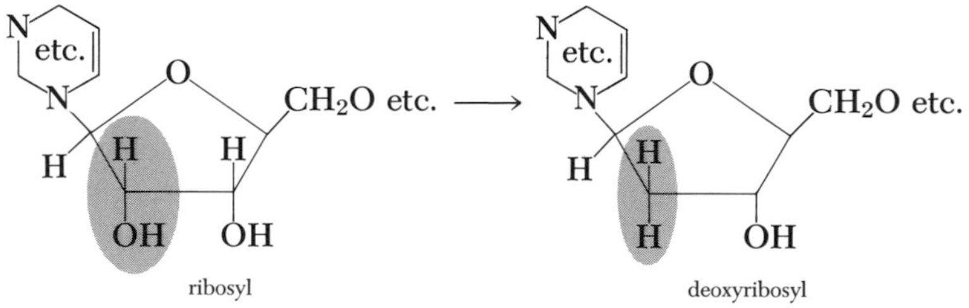

ribosyl   deoxyribosyl

Pantothenic Acid

Structure: This vitamin occurs in nature primarily as coenzyme A.

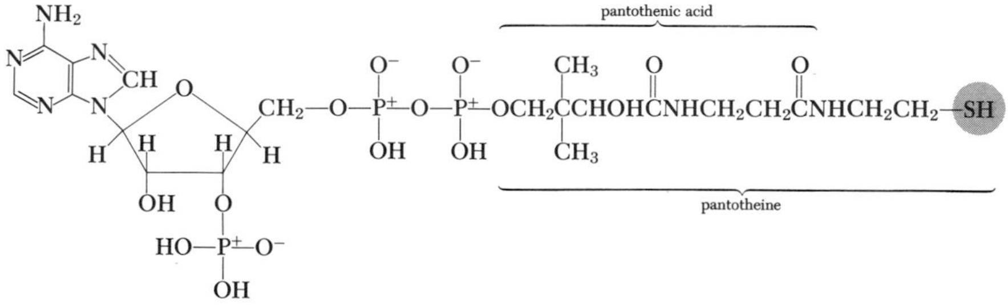

coenzyme A or CoA-SH

Occurrence: Pantothenic acid, which was isolated because of its ability to stimulate the growth of yeast, is required by higher animals as well as by other micro-organisms. Because an unknown cofactor was required for the enzymic acetylation of aromatic amines by acetate, the term coenzyme A was coined to describe the acetylation cofactor. Coenzyme A was isolated and its structure determined in the late 1940's by Lipmann, then of Harvard. The complete chemical synthesis of the coenzyme was described by Khorana in 1959.

Biochemical Function: Coenzyme A functions as a thioester of carboxylic acids:

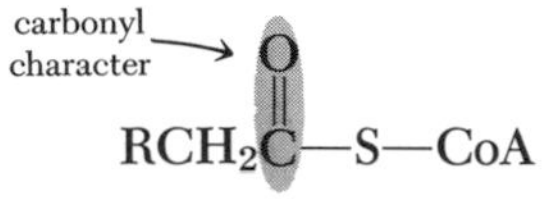

Although oxygen esters have two resonating forms,

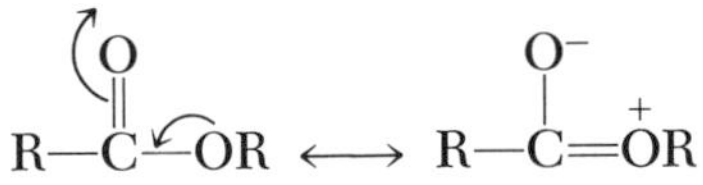

$$R-\overset{\overset{\displaystyle O}{\parallel}}{C}-OR \longleftrightarrow R-\overset{\overset{\displaystyle O^-}{|}}{\underset{}{C}}=\overset{+}{O}R$$

sulfur does not readily release its electrons for double-bond formation and hence thioesters do not exhibit the resonating forms of oxygen esters. Rather, thioesters exhibit considerable carbonyl character. With a fractional positive charge on the carbonyl carbon the hydrogen atom on the α-carbon atom will tend to separate as a proton, placing a fractional negative charge (or a nucleophilic site) on the carbon atom adjacent to the carbonyl carbon.

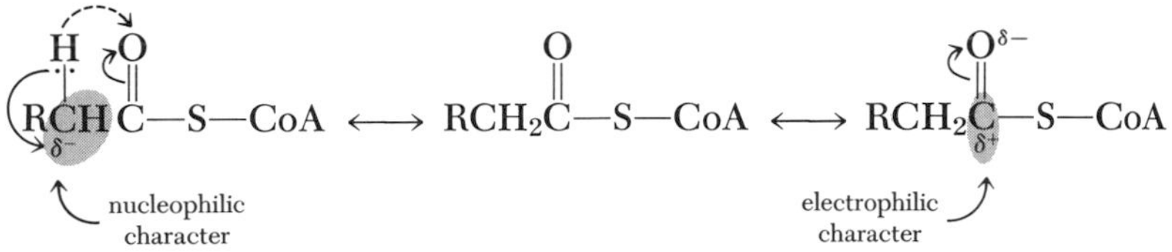

$$\underset{\substack{\text{nucleophilic}\\\text{character}}}{\overset{\overset{\displaystyle H \quad O}{}}{RCH\,C}-S-CoA} \longleftrightarrow RCH_2\overset{\overset{\displaystyle O}{\parallel}}{C}-S-CoA \longleftrightarrow \underset{\substack{\text{electrophilic}\\\text{character}}}{RCH_2\overset{\overset{\displaystyle O^{\delta-}}{}}{\underset{\delta+}{C}}-S-CoA}$$

Nucleophiles such as amines, ammonia, water, thio compounds, and phosphoric acid can attack the electrophilic site and displace the : S-CoA group. An electrophile such as CO_2, acyl-CoA, or the CO_2-biotinyl complex can in turn attack the nucleophilic site. Throughout the text numerous examples are given of the reactivities of thioesters of coenzyme A. Suffice it to say that most if not all the reactions can be explained on the basis of the dual reactivity of acyl thioesters. The student should, in his study of the book, attempt to gather together the many CoA-SH reactions and explain the mechanisms to his own satisfaction. Several examples and a further discussion will be found in Chapter 13.

Vitamins Lacking True Coenzyme Function

Vitamin K

Structure:

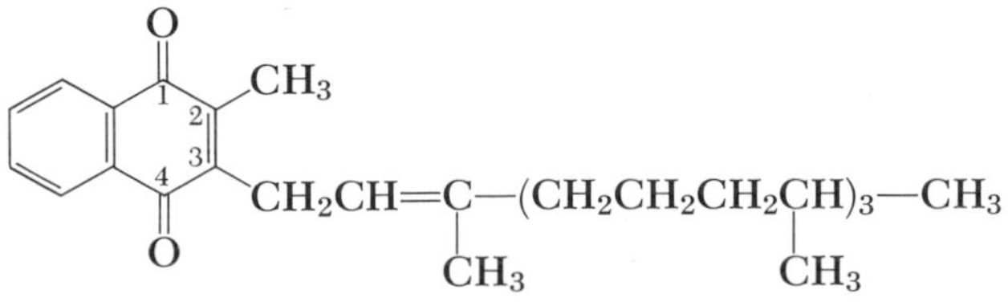

vitamin K₁

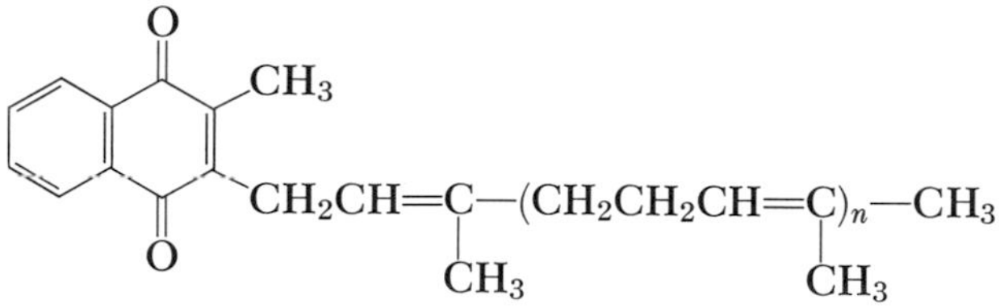

vitamin K_2 series

Occurrence: Vitamin K_1 (phylloquinone) occurs in green plants, whereas the members of the vitamin K_2 series are found in bacteria; all are fat soluble.   Essential features of the vitamin K napthoquinone derivatives are (1) that the methyl group be in the 2-position, (2) that there be an unsubstituted benzene ring, and (3) that certain specific requirements be fulfilled regarding the aliphatic substituent in the 3-position.   These compounds readily undergo oxidation and reduction but are well stabilized as quinones.   Light rapidly inactivates the K vitamins irreversibly.

Biochemical Function: No clear role has been found for vitamin K in enzyme systems although several well-defined roles have been assigned to the vitamin from the physiological point of view.   These include blood coagulation.

The process of blood coagulation is a complicated process and is under sensitive control.   In its simplest form it may be represented as follows:

fibrinogen

$$\text{thrombin} \xleftarrow[\text{thromboplastin}]{Ca^{2+}} \text{prothrombin}$$

fibrin (blood clot)

The clot that forms to prevent loss of blood consists of an insoluble protein known as *fibrin*.   Fibrin is formed from its precursor *fibrinogen,* a soluble protein which is present in normal plasma.   The conversion requires the presence of an enzyme known as *thrombin* and involves the release of two soluble peptides from the fibrinogen molecule.   It has been suggested that thrombin is a proteolytic enzyme which hydrolyzes off specific peptides from the fibrinogen and thus allows the residue to polymerize and so to form the insoluble clot.

The blood plasma, in turn, does not contain thrombin, but it does contain its precursor prothrombin.   In the presence of Ca^{2+} ions and another protein, thromboplastin, prothrombin is converted to thrombin. Other factors also play a role in the activation of thrombin, but they cannot be discussed here.   The requirement of Ca^{2+} in the blood-clotting process is one of the easiest to demonstrate, since the addition of effective complexing agents such as citric or oxalic acid to blood will prevent it from clotting.   Thromboplastin is found in many tissues in addition to the blood.

If the dietary intake of vitamin K is not adequate, the prothrombin level decreases.   The exact function of vitamin K in the clotting phenomenon is not known, but it is believed to participate in some manner in the synthesis of prothrombin in the liver.

Considerable work has also implicated vitamin K in oxidative phosphorylation and electron-transporting systems.   Much of this work is controversial in nature and need not be discussed here.   It should be pointed out, however, that in vitamin K-deficient animals growth and respiration appear normal; death takes place as a result of bleeding and not by some blockage in the respiratory chain.

In summary, vitamin K is strongly implicated in prothrombin biosynthesis.   Its role in other biochemical activities is not clear.

Vitamin E

Structure:

tocopherol
where R_1, R_2, R_3 may be a
combination of methyl groups and H atoms

Occurrence: The α-tocopherols are widespread in plant oils.   Large amounts are found in wheat germ oil and corn oil, for example.   Tocopherols are also found in animal body fat.   There is some evidence that all α-tocopherol in heart muscle is localized in the mitochondria.

Biochemical Function: Characteristic symptoms of avitaminosis E vary with the animal species.   In mature female rats, reproductive failure occurs because of fetal reabsorption; with the male rat germinal tissue degenerates.   With rabbits and guinea pigs acute muscular dystrophy results; in chickens vascular abnormalities occur.   In humans no well-defined syndrome of vitamin E deficiency has been detected.

The most prominent effect that tocopherol has in *in vitro* systems is a strong antioxidant activity.   It has been suggested that the biochemical activity of tocopherol is its capacity to protect sensitive mitochondrial systems from irreversible inhibition by lipid peroxides. Thus in mitochondria prepared from tocopherol-deficient animals, there is a profound deterioration of mitochondrial activity due to hematin-catalyzed peroxidation of highly unsaturated fatty acids normally present in these particles. Addition of tocopherol prevents this deterioration by acting as an antioxidant for peroxidation.

Many workers have observed that tocopherol-deficient muscle shows a high oxygen uptake. Administration of tocopherol to deficient animals lowers the oxygen consumption to normal. The evidence suggests that although the deficiency in some manner interferes with normal oxidative phosphorylation, it may only be a secondary interference, perhaps related to its known antioxidant properties.

Vitamin A

Structure: (a) Parent substance—α-carotene:

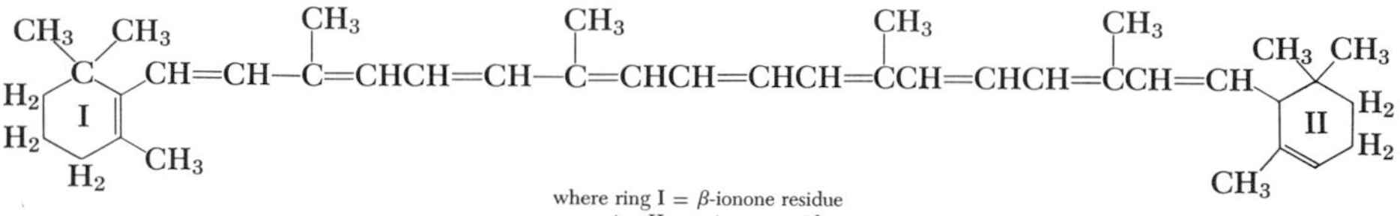

where ring I = β-ionone residue
ring II = α-ionone residue

(b) Vitamin A₁ (all *trans*)

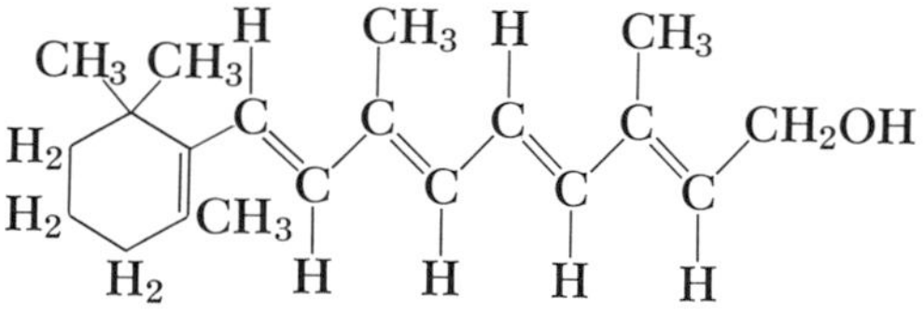

Occurrence: The parent substance is found widespread in the lower and higher forms of plants. Carotenoids, which are more saturated and oxygenated, are also found widely distributed. They occur in tissues of vertebrate and invertebrate animals, particularly in fat deposits, milk, and eye tissue. It is believed that in the small intestine the parent substances are oxidatively broken down to vitamin A.

It is interesting that the major proportion of the naturally occurring carotenoid molecules have all their double bonds in the *trans* configuration, although chemical isomerization can occur readily.

Biochemical Functions: George Wald of Harvard has made major contributions to our understanding of the role of vitamin A₁ in visual processes. The results can be outlined as in the diagram that follows.

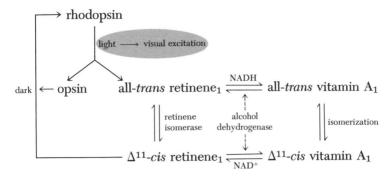

Rhodopsin is a visual pigment that consists of a carotenoid-protein complex found in the rods of the retina. The carotenoid is Δ^{11}-*cis* retinene$_1$, which has five double bonds, all *trans*, except the one between the C-11 and C-12 carbon atoms, which is *cis*. As can be seen

in the sketch, Δ^{11}-*cis* retinene$_1$ is the aldehyde corresponding to Δ^{11}-*cis* vitamin A$_1$.

When light strikes the visual pigment, isomerization of the Δ^{11}-*cis* double bond to the *trans* configuration occurs with the formation of all *trans* retinene$_1$; the protein-carotenoid complex subsequently dissociates yielding opsin and all-*trans* retinene$_1$. The latter compound may then be reduced by NADH and alcohol dehydrogenase in retinal tissue to all-*trans* vitamin A$_1$.

Light has a second role in the rhodopsin cycle; it labilizes the association of Δ^{11}-*cis* retinene$_1$ with opsin to regenerate rhodopsin. Δ^{11}-*cis* Retinene$_1$ in turn can be regenerated either by the isomerization of all-*trans* retinene$_1$ or by the oxidation of Δ^{11}-*cis* vitamin A$_1$. This compound may be formed by the enzymic isomerization of all-*trans* vitamin A. Of primary concern is the problem of how the action of light on rhodopsin results in a nervous excitation leading to vision. It has been suggested that just as trypsinogen is catalytically converted to trypsin, the conversion of rhodopsin to opsin and all-*trans* retinene may "uncork" an enzymic or other related reaction which is responsible for the actual visual mechanism.

It should be emphasized that avitaminosis A in rats is also characterized by loss of weight, skeletal abnormalities, and disturbances in normal sexual processes. It is therefore obvious that vitamin A has functions other than the visual process. There is indeed recent evidence that it may be involved in mucopolysaccharide biosynthesis.

Vitamin D

Structure:

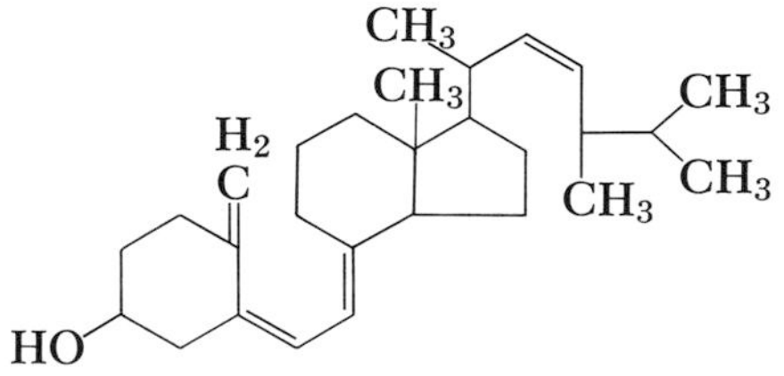

vitamin D₂ (calciferol)

Occurrence: Several compounds are known to be effective in preventing rickets; all are derived by irradiation of different forms of provitamin D. Thus vitamin D_2 (calciferol) is produced commercially by the irradiation of a steroid, ergosterol, which is found in plants. In animal tissues the provitamin D, 7-dehydrocholesterol, which occurs there naturally, can be converted by irradiation with ultraviolet light to vitamin D_3. The latter vitamin is also present in fish oil.

Biochemical Function: The classic symptom of vitamin D deficiency is the childhood disease known as rickets. In this deficiency the metabolism of calcium and phosphate is abnormal to the extent of producing structural changes in bones and teeth. The manner in which an adequate supply of vitamin D prevents these symptoms is unknown, although the vitamin is known to stimulate the absorption of Ca^{2+} from the intestine.

Ascorbic Acid or Vitamin C

Structure:

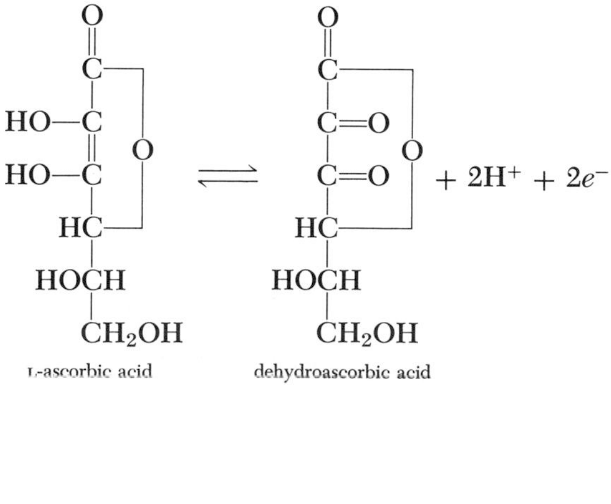

l-ascorbic acid   dehydroascorbic acid

Occurrence: Ascorbic acid is synthesized in a great variety of plants and in all known mammals except the primates and the guinea pig. In the tissues of these species the enzyme responsible for the conversion of L-gulonolactone to L-ascorbic acid is missing. The precise steps in the biosynthesis of ascorbic acid from glucose have been determined, but will not be discussed in this book. The student is referred to the literature for this information.

Biochemical Function: It is a historical fact that scurvy was remarkably cured by administering fresh vegetables to victims of the disease. The active component in fresh vegetables is L-ascorbic acid. Despite its dramatic effect on the disease, little information is at present available on the biochemical nature of the deficiency.

The following functions may be considered for L-ascorbic acid, however:

(a) Ascorbic acid is a powerful reducing agent and is reversibly converted to dehydroascorbic acid, the oxidized product. A plant enzyme that catalyzes this reaction is the copper-containing enzyme ascorbic acid oxidase:

$$\text{ascorbic acid} + \tfrac{1}{2}O_2 \longrightarrow \text{dehydroascorbic acid} + H_2O$$

The possibility that ascorbic acid may be a member of an electron-transport system remains open.

(b) Ascorbic acid is present in significant amounts in the adrenal cortex and may participate in the biosynthesis of adrenal steroid hormones.

(c) Ascorbic acid may be involved in the hydroxylation of aromatic compounds. The rate of hydroxylation is known to be markedly reduced in ascorbic-deficient guinea pigs and is restored on addition of the vitamin to the diets of the animals.

Table 8-3. Typical Metallo-Enzymes

Metal	Enzyme
Iron	Cytochromes, peroxidases
Copper	Tyrosinase, ascorbic oxidase
Zinc	Peptidase, carbonic anydrase
Magnesium	Phosphatases, kinases
Manganese	Kinases, peptidases, arginase
Molybdenum	Xanthine oxidase, nitrate reductase
Cobalt	Vitamin B_{12} coenzyme complexes
Potassium	Pyruvic kinase, β-methyl aspartase

Trace Metals

There is good evidence that all metals nutritionally required in trace quantities participate on a molecular level either as cofactors for enzymes or as structural components of enzymes. This may be best summarized in Table 8-3.

REFERENCES

1. *The Enzymes,* edited by Paul D. Boyer, Henry Lardy, and Karl Myrbäck, Academic Press, New York, 1960, Vols. 2 and 3.

   These two volumes contain comprehensive reviews on coenzymes.
2. C. H. Best and N. B. Taylor, *Physiological Basis of Medical Practice,* Williams and Wilkins, Baltimore, 6th edition, 1955, Chapters 54 and 55.

   An excellent description of the physiological aspects of the nutrition of vitamins.

Nine

Anaerobic Carbohydrate Metabolism

Introduction

Carbohydrates are a major source of energy for living organisms. In man's food the chief source of carbohydrate is starch, a polysaccharide produced by plants. The biological organism may store carbohydrate as a polymer within its own cells in times of abundant supply, to be used later when there is a demand for energy production. In man this stored form of carbohydrate is the polysaccharide glycogen.

Simple sugars such as sucrose, glucose, fructose, mannose, and galactose are also encountered in nature and are utilized by living forms as food. The process by which the chemical energy in these compounds is made available to and utilized by biological organisms is a matter of major concern in this text. The intermediary metabolism of carbohydrates, together with that of lipids, amino acids, and proteins, is indeed the backbone of biochemistry, and we are now prepared to consider the metabolism of the carbohydrates.

It is convenient to separate the intermediary metabolism of carbohydrates into an anaerobic phase and certain aerobic processes which will be described later. The term _glycolysis is generally used to refer to_ the anaerobic degradation of carbohydrates in living cells. It may also be used more specifically to describe the sequence of reactions leading to lactic acid formation in the muscles of higher animals. _Alcoholic fermentation_ on the other hand refers to the anaerobic degradation of carbohydrates as it occurs in yeast. This process leads to ethanol and CO_2 production. Fortunately the reactions involved are identical except for the initial and final stages, where different reactants and products are encountered.

The sequence of reactions of glycolysis and alcoholic fermentation as it exists today was developed by the pioneers in enzymology. In 1897 the Buchners obtained a cell-free extract of yeast which fermented sugars to CO_2 and ethanol. Shortly thereafter the work of Harden and Young in England implicated phosphorylated derivatives of the sugars in alcoholic fermentation. Today the glycolytic sequence is recognized as being composed of the reactions outlined inside the front cover of this text. A list of the pioneers in the field who were the architects of this scheme includes Embden, Meyerhof, Robison, Neuberg, the Coris, Parnas, and Warburg. Each reaction of the glycolytic process will be considered in turn in order to appreciate the significance of the overall sequence.

Reactions of the Glycolytic Sequence

PHOSPHORYLASE

The utilization of starchlike polysaccharides is effected by *phosphorylase*, an enzyme which is widely distributed in nature. Although the phosphorylases from different sources vary in certain respects, they all catalyze the phosphorylytic cleavage or synthesis of the α-1,4-glucosidic linkage at the nonreducing end of the starch or glycogen chain. The reaction is reversible and is represented as follows:

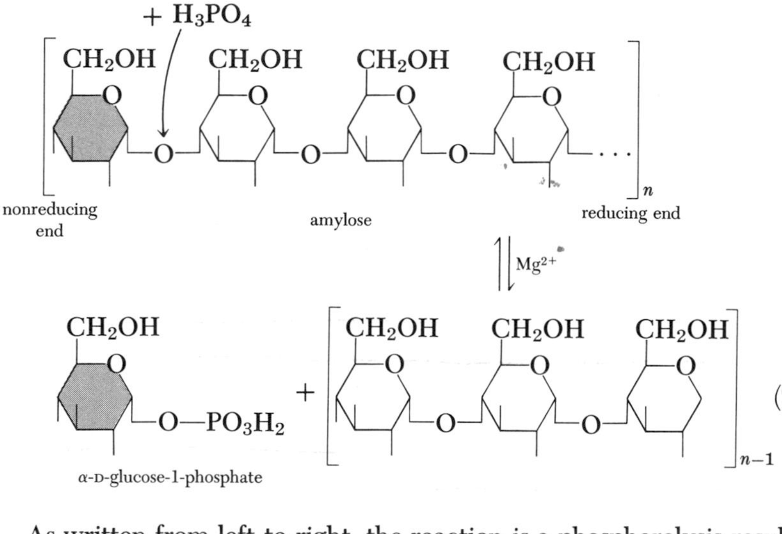

$$\text{(9-1)}$$

As written from left to right, the reaction is a phosphorolysis resulting in the formation of α-D-glucose-1-phosphate and the loss of one glucose unit from the nonreducing end of the polysaccharide chain. In the reverse reaction, inorganic phosphate is liberated from α-D-glucose-1-phosphate with a lengthening of the polysaccharide chain at the nonreducing end.

Synthesis of polysaccharide from α-glucose-1-phosphate does not occur unless a small amount of starch, glycogen, or dextrin is present as a priming agent. The primer is necessary because the enzyme is able to catalyze only very slowly the direct condensation of glucose-1-phosphate units in its absence. In the presence of the primer, the enzyme rapidly adds glucose units to the pre-existing polysaccharide chain. The nature of the primer required varies with the source of the phosphorylase. The enzyme from muscle requires the highly branched glycogen; the enzyme from potato can utilize the trisaccharide maltotriose as a primer. All phosphorylases are specific in that they react only with α-D-glucopyranosyl-1-phosphate and form only the α-1-4-maltosidic bond.

Phosphorylase will catalyze the complete degradation of the unbranched amylose chain to glucose-1-phosphate. Branched polysaccharides such as amylopectin are degraded only about 55 per cent; the residue is called *limit dextrin*. In amylopectin the branching of the polysaccharide chains is accomplished by an α-1-6-glucosidic linkage; this linkage constitutes a barrier upon which the enzyme is inactive. Figure 9-1 indicates the action of phosphorylase on amylopectin.

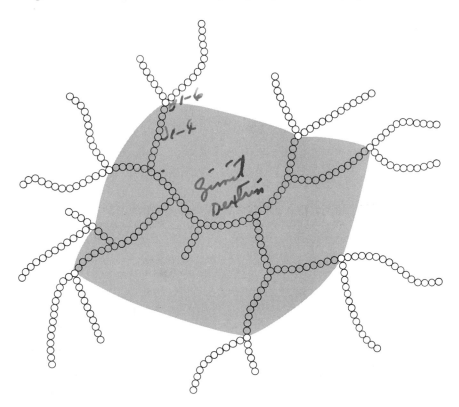

Fig. 9-1. Action of phosphorylase on amylopectin. The branched-chain polysaccharide is amylopectin. Phosphorylase degrades until a branching point is reached. Within the shaded area is limit dextrin on which phosphorylase does not act.

The equilibrium of the phosphorylase reaction, which is readily reversible, is independent of the polysaccharide concentration, provided a certain minimum concentration is exceeded. Thus in the following expression for K_{eq} the polysaccharide concentrations represent the number of nonreducing chain termini, *a number that does not change*. It then follows that at any pH the K_{eq} is determined by the relative concentrations of glucose-1-phosphate and inorganic phosphate.

$$K_{eq} = \frac{[C_6H_{10}O_5]_{n-1} \, [\text{glucose-1-PO}_4]}{[C_6H_{10}O_5]_n \, [H_3PO_4]}$$
$$= \frac{[\text{glucose-1-PO}_4]}{[H_3PO_4]}$$
$$= 0.3$$
$$\text{(pH 7.0)}$$

Although the reaction catalyzed by phosphorylase is readily reversible, the role of the enzyme is apparently largely degradative in nature. As described on page 188, a different enzyme and a different reaction (involving uridine diphosphoglucose) accounts for the synthesis of glycogen from monosaccharides.

The phosphorylase of rabbit muscle exists in two forms, *a* and *b*. Phosphorylase *a*, active as obtained, is converted to phosphorylase *b*, an inactive form with half the molecular weight of phosphorylase *a*, by the enzyme *phosphorylase phosphatase.* This involves the release of 4 moles of inorganic phosphate and the formation of 2 moles of phosphorylase *b*.

$$\text{phosphorylase } a \xrightarrow[\text{phosphatase}]{\text{phosphorylase}} 2 \text{ phosphorylase } b + 4H_3PO_4 \qquad (9\text{-}2)$$

The activity of phosphorylase *b* is partially restored in the presence of adenosine-5′-monophosphate. Phosphorylase *b* is also converted back to active phosphorylase *a* by the action of ATP and a specific kinase.

$$2 \text{ phosphorylase } b + 4ATP \xrightarrow[\text{Mn}^{2+}]{\text{kinase}} \text{phosphorylase } a + 4ADP \qquad (9\text{-}3)$$

Reliable data indicate that it involves formation of a dimer with twice the molecular weight and the uptake of 4 moles of phosphate.

PHOSPHOGLUCOMUTASE

This enzyme catalyzes the conversion of glucose-1-phosphate to glucose-6-phosphate in the presence of Mg^{2+} ions. Phosphoglucomutase has been crystallized (mol wt 74,000) from rabbit skeletal muscle, of which it constitutes almost 2 per cent of the water-soluble protein. The mechanism of the reaction has been studied by the Argentinian biochemist Leloir and his colleagues; more recent information has been contributed from the American laboratory of Najjar.

Leloir's group showed that phosphoglucomutase required glucose-1-6-diphosphate as a cofactor. It was originally proposed that the role of the diphosphate was to donate phosphate reversibly to glucose-1-phosphate or glucose-6-phosphate. Najjar's studies required a revision of the original mechanism, however. Phosphoglucomutase isolated in the active form from rabbit muscle is a *phosphoenzyme* containing one atom of phosphorous per molecule of enzyme; the phosphate is attached to a serine residue in the protein. Thus it can react with either glucose-1-phosphate or glucose-6-phosphate reversibly to form the coenzyme.

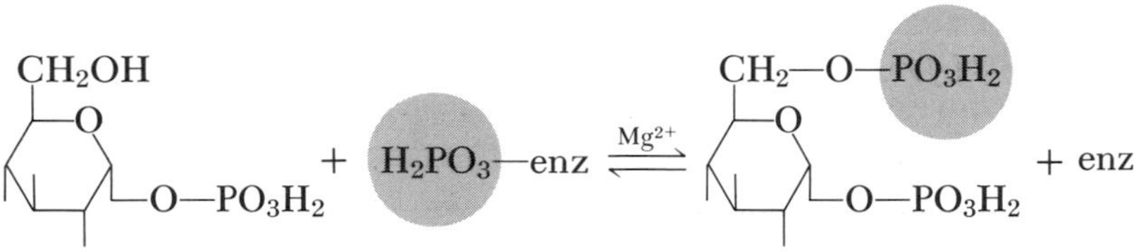

$$
\text{glucose-1-phosphate} + \text{H}_2\text{PO}_3\text{-enz (phosphoenzyme)} \underset{}{\overset{\text{Mg}^{2+}}{\rightleftharpoons}} \text{glucose-1-6-diphosphate} + \text{enz (dephosphoenzyme)}
$$

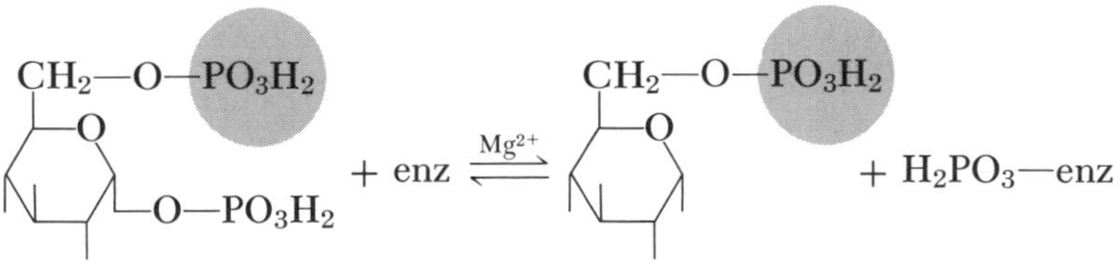

$$
\text{glucose-1-6-diphosphate} + \text{enz (dephosphoenzyme)} \underset{}{\overset{\text{Mg}^{2+}}{\rightleftharpoons}} \text{glucose-6-phosphate} + \text{H}_2\text{PO}_3\text{-enz (phosphoenzyme)}
$$

The sum of these reactions is:

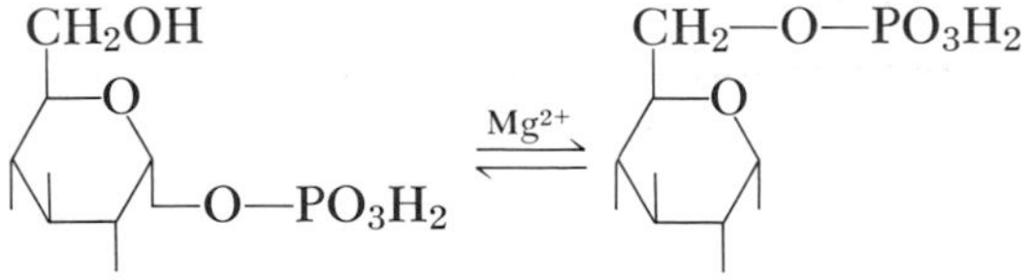

$$
\text{glucose-1-phosphate} \underset{}{\overset{\text{Mg}^{2+}}{\rightleftharpoons}} \text{glucose-6-phosphate} \tag{9-4}
$$

The K_{eq} of the reaction from left to right is 19 at pH 7.0 and favors the formation of glucose-6-phosphate. The coenzyme glucose-1-6-diphosphate has been found in all living tissues.

HEXOKINASE

The initial step in the utilization of glucose by many living organisms is its phosphorylation by ATP to yield glucose-6-phosphate.

$$\text{glucose} + \text{ATP} \underset{}{\overset{Mg^{2+}}{\rightleftharpoons}} \text{glucose-6-phosphate} + \text{ADP} \qquad (9\text{-}5)$$

The enzyme hexokinase which catalyzes this reaction was first discovered in yeast by Meyerhof in 1927. The enzyme from yeast has been crystallized (mol wt 96,000) and shows a rather broad specificity in that it will catalyze the transfer of phosphate from ATP not only to glucose, but also to fructose, mannose, and glucosamine. The relative rates of reaction depend on the concentration of the sugars in the reaction mixture; fructose is phosphorylated most rapidly at high concentrations.

It is informative to consider the energy changes that occur in this reaction. When glucose is phosphorylated to form glucose-6-phosphate, a compound having a low-energy phosphate ester grouping has been produced. The free energy of hydrolysis of this compound is about -3000 cal.

$$\text{glucose-6-phosphate} + H_2O \longrightarrow \text{glucose} + H_3PO_4$$
$$\Delta F' = -3000 \text{ cal (pH 7.0)}$$

The phosphate group attached to the sugar was obtained from the terminal phosphate group of ATP. When this group is hydrolyzed to ADP and inorganic phosphate, the free energy of hydrolysis is about -8000 cal.

$$\text{ATP} + H_2O \longrightarrow \text{ADP} + H_3PO_4 \qquad (9\text{-}6)$$
$$\Delta F' = -8000 \text{ cal (pH 7.0)}.$$

Inspection reveals that in the hexokinase reaction a high-energy bond of ATP was utilized and a low-energy structure (that of glucose-6-phosphate) was formed. In the terminology of the biochemist, the reaction catalyzed by hexokinase is said to involve the *formation of a low-energy phosphate compound by the expenditure of an energy-rich phosphate structure.* Normally the loss of a high-energy bond by hydrolysis (reaction 9-6) would result in the liberation of the -8000 cal as heat if changes in entropy are neglected. In the hexokinase reaction part of that energy (-3000 cal) is conserved in the formation of the low-energy structure and the remainder (-5000 cal) is liberated as heat, again neglecting entropy changes.   Thus we may estimate the free-energy change for the hexokinase reaction to be almost -5000 cal; that is, the reaction is strongly exergonic.   An equilibrium constant of 5.5×10^3 corresponding to a $\Delta F'$ of -5100 has been measured experimentally. The equilibrium in this reaction is clearly far to the right.

PHOSPHOHEXOISOMERASES

The next reaction in the anaerobic degradation of glucose is the isomerization of glucose-6-phosphate, which is catalyzed by phosphoglucoisomerase.

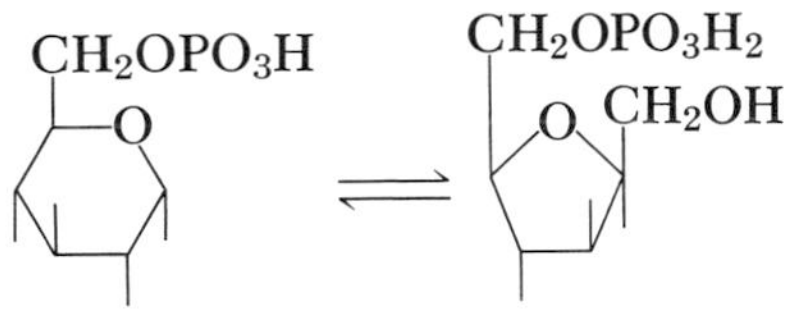

$$CH_2OPO_3H \qquad CH_2OPO_3H_2$$

glucose-6-phosphate   fructose-6-phosphate

$$(9\text{-}7)$$

The enzyme, which has been extensively purified from skeletal muscle, does not require a cofactor; the K_{eq} for the reaction from left to right is approximately 0.5.   A similar enzyme that catalyzes the isomerization of mannose-6-phosphate to fructose-6-phosphate has been isolated from rabbit muscle.   Since the three sugars glucose, fructose, and mannose are readily interconverted in dilute alkali (the Lobry-de Bruyn-Von Ekenstein transformation), it is interesting to note that the two enzymes are highly specific for fructose-6-phosphate and the corresponding hexose-6-phosphate for which they are named.

PHOSPHOFRUCTOKINASE

The kinase that catalyzes the phosphorylation of fructose-6-phosphate by ATP has been purified from both yeast and muscle.   The enzyme requires Mg^{2+} and is specific for fructose-6-phosphate.

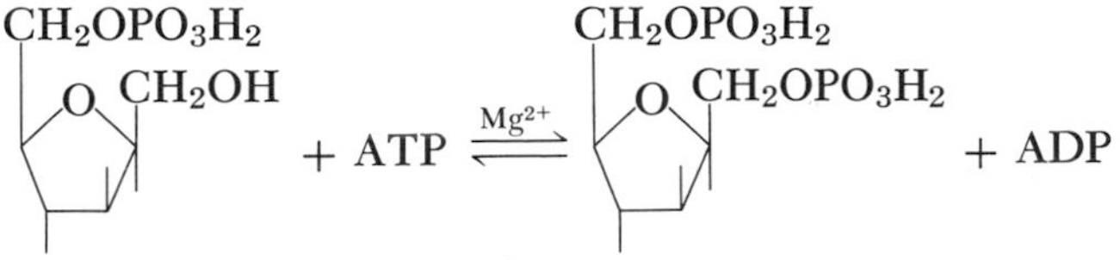

$$CH_2OPO_3H_2 \qquad CH_2OPO_3H_2$$

fructose-6-phosphate   fructose-1-6-diphosphate

$$(9\text{-}8)$$

As with hexokinase, the high-energy bond of ATP is utilized to synthesize the low-energy 1-phosphate bond of fructose-1-6-diphosphate.   Using the arguments presented in the former case, we may expect that this reaction, too, should proceed with a large decrease in free energy and therefore should not be freely reversible. The $\Delta F'$ is -4200 cal/mole.

ALDOLASE

The next reaction in the glycolytic sequence involves the cleavage of fructose-1-6-diphosphate to form two molecules of triose sugars, dihydroxyacetone phosphate, and D-glyceraldehyde-3-phosphate.

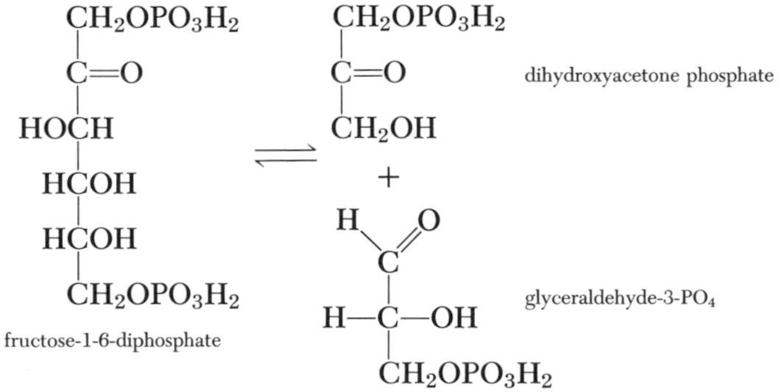

$$
\begin{array}{ccc}
\text{CH}_2\text{OPO}_3\text{H}_2 & \text{CH}_2\text{OPO}_3\text{H}_2 & \\
| & | & \\
\text{C}=\text{O} & \text{C}=\text{O} & \text{dihydroxyacetone phosphate} \\
| & | & \\
\text{HOCH} & \text{CH}_2\text{OH} & \\
| & + & \quad\quad\quad (9\text{-}9) \\
\text{HCOH} & & \\
| & \text{H}\quad\text{O} & \\
\text{HCOH} & \text{C} & \\
| & | & \\
\text{CH}_2\text{OPO}_3\text{H}_2 & \text{H}-\text{C}-\text{OH} & \text{glyceraldehyde-3-PO}_4 \\
\text{fructose-1-6-diphosphate} & | & \\
 & \text{CH}_2\text{OPO}_3\text{H}_2 & \\
\end{array}
$$

The enzyme aldolase which catalyzes this reaction was extensively purified from yeast and studied by Warburg, and has been crystallized (mol wt of 147,000) from rabbit muscle in the Cori laboratory. The reaction is readily reversible and the equilibrium constant $K_{eq} = 9.1 \times 10^{-5}$, favors the formation of the hexose diphosphate. The formation of hexose diphosphate constitutes an aldol condensation from which the enzyme receives its name.

It is interesting to note the stereospecificity of the condensation reaction; the aldol condensation results in the formation of two asymmetric carbon atoms. Hence four different isomers of the hexosediphosphate theoretically could be formed. Nevertheless the enzyme specifically catalyzes the formation of only one, fructose-1-6-diphosphate, from dihydroxyacetone phosphate and D-glyceraldehyde-3-phosphate. As regards the specificity for the trioses, a number of aldehydes will substitute for D-glyceraldehyde-3-phosphate; the specificity for dihydroxyacetone phosphate is absolute, however. Thus when D-erythrose-4-phosphate is substituted for D-glyceraldehyde-3-phosphate, sedoheptulose-1-7-diphosphate is formed. Similarly, if formaldehyde is supplied instead of glyceraldehyde, D-erythrulose-1-phosphate is formed.

Yeast aldolase is inactivated by cysteine and may be reactivated by zinc, ferrous, or cobalt ions. On the other hand, the aldolase from higher plants (peas) does not exhibit these properties.

TRIOSEPHOSPHATE ISOMERASE

Meyerhof was the first to describe the equilibrium between the triosephosphates which is catalyzed by this enzyme.

$$
\begin{array}{ccc}
\underset{\text{glyceraldehyde-3-phosphate}}{\begin{array}{c} H \\ \diagdown \\ C \diagup\!\!\!\diagdown O \\ | \\ H-C-OH \\ | \\ CH_2OPO_3H_2 \end{array}}
&
\rightleftharpoons
&
\underset{\text{dihydroxyacetone-phosphate}}{\begin{array}{c} CH_2OH \\ | \\ C=O \\ | \\ CH_2OPO_3H_2 \end{array}}
\end{array}
\qquad (9\text{-}10)
$$

The reaction is analagous to the isomerization of the hexoses (reaction 9-7) and its significance is realized when subsequent degradation of the trioses is shown to involve only D-glyceraldehyde-3-phosphate and not dihydroxyacetone phosphate. Although at equilibrium the acetone derivative predominates ($K_{eq} = 22$), the presence of even a small amount of this enzyme, which has a high turnover number, insures that an immediate conversion of the acetone derivative will result to establish the equilibrium. The turnover number of calf muscle triosephosphate isomerase is $2 \times 10^6/10^6$ g of enzyme.

PHOSPHOGLYCERALDEHYDE DEHYDROGENASE

This reaction is the first one in the glycolytic sequence to involve oxidation reduction. As may be seen from the overall reaction, it is also the first reaction in which a high-energy phosphate bond has been formed where none previously existed.

$$
\underset{\text{glyceraldehyde-3-phosphate}}{\begin{array}{c} H \\ \diagdown \\ C \diagup\!\!\!\diagdown O \\ | \\ H-C-OH \\ | \\ CH_2OPO_3H_2 \end{array}} + NAD^+ + H_3PO_4 \rightleftharpoons \underset{\text{1,3-diphosphoglyceric acid}}{\begin{array}{c} O \\ || \\ C-OPO_3H_2 \\ | \\ H-C-OH \\ | \\ CH_2OPO_3H_2 \end{array}} + NADH + H^+
$$

$$(9\text{-}11)$$

As a result of the oxidation of an aldehyde group to the level of an acid, some of the energy which presumably would have been released in the form of heat has been conserved in the formation of the acyl phosphate group of 1,3-diphosphoglyceric acid. The oxidizing agent involved is NAD^+.

To consider the mechanism whereby the enzyme brings about this remarkable reaction some of the properties of the protein need to be discussed. The enzyme, which has been crystallized from rabbit mus-

cle, possesses sulfhydryl groups which must be fully reduced for catalytic activity. The oxidized, inactive form of the enzyme may be
readily activated by reduction with glutathione or cysteine. The
reduced, active form of the enzyme is irreversibly inactivated by iodo-
acetic acid. In addition, the crystalline rabbit muscle enzyme contains
two molecules of NAD^+ that are tightly bound to the enzyme. The
NAD^+-free protein cannot in fact be crystallized unless NAD^+ is added
back to it. Thus triosephosphate dehydrogenase constitutes an important exception to the statement made earlier that the pyridine nucleotide dehydrogenases are isolated without the coenzyme being associated
with the protein.

One mechanism recently proposed may be written as follows. In the
initial reaction the aldehyde is oxidized to a thioester in the presence of
the dehydrogenase-NAD^+; the sulfur atom participating in the thioester
linkage is represented as a sulfhydryl group of the enzyme.

$$R-C\overset{H}{\underset{O}{\diagdown}} + HS-enz-NAD^+ \rightleftharpoons R-\underset{O}{\overset{||}{C}}-S-enz-NADH + H^+$$

The acyl-enzyme compound then exchanges its NADH for NAD^+.

$$R-\underset{O}{\overset{||}{C}}-S-enz-NADH + NAD^+ \rightleftharpoons R-\underset{O}{\overset{||}{C}}-S-enz-NAD^+ + NADH$$

Finally, the acyl group on the enzyme is transferred to inorganic
phosphate.

$$R-\underset{O}{\overset{||}{C}}-S-enz-NAD^+ + H_3PO_4 \rightleftharpoons R-\underset{O}{\overset{||}{C}}-OPO_3H_2 + HS-enz-NAD^+$$

The sum of these three reactions is the overall reaction 9-11.

PHOSPHOGLYCERYL KINASE

This reaction accomplishes the transfer of the phosphate from the
acyl phosphate formed in the preceding reaction to ADP to form ATP.
The name of the enzyme is derived from the reverse reaction, in which
a high-energy phosphate is transferred from ATP to 3-phosphoglyceric
acid.

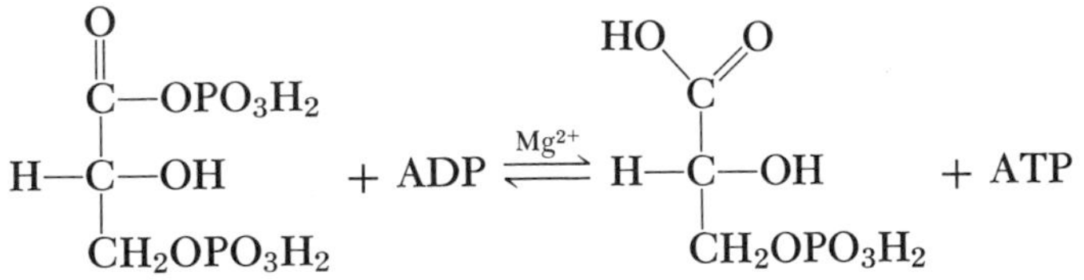

$$
\begin{array}{c}
\overset{\displaystyle O}{\underset{\displaystyle \|}{}} \\
C{-}OPO_3H_2 \\
| \\
H{-}C{-}OH \\
| \\
CH_2OPO_3H_2
\end{array}
\quad + ADP \overset{Mg^{2+}}{\underset{}{\rightleftharpoons}}
\begin{array}{c}
HO \;\; O \\
\diagdown C \diagup \\
| \\
H{-}C{-}OH \\
| \\
CH_2OPO_3H_2
\end{array}
\quad + ATP \quad (9\text{-}12)
$$

1,3-diphosphoglyceric acid   3-phosphoglyceric acid

The equilibrium for this reaction lies far to the right. The K_{eq} for the reaction from left to right is approximately 3.1×10^3, which means that the free-energy change is about -4700 cal. This value in turn, then, means that the $\Delta F'$ of hydrolysis of the acyl phosphate group of 1,3-diphosphoglyceric acid is about $(-8000) + (-4700)$ or about $-12,000$ cal at pH 7. These approximate calculations are similar to those discussed in the reaction catalyzed by hexokinase.

PHOSPHOGLYCEROMUTASE

Both 3-phosphoglyceric acid and 2-phosphoglyceric acid are converted to pyruvic acid by extracts of yeast, bacteria, and animal and plant tissues. The enzyme that catalyzes the interconversions of these two acids is phosphoglyceromutase.

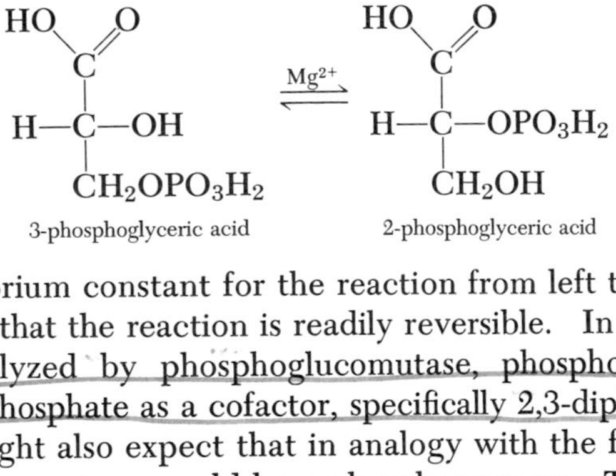

$$
\begin{array}{c}
HO \;\; O \\
\diagdown C \diagup \\
| \\
H{-}C{-}OH \\
| \\
CH_2OPO_3H_2
\end{array}
\quad \overset{Mg^{2+}}{\underset{}{\rightleftharpoons}}
\begin{array}{c}
HO \;\; O \\
\diagdown C \diagup \\
| \\
H{-}C{-}OPO_3H_2 \\
| \\
CH_2OH
\end{array}
\qquad (9\text{-}13)
$$

3-phosphoglyceric acid   2-phosphoglyceric acid

The equilibrium constant for the reaction from left to right is 0.17, which means that the reaction is readily reversible. In analogy to the reaction catalyzed by phosphoglucomutase, phosphoglyceromutase requires a diphosphate as a cofactor, specifically 2,3-diphosphoglyceric acid. We might also expect that in analogy with the former enzyme phosphoglyceromutase would be a phosphoenzyme. There is no evidence for or against this point, however. The enzyme crystallized from yeast has a mol wt of 112,000.

ENOLASE

The next reaction in the degradation of glucose involves the dehydration of 2-phosphoglyceric acid to form phosphoenolpyruvic acid, a compound with a high-energy enolic phosphate group.

$$\underset{\substack{\text{2-phosphoglyceric acid}}}{\overset{\displaystyle\text{HO}\diagdown\diagup\text{O}}{\underset{\displaystyle\text{CH}_2\text{OH}}{\overset{\displaystyle\text{C}}{\underset{\displaystyle\text{H—C—OPO}_3\text{H}_2}{}}}}} \overset{\text{Mg}^{2+}}{\rightleftharpoons} \underset{\substack{\text{phosphoenolpyruvic acid}}}{\overset{\displaystyle\text{HO}\diagdown\diagup\text{O}}{\underset{\displaystyle\text{CH}_2}{\overset{\displaystyle\text{C}}{\underset{\displaystyle\text{C—OPO}_3\text{H}_2}{}}}}} + \text{H}_2\text{O} \qquad (9\text{-}14)$$

The equilibrium constant for this reaction is 3; thus the reaction is freely reversible. It is hence interesting that by this process of dehydration an enolic phosphate ($\Delta F'$ of hydrolysis $= -12{,}800$ cal) is formed.

Enolase requires Mg^{2+} for activity. In the presence of Mg^{2+} and phosphate, fluoride ions strongly inhibit the enzyme. This effect is related to the formation of a magnesium-fluorophosphate complex which is only slightly dissociated and thereby effectively removes Mg^{2+} from the reaction mixture.

PYRUVIC KINASE

This reaction involves a transfer of phosphate from phosphoenol pyruvate to ADP to yield ATP and pyruvic acid.

$$\underset{\substack{\text{phosphoenolpyruvic acid}}}{\overset{\displaystyle\text{HO}\diagdown\diagup\text{O}}{\underset{\displaystyle\text{CH}_2}{\overset{\displaystyle\text{C}}{\underset{\displaystyle\text{C—OPO}_3\text{H}_2}{}}}}} + \text{ADP} \overset{\text{Mg}^{2+}}{\underset{\text{K}^+}{\rightleftharpoons}} \underset{\substack{\text{pyruvic acid}}}{\overset{\displaystyle\text{HO}\diagdown\diagup\text{O}}{\underset{\displaystyle\text{CH}_3}{\overset{\displaystyle\text{C}}{\underset{\displaystyle\text{C}=\text{O}}{}}}}} + \text{ATP} \qquad (9\text{-}15)$$

The enzyme, which has been crystallized from human and rat muscle, requires both Mg^{2+} and K^+ ions for activity. For many years the reaction was believed not to be reversible and only in 1945 was reversibility demonstrated by Boyer and Lardy when K^+ (or $\text{NH}_4{}^+$) was provided as well as Mg^{2+} and ATP. Since the $\Delta F'$ of hydrolysis of the enolic phosphate ($-12{,}800$) is somewhat larger than that for the pyrophosphate of ATP, the K_{eq} can be calculated to be 3.2×10^3.

Further Reactions Involving Pyruvate

Up to this point the reactions of glycolysis and alcoholic fermentation have been identical save for the initial reactants. Once pyruvate is produced, however, there is a difference in the way this compound is metabolized. In muscle tissue the enzyme *lactic dehydrogenase* is present and catalyzes the reduction of pyruvate to L-lactic acid in the presence of NADH and H^+.

$$\underset{\text{pyruvate}}{\overset{\displaystyle HO\diagdown\diagup O}{\underset{\displaystyle CH_3}{\overset{\displaystyle C}{\underset{\displaystyle C=O}{|}}}}} + NADH + H^+ \rightleftharpoons \underset{\text{L-(+)-lactic acid}}{\overset{\displaystyle HO\diagdown\diagup O}{\underset{\displaystyle CH_3}{\overset{\displaystyle C}{\underset{\displaystyle HO-C-H}{|}}}}} + NAD^+ \quad (9\text{-}16)$$

Thus in muscle the anaerobic metabolism of carbohydrates starts with glycogen and ends with lactic acid, 2 moles of lactate being formed per glucosyl unit of polysaccharide utilized. Lactic dehydrogenase, which has been crystallized from several animal tissues, catalyzes an equilibrium ($\Delta F' = -6000$ cal) which is in the direction of NADH oxidation or lactate formation at physiological pH.

Organisms such as yeast that carry out alcoholic fermentation contain the enzyme *pyruvic carboxylase*, which catalyzes the decarboxylation of pyruvate to acetaldehyde and CO_2. The enzyme requires thiamin

$$\underset{\text{pyruvate}}{\overset{\displaystyle HO\diagdown\diagup O}{\underset{\displaystyle CH_3}{\overset{\displaystyle C}{\underset{\displaystyle C=O}{|}}}}} \xrightarrow[\text{TPP}]{\text{Mg}^{2+}} \underset{\text{acetaldehyde}}{\overset{\displaystyle H\diagdown\diagup O}{\underset{\displaystyle CH_3}{\overset{\displaystyle C}{|}}}} + CO_2 \quad (9\text{-}17)$$

pyrophosphate (cocarboxylase) and Mg^{2+} as cofactors. The mechanism for this reaction was discussed in Chapter 8.

In the final reaction of alcoholic fermentation, acetaldehyde is reduced to ethanol by NADH in the presence of *alcohol dehydrogenase*.

$$\underset{\text{acetaldehyde}}{\overset{\displaystyle H\diagdown\diagup O}{\underset{\displaystyle CH_3}{\overset{\displaystyle C}{|}}}} + NADH + H^+ \rightleftharpoons \underset{\text{ethanol}}{\overset{\displaystyle CH_2OH}{\underset{\displaystyle CH_3}{|}}} + NAD^+ \quad (9\text{-}18)$$

Thus the process of alcoholic fermentation results in the formation of 2 moles of ethanol and 2 moles of CO_2 per mole of glucose utilized. The enzyme alcohol dehydrogenase is widely distributed in nature and has been crystallized from baker's yeast and horse liver.

Important Aspects of Anaerobic Carbohydrate Metabolism

In considering the overall features of the glycolytic sequence, it is possible to divide the reactions into different groups. Initially the problem is one of modifying glucose or the glycosyl unit of a polysaccharide into a metabolizable form. The preliminary phosphorylation is accomplished at the expense of the energy-rich phosphate bonds of ATP (reactions 9-5 and 9-8) or by the action of phosphorylase (reaction 9-1). Only when hexose diphosphate is available does the degradative sequence begin with a cleavage of the hexose phosphate to triose phosphates. Then an oxidation-reduction reaction, which results in the entrapment of some of the energy of the hexose molecule into a form readily utilized by the organism, is encountered. The further modification of 3-phosphoglyceric acid results in the formation of another energy-rich compound and eventually leads to the production of pyruvic acid, a key intermediate in glycolysis. The fate of pyruvate in turn depends on the organism under consideration or, more properly, on the enzymes present in that organism.

CLASSIFICATION OF ENZYMES

The student will be aided in his mastery of the glycolytic sequence if he recognizes that most of the enzymes involved belong to one of four following classes.

The *kinases* catalyze the transfer of a phosphate group from ATP to some acceptor molecule. If the phosphorylated acceptor contains an energy-rich phosphate structure, the transfer is said to have occurred at a high-energy level, and the reaction will be reversible. An example of such a reaction is that catalyzed by 3-phosphoglyceric kinase (reaction 9-12). If the transfer involves a transfer from a high-energy level in ATP to a low-energy level, as in the hexokinase reaction (reaction 9-5), the reaction will not be readily reversible.

The *mutases* catalyze the transfer of phosphate groups at a low-energy level from one position on a carbohydrate molecule to another position on the same molecule. The *isomerases*, on the other hand, catalyze the isomerization of aldose sugars to ketose sugars; these enzymes, unlike the kinases and mutases, do not require Mg^{2+}. Finally, the *dehydrogenases* constitute the fourth general class of enzyme encountered in anaerobic carbohydrate metabolism.

BALANCE OF COENZYMES

Anaerobic carbohydrate metabolism occurs in the absence of oxygen. How then does the oxidation of D-glyceraldehyde-3-phosphate proceed uninterruptedly in a cell during glycolysis? Inspection of reaction 9-11 shows that NAD^+ is the primary oxidizing agent which accepts the electrons in the oxidation of the triose phosphate. Since the amount of

NAD^+ in any cell is limited, the reaction will cease as soon as all the NAD^+ is reduced, *unless* there is a mechanism for reoxidation of the reduced pyridine nucleotide.   In alcoholic fermentation that reoxidation is accomplished when acetaldehyde is reduced to ethanol in the presence of alcohol dehydrogenase (reaction 9-18).   In muscle tissue the reoxidation occurs when pyruvate is reduced to lactate (reaction 9-16). Thus NAD^+ serves as a carrier of electrons which are transferred from triosephosphate to either acetaldehyde or pyruvate depending on the tissue involved.   This may be represented for the latter compound as in our diagram.

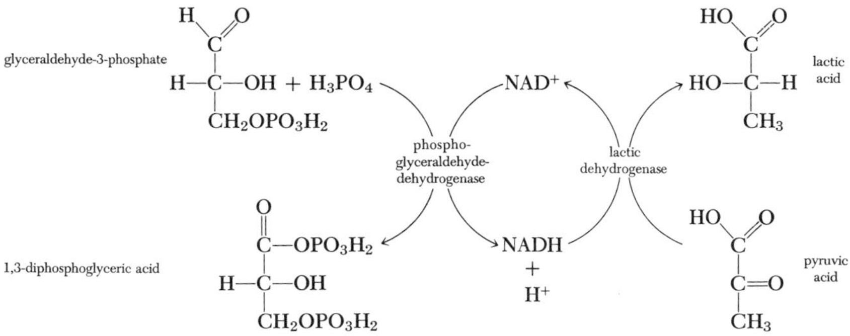

PRODUCTION   OF   HIGH-ENERGY   PHOSPHATE

By considering the precise reactions involved it is possible to show that there is a net formation of high-energy phosphate in the form of ATP in both glycolysis and alcoholic fermentation.   The number of such bonds formed differs for the two processes.   In alcoholic fermentation, a high-energy bond is produced (reaction 9-11) when triosephosphate is oxidized and is made available to the cell in the form of ATP in the subsequent reaction (reaction 9-12).   Two trioses are produced, moreover, from each molecule of hexose metabolized, and both the trioses are oxidized to 1,3-diphosphoglyceric acid in the presence of the enzymes *triosephosphate isomerase* (reaction 9-10) and *triosephosphate dehydrogenase* (reaction 9-11).   In the absence of the isomerase half of the hexose molecule would remain as dihydroxyacetone phosphate and would not be converted to pyruvate.   Since triosephate isomerase is widely distributed in nature, however, both trioses can be oxidized, and two high-energy phosphates per mole of hexose will be produced in the oxidative step.

Similarly, in reaction 9-14 a high-energy phosphate bond is produced from a mole of triose where none previously existed.   This again is transferred to ADP in the subsequent step (reaction 9-15) to make

ATP. Thus for each mole of hexose two moles of ATP will be formed at this stage of the pathway. Hence the total is *four*, but this is not a *net* achievement. In alcoholic fermentation glucose must first be phosphorylated to glucose-6-phosphate, and fructose-6-phosphate must be phosphorylated to fructose diphosphate before cleavage into the triose phosphates and subsequent degradation can proceed. Thus *two* high-energy phosphate bonds are *expended* in the initial steps (reactions 9-5 and 9-8) of the alcoholic fermentation. The *net* production of high-energy phosphate is therefore *two* per mole of glucose fermented to ethanol and CO_2.

Now the $\Delta F'$ for the conversion of glucose to ethanol and CO_2 can be calculated from various thermodynamic data:

$$C_6H_{12}O_6 \longrightarrow 2C_2H_5OH + 2CO_2$$

$$\Delta F' = -56,000 \text{ cal}$$

Neglecting entropy changes, this amount of energy could be liberated as heat. In the yeast cell, however, at least 16,000 (2×-8000) cal of this free energy are conserved in the production of 2 moles of high-energy phosphate. We may speak of this as an efficiency of energy conservation of $-16,000/-56,000$ or 29 per cent. At this point it is well to point out that the ΔF for the hydrolysis of ATP (reaction 9-6) under the conditions that exist in a cell may be more negative by 4000 calories than the standard free-energy change ($\Delta F' = -8000$ cal). This is due of course to the fact that the concentrations of reactants in reaction 9-6 are not at standard values (see Chapter 6). If the ΔF for *formation* of ATP is indeed $+12,000$ cal, the efficiency of energy conservation will be $24,000/56,000$ or 43 per cent.

The same type of calculation may be made for glycolysis where 4 moles of high-energy phosphate are again produced per mole of glucosyl unit of glycogen, which is degraded to lactic acid. Here, however, careful inspection of the reactions involved shows that it is necessary to expend only one high-energy bond in reaction 9-8 in order to produce the hexose diphosphate which is subsequently degraded to lactic acid. Thus the net production of high-energy phosphate bonds is three. The $\Delta F'$ for the conversion of a glucosyl unit of glycogen to lactic acid may also be estimated from various data:

$$
(C_6H_{12}O_6)_n \longrightarrow 2CH_3-\underset{\underset{\text{H}}{|}}{\overset{\overset{\text{O}}{|}}{\text{C}}}-COOH + (C_6H_{12}O_6)_{n-1}
$$

$$\Delta F' = -52,000 \text{ cal}$$

Since three high-energy bonds were produced, the efficiency of this energy conserving process is $-24,000/52,000$ or 43 per cent. Although these figures are relatively high in comparison to those exhibited by most man-made machines in doing work, the comparison is not valid. The overall efficiency of a living cell is not much greater than that of mechanical devices made by man.

At first glance it might appear that glycolysis is more efficient than alcoholic fermentation. It is important to stress that this efficiency is only apparent and to emphasize that energy was utilized in attaching the glucosyl unit onto the glycogen polymer. Indeed, if the glycogen unit is lengthened one glycosyl unit by a combination of reaction 9-5, reaction 9-4, and reaction 9-1 catalyzed by phosphorylase, one high-energy phosphate would be expended in lengthening the glycogen chain. The net production of high-energy phosphate from glucose would then be the same in either glycolysis or alcoholic fermentation.

REVERSAL OF GLYCOLYSIS OR ALCOHOLIC FERMENTATION

All the reactions in the glycolytic sequence are reversible, and it is an experimental fact that lactic acid in a resting muscle can be converted to glycogen provided an energy source is available. It has sometimes been assumed that this occurs by a reversal of each reaction of the glycolytic sequence. Consideration of the equilibrium constants of the individual reactions reveals, however, and it has been amply demonstrated, that three reactions (reactions 9-5, 9-8, and 9-15) are not readily reversed. Moreover if we consider the concentrations of ATP (or ADP) required to reverse these reactions, it may be seen that a high concentration of ATP (and low ADP concentration) is required to drive reaction 9-15 in the direction of carbohydrate synthesis while a high ADP (and low ATP) concentration is required to drive reactions 9-5 and 9-8 in the direction of carbohydrate synthesis. Since these conditions can hardly exist side by side in the cell, it is apparent that some other reactions must be involved in order to effect a reversal of glycolysis. These are known and have been described.

In the case of reaction 9-15 the reversal is effected by a complex mechanism involving three enzymes described in detail in Chapter 11. The first of these is the reaction catalyzed by *malic enzyme. Malic*

$$\begin{array}{c} COOH \\ | \\ C{=}O \\ | \\ CH_3 \end{array} + CO_2 + NADPH + H^+ \rightleftharpoons \begin{array}{c} COOH \\ | \\ HO{-}C{-}H \\ | \\ CH_2 \\ | \\ COOH \end{array} + NADP^+ \qquad (9\text{-}19)$$

pyruvic
acid

l-malic acid

dehydrogenase then converts malic acid to oxalacetic acid. The

$$
\begin{array}{c}
\text{COOH} \\
| \\
\text{HO—C—H} \\
| \\
\text{CH}_2 \\
| \\
\text{COOH}
\end{array}
\;+\; \text{NAD}^+ \;\rightleftharpoons\;
\begin{array}{c}
\text{COOH} \\
| \\
\text{C=O} \\
| \\
\text{CH}_2 \\
| \\
\text{COOH}
\end{array}
\;+\; \text{NADH} + \text{H}^+ \qquad (9\text{-}20)
$$

L-malic acid   oxalacetic acid

oxalacetic acid then undergoes conversion to phosphoenol pyruvic acid in the presence of *phosphoenolpyruvic carboxykinase*. The sum of

$$
\begin{array}{c}
\text{COOH} \\
| \\
\text{C=O} \\
| \\
\text{CH}_2 \\
| \\
\text{COOH}
\end{array}
\;+\; \text{ITP} \;\rightleftharpoons\;
\begin{array}{c}
\text{COOH} \\
| \\
\text{C—OPO}_3\text{H}_2 \\
\| \\
\text{CH}_2
\end{array}
\;+\; \text{CO}_2 + \text{IDP} \qquad (9\text{-}21)
$$

oxalacetic acid   phosphoenol pyruvic acid

these three reactions is shown as reaction 9-22 and results in the formation of phosphoenol pyruvic acid from pyruvic acid.

$$
\begin{array}{c}
\text{COOH} \\
| \\
\text{C=O} \\
| \\
\text{CH}_3
\end{array}
\;+\; \text{NADPH} + \text{NAD}^+ + \text{ITP} \;\rightleftharpoons\;
\begin{array}{c}
\text{COOH} \\
| \\
\text{C—OPO}_3\text{H}_2 \\
\| \\
\text{CH}_2
\end{array}
\;+\; \text{NADP}^+ + \text{NADH} + \text{IDP} \quad (9\text{-}22)
$$

Although the same energy barrier exists in this reaction in going from pyruvate to phosphoenol pyruvate, reaction 9-22 can be driven by coupled reactions which produce NADPH, NAD$^+$, and ITP or by reactions utilizing NADP$^+$, NADH, or IDP.

There is an enzyme in yeast, in plants, and in muscle which catalyzes the *hydrolysis* of fructose-1-6-diphosphate to form fructose-6-phosphate.

$$
\text{fructose-1-6-diphosphate} + \text{H}_2\text{O} \longrightarrow \text{fructose-6-phosphate} + \text{H}_3\text{PO}_4 \qquad (9\text{-}23)
$$

fructose-1-6-diphosphate   fructose-6-phosphate

Although this is not a reverse of reaction 9-8, which involves ATP and ADP, the presence of the phosphatase does account for the formation of fructose-6-phosphate from hexose diphosphate and thus provides a means by which glycogen or glucose can subsequently be formed from hexose diphosphate.

The production of free *glucose* from lactic acid or pyruvic acid occurs by reversal of the sequence from pyruvate to fructose-1-6-diphosphate hydrolysis to fructose-6-phosphate and isomerization to glucose-6-phosphate. At this point a second specific phosphatase, glucose-6-phosphatase, catalyzes the hydrolysis of this ester to yield free glucose.

$$CH_2OPO_3H_2 \quad + H_2O \longrightarrow \quad CH_2OH \quad + H_3PO_4 \quad \quad (9\text{-}24)$$

glucose-6-phosphate   glucose

Like reaction 9-23, this reaction is not the reverse of the phosphorylation reaction catalyzed by hexokinase. It is instead a hydrolytic reaction which accounts for the formation of free glucose from glucose-6-phosphate.

A reaction of alcoholic fermentation that is not demonstrably reversible is the decarboxylation of pyruvate to form acetaldehyde and CO_2 (reaction 9-17). There is no analagous enzyme which in effect reverses this reaction, and the formation of the aldehyde in alcoholic fermentation is a truly irreversible process.

It is well to emphasize that although the necessary enzymes are available for explaining the conversion of pyruvate (or lactate) to glucose or glycogen, an essential requirement for reversibility is the necessary energy. The production of lactate or ethanol and CO_2 has been shown on p. 178 to involve a *net* formation of high-energy phosphate. In order to reverse this process clearly energy must be supplied. This is done in reactions 9-12 and 9-22 where a nucleotide triphosphate (ATP or ITP) is utilized; additional energy is also supplied in reactions 9-11 and 9-22 where NADH and NADPH are utilized. These reactions emphasize that NADH and NADPH also represent a form of potential chemical energy.

Evidence for Occurrence of the Glycolytic Sequence

There is little doubt that the sequence of reactions under discussion accounts for the process of alcoholic fermentation in intact yeast cells. Indeed the process goes on much more rapidly in intact cells than in the properly supplemented cell-free extracts in which the individual reactions may be studied. The high rate of reaction in intact cells suggests that in the cell the enzymes and coenzymes are arranged in an orderly, definite manner rather than in the random distribution which exists in the extract.

The glycolytic sequence could not have been worked out without the use of cell-free extracts which accomplish alcoholic fermentation. It is sobering to consider the consequences of this accomplishment of the brothers Buchner, especially since their discovery, like so many in scientific history, had an element of chance in it.

When in 1897 the Buchners first prepared their yeast extracts by grinding with sand and filtering to remove intact cells, their object was to obtain a preparation which could be injected into animals for medicinal purposes. Since the preparations were to be introduced into living animals, ordinary preservatives such as toluene could not be used, and they employed the housewife's procedure for preserving food, namely, the addition of high concentrations of sugar. In this way the fermentative ability of the extracts was discovered!

A more important consequence of the Buchners' discovery was that it served as the proper stimulus for intensive studies by the pioneers of biochemistry and resulted in the elucidation of the glycolytic sequence. As a result of this development some of our most detailed information on the nature and mechanism of enzymes has been obtained. At least three major coenzymes, NAD^+, ATP, and thiamin pyrophosphate were discovered as the pathway was worked out.

If we are interested today in establishing whether the glycolytic sequence functions in a given tissue, we must essentially repeat the observations of the pioneers in this work. These are some of the questions asked: Does the intact tissue carry out the anaerobic conversion of glucose or some polysaccharide to ethanol and CO_2 or lactic acid? Is it possible to obtain cell-free extracts that accomplish the fermentation (the observation of the Buchners)? Does continuous fermentation in cell-free extracts require the addition of inorganic phosphate and result in the accumulation of phosphorylated sugars (the work of Harden and Young)? Can the preparation be inactivated by dialysis and reactivated by the addition of NAD^+, ATP, thiamin pyrophosphate, Mg^{2+} ions, and inorganic phosphate? Is the fermentation strongly inhibited by iodoacetate (an inhibitor of triosephosphate dehydrogenase) and by fluoride (the inhibitor of enolase)? Can we demonstrate certain key enzymes such as aldolase, triosephosphate dehydrogenase, lactic dehydrogenase, or pyruvic carboxylase? Positive answers to these questions would fairly well define the glycolytic sequence in the particular tissue.

Studies on alcoholic fermentation greatly aided the working out of the details of anaerobic carbohydrate metabolism in muscle. By 1925 Meyerhof had described the preparation of cell-free extracts of muscle that converted glycogen to lactic acid. Dialysis of this extract removed coenzymes, and the addition of those required for alcoholic fermentation also restored the activity of the muscle extracts. In addition, several of these coenzymes as well as the phosphorylated intermediates encountered in alcoholic fermentation could be isolated from muscle tissue.

An obvious reason for studying the biochemical processes in muscle has been the hope that some clear correlation could be obtained between the physical work done by the muscle fiber and the chemical changes which occur therein. Hopkins, the distinguished English biochemist, was among the first to show, in 1907, that lactic acid was produced when a muscle contracts. When care was taken to chill the fibers and prevent further chemical changes, Hopkins demonstrated the following points in stimulated and control muscles: (a) Muscle can contract anaerobically; (b) lactic acid is produced during anaerobic contraction and accumulates until the muscle is fatigued; (c) if the fatigued muscle is exposed to oxygen, the lactic acid disappears and the ability of the muscle to contract is restored; (d) less lactic acid accumulates in a muscle that is stimulated in the presence of oxygen. Shortly thereafter Meyerhof showed that glycogen was the source of the lactic acid and that there was a correlation among the amount of work done by a contracting muscle, the heat produced, and the lactic acid formed.

The work on the details of the reaction sequence in muscle tissue paralleled that on the reaction in yeast for the most part. One compound was present in muscle tissue which had no counterpart in the scheme for alcoholic fermentation, however. This was the high-energy phosphate compound creatine phosphate, discovered in 1927.

creatine phosphate

This compound, which is present in all types of vertebrate muscle (smooth, striated, and cardiac), is apparently intimately associated with muscle action, since it is degraded to creatine and inorganic phosphate during stimulation and is resynthesized during rest. The role of creatine phosphate was made clearer in 1930 when Lundsgaard in a classic experiment showed that muscle fibers poisoned with iodoacetate nevertheless were capable of contraction. Moreover, in poisoned muscles, *no* lactic acid was formed and the contraction continued only until the supply of creatine phosphate was exhausted. It was concluded that the iodoacetate prevented glycolysis since it inhibited triosephosphate dehydrogenase; as a result ATP synthesis did not occur and lactic acid was not formed. Instead creatine phosphate served as a source of energy for muscular contraction. It was soon demonstrated that the role of creatine phosphate was to generate ATP. The Russian physiologist Englehardt provided evidence in 1939 that ATP is the primary energy source for muscular contraction. The formation of ATP at the expense of creatine phosphate is accomplished by the enzyme *creatine kinase,* which is present in high concentration in muscle.

$$
\begin{array}{ccc}
\underset{\substack{\text{creatine phosphate}}}{\substack{\text{HN} \\ \diagdown \\ \text{C} \\ \diagup \\ \text{N--CH}_2\text{--COOH} \\ \text{CH}_3}} & + \text{ADP} \rightleftharpoons & \underset{\substack{\text{creatine}}}{\substack{\text{HN} \\ \diagdown \\ \text{C} \\ \diagup}} & + \text{ATP} \quad (9\text{-}25)
\end{array}
$$

This reaction is readily reversible ($K_{eq} = 0.6$) and when there is an abundant amount of ATP, as the result of vigorous glycolysis for example, most of the high-energy phosphate produced is stored as creatine phosphate. Then, when ATP is required for muscular work, it can be resynthesized from ADP in the presence of creatine phosphate. It is obvious that this process requires a constant source of ADP, which fortunately is formed when muscular work is done. Although the details of muscle action cannot be spelled out precisely, it is clear that as work is done ATP is converted to ADP and inorganic phosphate:

$$
\text{ATP} \xrightarrow[\text{work}]{\text{muscular}} \text{ADP} + \text{H}_3\text{PO}_4
$$

We mentioned earlier that an excised muscle which has been stimulated to the point of exhaustion will recover if placed in oxygen; this results in the resynthesis of glycogen. Quantitative studies have shown, however, that not all the lactic acid is converted back to glycogen during the recovery period. As we discussed in the preceding section, this process of reversal requires energy in the form of ATP and NADH. These compounds can be formed when lactic acid is further oxidized to CO_2 and H_2O in an aerobic process (the Krebs cycle).

The data in fact indicate that approximately 15 per cent of the lactic acid in a stimulated muscle is oxidized in order to furnish the energy for the formation of glycogen from the remaining 85 per cent. There is doubt that this pathway of oxidative recovery is of significance *in vivo,* however. Lactic acid diffuses out of muscle into the blood stream where, after returning to the liver, it is resynthesized into liver glycogen.

The muscle glycogen is probably resynthesized from blood glucose, in a sequence involving only a few enzymes.

There is little doubt that the glycolytic sequence can account for the conversion of glucose to pyruvic acid in many organisms. In addition to the type of evidence previously cited, confirming data may be obtained with the use of radioisotopes. If glucose labeled with carbon-14 (C^{14}) in carbon atoms 3 and 4 is administered to animals or to a yeast culture, the lactic acid produced by the former will contain radioactivity in its carboxyl group, and the CO_2 produced in alcoholic fermentation will be radioactive.

When criteria like these and the ones described earlier are applied, it is evident that the anaerobic phase of carbohydrate metabolism occurs in many living organisms ranging in complexity from bacteria to man. The glycolytic sequence is functional in trypanosomes and other protozoa, and is found in the leg muscle of the cockroach and the wing muscle of the grasshopper. The skeletal muscle of the dolphin, the hearts of eel, toad, and turtle, the gastric mucosa of man, and numerous carcinomas degrade glucose by this sequence of reactions. Higher plants also have the glycolytic sequence and can produce either ethanol and CO_2 or lactic acid.

Although the Embden-Meyerhof scheme has been stressed as a sequence of reactions for the degradation of glucose, it must be emphasized that this is not the only possibility. Another important process for the degradation of glucose is discussed in the next chapter.

Utilization of Other Sugars

The ability of yeast hexokinase to phosphorylate glucose, fructose, and mannose as the corresponding hexose-6-phosphate has been referred to previously. Mannose-6-phosphate thus formed can be converted to fructose-6-phosphate by the action of phosphomannose isomerase and thus can be accommodated in the glycolytic sequence.

Disaccharides such as lactose and sucrose are extremely common sources of carbohydrate in the diet of animals. The initial steps in their utilization involve hydrolysis to the component monosaccharides by digestive enzymes. The hydrolysis of lactose yields glucose and galactose; the subsequent metabolism of this latter monosaccharide is a story which has only recently unfolded.

The fermentation of galactose requires phosphorylation initially by ATP in the presence of a *galactokinase* found in both animal and yeast cells. The utilization of the phosphorylated galactose involves a reac-

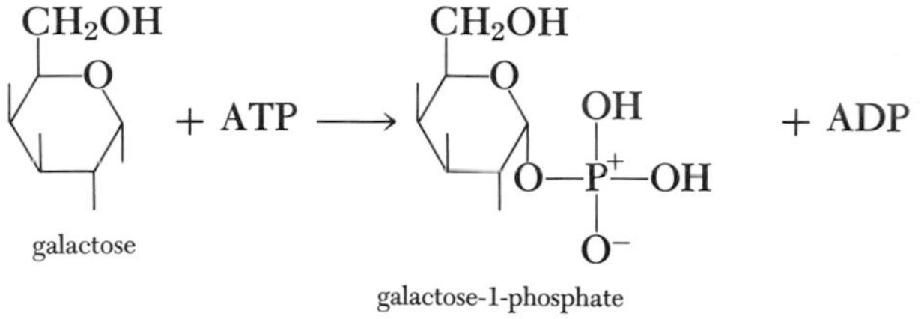

$$\text{galactose} + ATP \longrightarrow \text{galactose-1-phosphate} + ADP \qquad (9\text{-}26)$$

tion with uridine diphosphate glucose (UDPG) first described by Leloir in 1950.

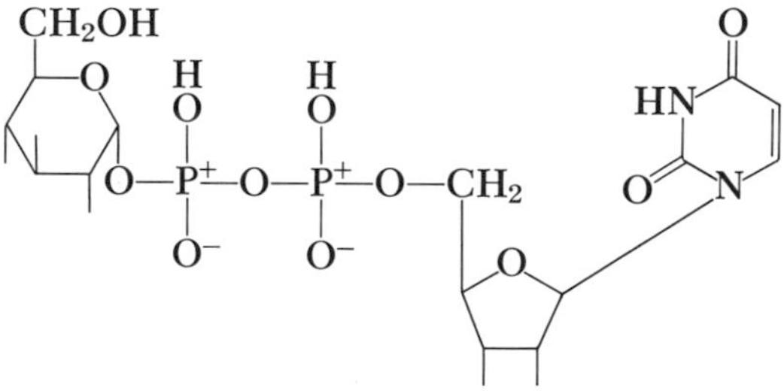

uridine diphosphate glucose
(UDPG)

In the presence of the enzyme *uridyl transferase* an exchange of the galactose phosphate moiety with the glucose phosphate moiety attached to UMP occurs which results in the formation of glucose-1-phosphate and UDP-galactose. This reaction will proceed until the supply of UDPG in the organism is exhausted, were it not for the fact that a third enzyme *UDP-galactose-4-epimerase* catalyzes the conversion of UDP-

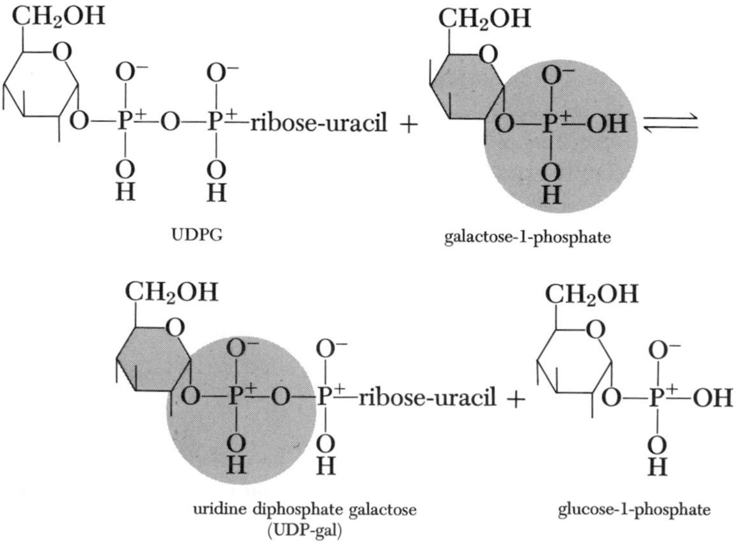

UDPG   galactose-1-phosphate

uridine diphosphate galactose   glucose-1-phosphate
(UDP-gal)

$$(9\text{-}27)$$

galactose to UDPG. This reaction involves an inversion in the configuration about the carbon atom 4 of the galactosyl residue to form a glucosyl moiety.

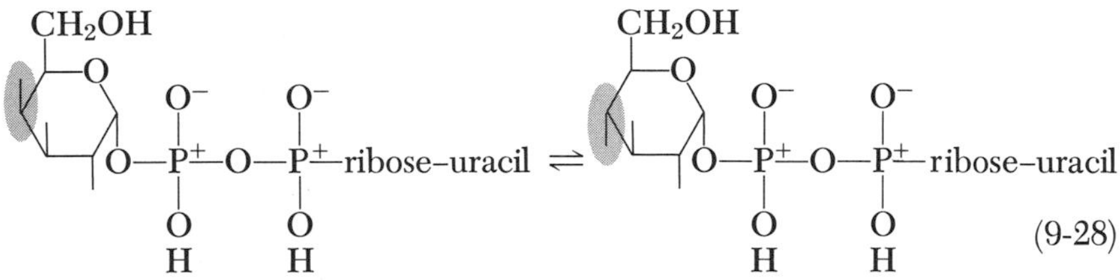

UDP-galactose   UDPG   (9-28)

The sum of reactions 9-27 and 9-28 is:

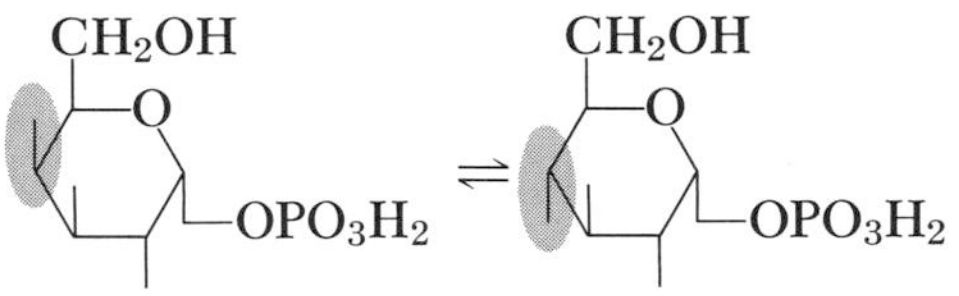

α-D-galactose-1-phosphate   α-D-glucose-1-phosphate   (9-29)

These reactions, accounting for the metabolism of galactose, have recently been related to the medical abnormality known as *galactosemia,* a disease of infants in which the child is unable to metabolize galactose. The child consequently excretes massive amounts of galactose in the urine. In infants the disease can be fatal unless the situation is recognized and another carbohydrate is substituted for the lactose in the milk of the child's diet. Kalckar has shown that this abnormality, which is hereditary, is due to a deficiency in the amount of uridyl transferase (reaction 9-27) normally present in the liver.

In addition to functioning in the metabolism of galactose, UDPG and other UDP-sugar derivatives (for example, UDP-glucuronic acid) have been found to have important roles in biosynthetic reactions. Two such reactions in which UDPG participates will be described. An enzyme discovered by Leloir in wheat germ has been shown to catalyze the formation of sucrose phosphate from UDPG and fructose-6-phosphate. In this reaction the enzyme catalyzes the transfer of the glucosyl moiety of UDPG to fructose-6-PO_4 with the formation of UDP and sucrose phosphate. This enzyme, together with one that catalyzes the transfer of glucose from UDPG to fructose

$$UDPG + fructose \rightleftharpoons sucrose + UDP$$

may account for the formation of sucrose in higher plants.

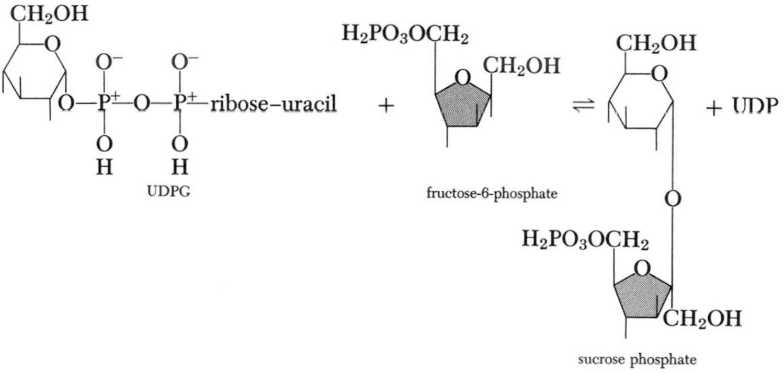

$$\text{UDPG} + \text{fructose-6-phosphate} \rightleftharpoons \text{sucrose phosphate} + \text{UDP} \quad (9\text{-}30)$$

Another important reaction in which UDPG participates is the formation of glycogen. Enzymes in muscle and liver have recently been demonstrated to catalyze reaction 9-31. In this reaction a glucosyl unit

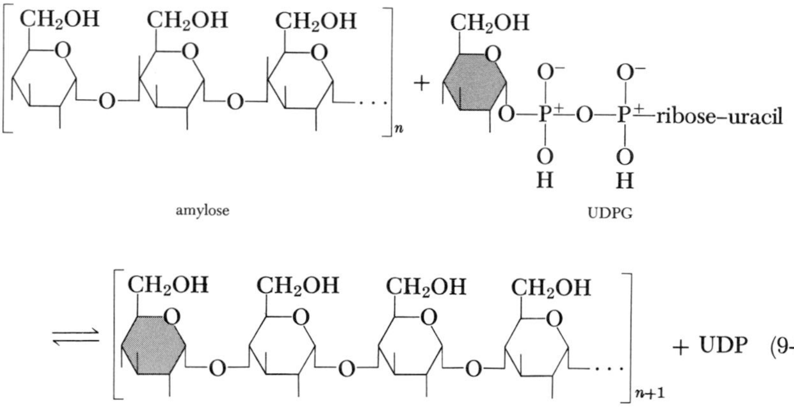

$$\text{amylose} + \text{UDPG} \rightleftharpoons [\ldots]_{n+1} + \text{UDP} \quad (9\text{-}31)$$

is transferred to a primer to lengthen the polysaccharide chain. The equilibrium for this reaction appears to be very much in the direction of polysaccharide synthesis. Preliminary evidence suggests that the role of this enzyme is strictly biosynthetic, whereas the action of phosphorylase may be chiefly concerned with degradation.

Formation of Glycerol and α-Glycerophosphate

Fermentation of glucose by yeast cells or extracts always gives rise to a small amount of glycerol. This can be readily accounted for by the presence in yeast of two enzymes, *α-glycerophosphate dehydrogenase,* which catalyzes reaction 9-32, and a phosphatase that specifically hydrolyzes the L-α-glycerophosphate produced.

$$\begin{matrix} CH_2OH \\ | \\ C=O \\ | \\ CH_2OPO_3H_2 \end{matrix} \quad + \text{ NADH } + \text{ H}^+ \rightleftharpoons \begin{matrix} CH_2OH \\ | \\ HO-C-H \\ | \\ CH_2OPO_3H_2 \end{matrix} \quad + \text{ NAD}^+ \quad (9\text{-}32)$$

dihydroxyacetone phosphate   L-α-glycerophosphate

The production of traces of glycerol in yeast fermentation is believed to occur at the beginning of the fermentation when most of the NAD^+ present in the cell has been reduced. It is argued that sufficient acetaldehyde has not yet been produced and that dihydroxyacetone phosphate and α-glycerophosphate dehydrogenase substitute as a mechanism for reoxidation of the NADH. Eventually acetaldehyde and alcohol dehydrogenase account for the majority of NADH reoxidized, probably because there is a high concentration of alcohol dehydrogenase in yeast.

Neuberg applied this principle during World War I to produce glycerol by yeast fermentations. The German biochemist found that, in the presence of $NaHSO_3$, acetaldehyde was firmly bound as its bisulfite addition product.

$$\begin{matrix} H \\ / \\ CH_3-C \\ \\ O \end{matrix} \quad + \text{ NaHSO}_3 \longrightarrow \begin{matrix} H \\ | \\ CH_3-C-SO_3Na \\ | \\ O \\ H \end{matrix} \quad (9\text{-}33)$$

acetaldehyde   bisulfite addition
product

As a result the normal pathway for reoxidation of NADH by reduction of acetaldehyde was unavailable to the cell and dihydroxyacetone phosphate was utilized instead. The α-glycerophosphate produced was subsequently hydrolyzed to produce glycerol.

The role of lactic dehydrogenase in reoxidizing NADH during the anaerobic degradation of glucose in muscle has already been mentioned. It is interesting to note that the flight muscle of insects is low in lactic dehydrogenase and in this tissue α-glycerophosphate plays an important part. Insect flight muscle contains an extremely active soluble α-glycerophosphate dehydrogenase, which by catalysis of reaction 9-32 brings about the necessary reoxidation of NADH produced in the oxidation of D-glyceraldehyde-3-phosphate. In the insect α-glycerophosphate is not hydrolyzed, however, and does not accumulate. Instead a second enzyme, α-glycerophosphate oxidase, is associated with the insoluble material (mitochondria) of the cell and catalyzes the aerobic oxidation of α-glycerophosphate to dihydroxyacetone phosphate.

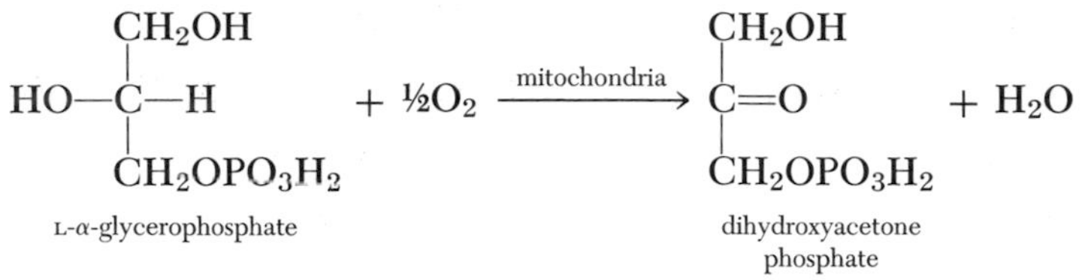

$$
\begin{array}{c}
CH_2OH \\
| \\
HO-C-H \\
| \\
CH_2OPO_3H_2
\end{array}
+ \ \tfrac{1}{2}O_2 \ \xrightarrow{\text{mitochondria}}
\begin{array}{c}
CH_2OH \\
| \\
C=O \\
| \\
CH_2OPO_3H_2
\end{array}
+ \ H_2O \quad (9\text{-}34)
$$

L-α-glycerophosphate   dihydroxyacetone
                                         phosphate

The net effect of reactions 9-32 and 9-34 is to accomplish the oxidation of NADH by molecular O_2.

REFERENCES

1. B. Axelrod in *Metabolic Pathways,* edited by D. M. Greenberg, Academic Press, New York, 2nd edition, 1960, Vol. 1, Chapter 3.
2. P. K. Stumpf in *Chemical Pathways of Metabolism,* edited by D. M. Greenberg, Academic Press, New York, 1st edition, 1954, Chapter 3.

   These two reviews in the first and second editions of the same treatise cover the subject of glycolysis quite thoroughly.
3. H. A. Krebs and H. L. Kornberg, *Ergebnisse der Physiologie, biologischen Chemie und experimentellen Pharmakologie, 49,* 212 (1957).

   A masterful survey of the energy transformations encountered in glycolysis and other metabolic routes.   Strongly recommended for the advanced student in biochemistry.

Ten

The Pentose Phosphate Pathway

Introduction

The Embden-Meyerhof scheme is a major anaerobic route for the degradation of hexoses to pyruvate. In view of the great emphasis that is placed on this sequence of reactions, we must take pains to stress that this is not the only pathway for the degradation of hexoses. For example, in all the forms of plant and animal life which have now been studied it is evident that there are several routes for the metabolism of glucose. It is impossible for reasons of space, and indeed it is unnecessary, to describe all of them, but the new student of biochemistry needs to be familiar with the details of one of these schemes. This is the pentose phosphate pathway, also known as the hexosemonophosphate shunt.

It was early recognized that an alternate route existed for the metabolism of glucose. Its existence was indicated by the fact that in some tissues the classical inhibitors of glycolysis, iodoacetate and fluoride, had no effect on the utilization of glucose. In addition, the experiments of Warburg, resulting in the discovery of $NADP^+$ and the oxidation of glucose-6-phosphate to phosphogluconic acid, led the glucose molecule into an unfamiliar area of metabolism. Moreover, with the advent of carbon-14, it could be shown in some instances that glucose labeled in the C-1 carbon atom was more readily oxidized to $C^{14}O_2$ than was glucose labeled in the C-6 position. If the glycolytic sequence were the only means whereby glucose could be converted to pyruvate-3-C^{14} and subsequently broken down to CO_2, then $C^{14}O_2$ should have been produced at an equal rate from glucose-1-C^{14} and glucose-6-C^{14}. These observations stimulated work, and the work has resulted in the delineation of pentose phosphate pathway. The pathway in its entirety is shown inside the front cover of this book, on the right-hand side. The chief architects of the pathway are the American biochemists Horecker and Racker; among the earlier workers three who should be mentioned are Warburg, Lipmann, and Dickens.

Enzymes of the Pentose Phosphate Pathway

GLUCOSE-6-PHOSPHATE DEHYDROGENASE

Warburg's discovery of this enzyme and its coenzyme $NADP^+$ is one of the classic episodes of biochemistry. From this work resulted our present knowledge that the function of a vitamin is established by its role as a constituent of a coenzyme.

Glucose-6-phosphate dehydrogenase, originally called *Zwischenferment*, catalyzes the following reaction:

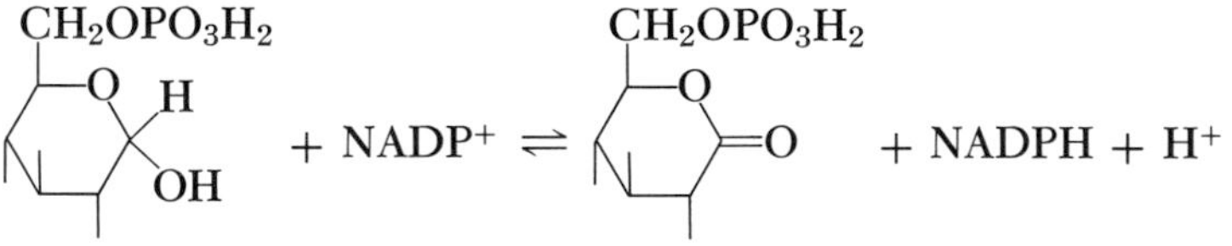

$$CH_2OPO_3H_2 \quad\quad\quad\quad CH_2OPO_3H_2$$

$$+ NADP^+ \rightleftharpoons \quad\quad + NADPH + H^+ \quad\quad (10\text{-}1)$$

glucose-6-phosphate   glucono-δ-lactone-6-phosphate

Although the product was initially believed to be phosphogluconic acid, there is good evidence that the δ-lactone of this acid is the first product. The reaction is reversible because the oxidation of NADPH occurs in the presence of the enzyme and the lactone. It is easy to visualize that the oxidation of the pyranosyl form of the substrate involves the removal of two hydrogen atoms and results in the formation of the lactone. *Zwischenferment* is widely distributed in nature and in some sources appears to require a divalent cation for activity.

6-PHOSPHOGLUCONOLACTONASE

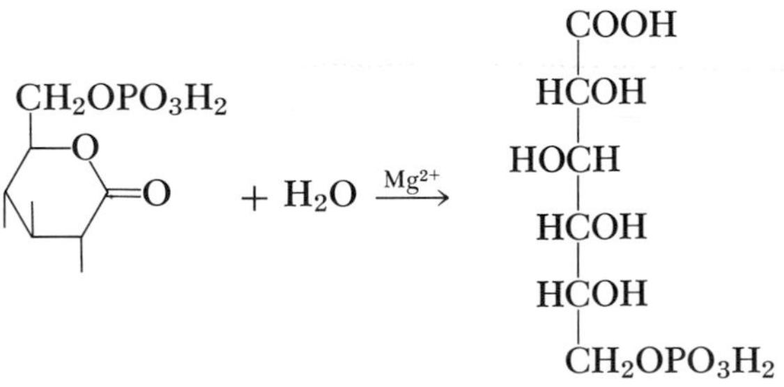

$$
\begin{array}{cc}
 & COOH \\
 & | \\
CH_2OPO_3H_2 & HCOH \\
 & | \\
 & HOCH \\
=O \quad + H_2O \xrightarrow{Mg^{2+}} & | \\
 & HCOH \\
 & | \\
 & HCOH \\
 & | \\
 & CH_2OPO_3H_2
\end{array}
\quad (10\text{-}2)
$$

glucono-δ-lactone-6-phosphate   6-phosphogluconic acid

An enzyme that catalyzes the hydrolysis of the lactone produced in reaction 10-1 has been described, although the nonenzymatic hydrolysis of the lactone is extremely rapid. The $\Delta F'$ for the hydrolysis of the lactone is large; therefore the overall oxidation of glucose-6-phosphate to phosphogluconic acid is irreversible.

6-PHOSPHOGLUCONIC ACID DEHYDROGENASE

This enzyme, which catalyzes reaction 10-3, was also implicated in the early work of Warburg, who showed that CO_2 was a product of a crude yeast extract which contained *Zwischenferment*.

$$
\begin{array}{c}
\text{COOH} \\
\text{HCOH} \\
\text{HOCH} \\
\text{HCOH} \\
\text{HCOH} \\
\text{CH}_2\text{OPO}_3\text{H}_2
\end{array}
+ \text{NADP}^+ \xrightarrow{\text{Mg}^{2+}}
\left[
\begin{array}{c}
\text{COOH} \\
\text{HCOH} \\
\text{C}=\text{O} \\
\text{HCOH} \\
\text{HCOH} \\
\text{CH}_2\text{OPO}_3\text{H}_2
\end{array}
\right]
\longrightarrow
\begin{array}{c}
\text{CO}_2 \\
+ \\
\text{CH}_2\text{OH} \\
\text{C}=\text{O} \\
\text{HCOH} \\
\text{HCOH} \\
\text{CH}_2\text{OPO}_3\text{H}_2
\end{array}
+ \text{NADPH} + \text{H}^+
\qquad (10\text{-}3)
$$

6-phosphogluconic   3-keto hexonic acid   D-ribulose-5-phosphate
acid   (postulated intermediate)

Because the reaction involves both an oxidation and decarboxylation, it was first suggested that a 3-keto-6-phosphohexonic acid might be an intermediate product prior to decarboxylation. No direct evidence in support of such a compound has been offered, and the reaction is hence believed to be a single-step oxidative decarboxylation resulting in the formation of ribulose-5-phosphate. The dehydrogenase, which is widely distributed, requires Mg^{2+} or other divalent cations for activity.

PHOSPHORIBOISOMERASE

This enzyme catalyzes the interconversion of the keto sugar ribulose-5-phosphate and the aldopentose phosphate ribose-5-phosphate. It is thus analogous in its action to the phosphohexoisomerase encountered in glycolysis. The K_{eq} for the reaction from left to right is approximately 3.

$$
\begin{array}{c}
\text{CH}_2\text{OH} \\
\text{C}=\text{O} \\
\text{HCOH} \\
\text{HCOH} \\
\text{CH}_2\text{OPO}_3\text{H}_2
\end{array}
\rightleftharpoons
\begin{array}{c}
\overset{\text{H}}{\underset{}{\diagdown}}\overset{\text{O}}{\underset{}{\diagup}} \\
\text{C} \\
\text{HCOH} \\
\text{HCOH} \\
\text{HCOH} \\
\text{CH}_2\text{OPO}_3\text{H}_2
\end{array}
\qquad (10\text{-}4)
$$

D-ribulose-5-phosphate   D-ribose-5-phosphate

PHOSPHOKETOPENTOEPIMERASE

The epimerase that catalyzes reaction 10-5 is also widely distributed in nature and occurs generally with the other enzymes of the pento-phosphate pathway.   The K_{eq} is 0.8.

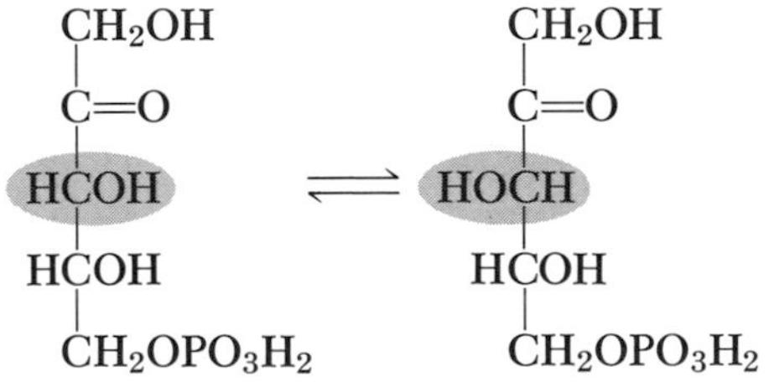

$$
\begin{array}{ccc}
CH_2OH & & CH_2OH \\
| & & | \\
C{=}O & & C{=}O \\
| & & | \\
HCOH & \rightleftharpoons & HOCH \\
| & & | \\
HCOH & & HCOH \\
| & & | \\
CH_2OPO_3H_2 & & CH_2OPO_3H_2
\end{array}
\qquad (10\text{-}5)
$$

D-ribulose-5-phosphate   D-xylulose-5-phosphate

The mechanism for this reaction is not known although it may possibly involve the enediol as an intermediate.

TRANSKETOLASE

Up to this point the enzymes have dealt with the oxidative degradation of the hexose chain of glucose-6-phosphate and the subsequent interrelations of the pentose phosphates produced.   During the period in which these reactions were being studied, chiefly in yeasts and bacteria, it was apparent that other sugars, including heptoses, tetroses, and trioses, were also formed.   Some clarification of the relations between the pentoses and these other sugars resulted when the enzyme *transketolase* was discovered and described.   This enzyme catalyzes the transfer of the ketol group from a donor molecule to an acceptor aldehyde.   The generalized reaction may be written as in the accompanying diagram.

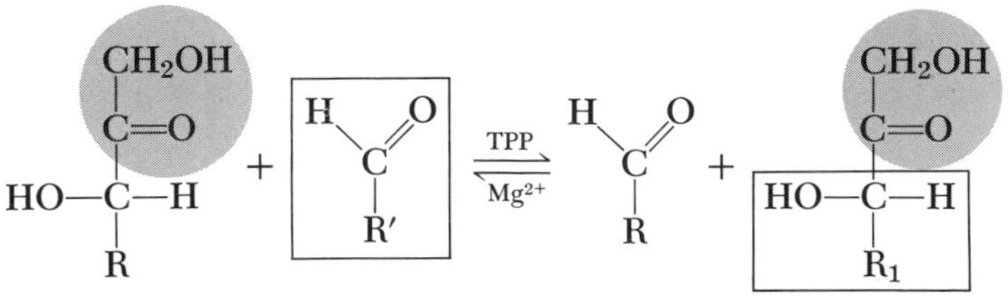

$$
\begin{array}{ccccc}
CH_2OH & & H & & CH_2OH \\
| & & \backslash \quad O & & | \\
C{=}O & & C & & C{=}O \\
| & + & | & \xrightleftharpoons[Mg^{2+}]{TPP} & \\
HO{-}C{-}H & & R' & & HO{-}C{-}H \\
| & & & & | \\
R & & & & R_1
\end{array}
$$

$$ (10\text{-}6) $$

ketol donor   acceptor   product   product ketol
                   aldehyde   aldehyde   donor

In a specific instance, transketolase catalyzes the transfer of a ketol group from xylulose-5-phosphate to ribose-5-phosphate to form sedo-heptulose-7-phosphate and glyceraldehyde-3-phosphate.

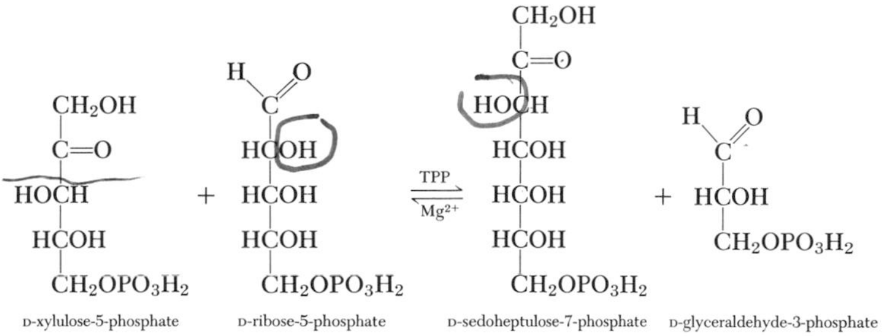

$$\text{D-xylulose-5-phosphate} + \text{D-ribose-5-phosphate} \underset{Mg^{2+}}{\overset{TPP}{\rightleftharpoons}} \text{D-sedoheptulose-7-phosphate} + \text{D-glyceraldehyde-3-phosphate} \quad (10\text{-}7)$$

Transketolase requires thiamin pyrophosphate (TPP) and Mg^{2+} as co-factors. The TPP functions because it is able to form a carbanion by dissociation of a proton at the C-2 carbon atom of the thiazole ring.

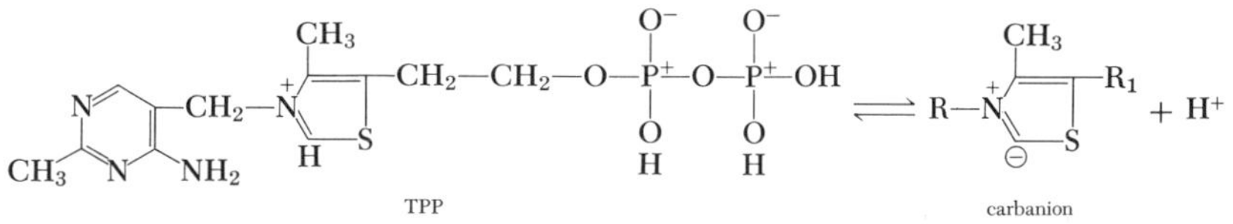

The resultant carbanion can in turn react with the ketol donor to form an addition product, I, which, by appropriate rearrangement of electrons, can dissociate in another manner to form the product alde-hyde and leave the ketol group on the TPP, II. The ketol-TPP addition

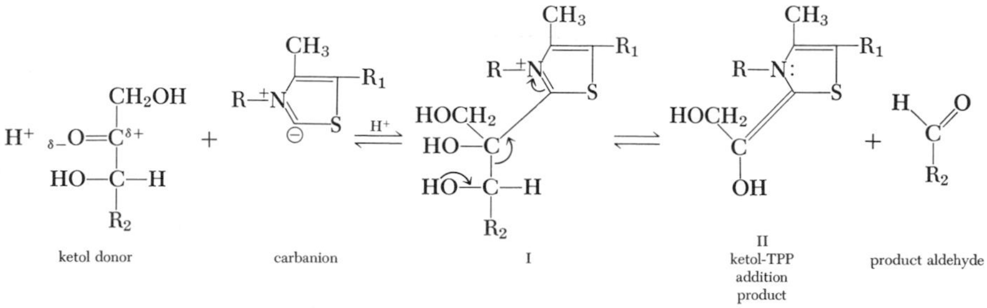

product II can then react with an acceptor aldehyde to form the product ketol donor and regenerate the carbanion.

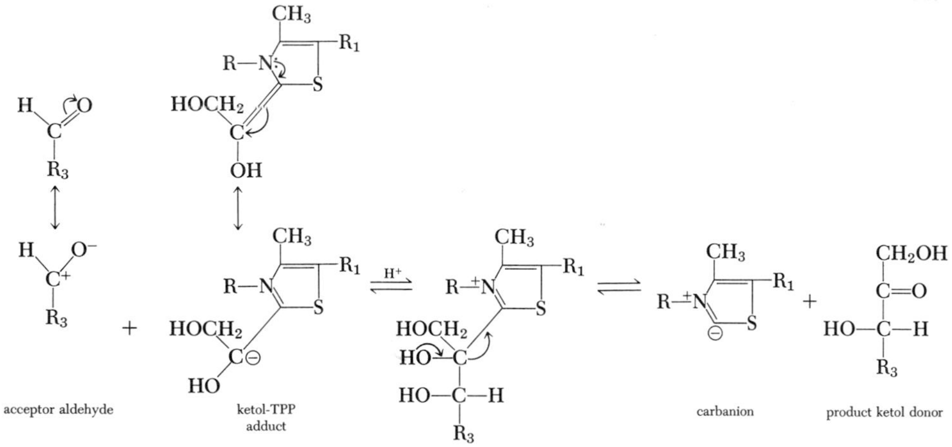

acceptor aldehyde   ketol-TPP   carbanion   product ketol donor
                           adduct

Transketolase may also catalyze the transfer of a ketol group from xylulose-5-phosphate to erythrose-4-phosphate to form fructose-6-phosphate and glyceraldehyde-3-phosphate (see inside of cover). Since this reaction as well as reaction 10-7 is readily reversible, we can list the following compounds which will serve as donor molecules and acceptor aldehydes for the enzyme.

Ketol Donors (Ketoses)	Acceptor Aldehydes (Aldoses)
D-Xylulose-5-PO$_4$	D-Ribose-5-PO$_4$
D-Fructose-6-PO$_4$	D-Glyceraldehyde-3-PO$_4$
D-Sedoheptulose-7-PO$_4$	D-Erythrose-4-PO$_4$

It is worthwhile to note that all the donor ketoses have the L-configuration at the C-3 position.

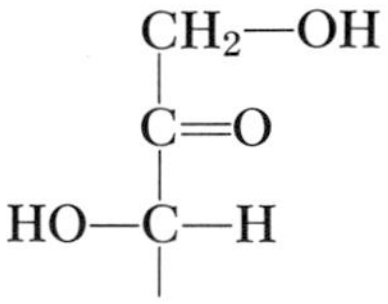

$$CH_2-OH$$
$$C=O$$
$$HO-C-H$$

TRANSALDOLASE

This enzyme, like transketolase, functions as a transferring enzyme by catalyzing the transfer of the dihydroxyacetone moiety of fructose-6-phosphate or sedoheptulose-7-phosphate to a suitable aldose. As represented in the scheme for pentose phosphate metabolism, the acceptor aldose may be glyceraldehyde-3-phosphate or, in the reverse direction, erthyrose-4-phosphate.

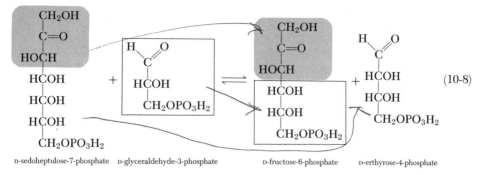

D-sedoheptulose-7-phosphate   D-glyceraldehyde-3-phosphate   D-fructose-6-phosphate   D-erthyrose-4-phosphate

Ribose-5-phosphate may also be an acceptor, in which case an octose, octulose-8-phosphate, is formed.

Significance of the Pentose Phosphate Pathway

As in the case of glycolysis it is tempting to postulate some definite stoichiometry from the sequence of reactions of the pentose phosphate pathway. One such stoichiometric relationship has the following inter- esting implications:

Consider the passage of six molecules of glucose-6-phosphate (hexose phosphate) through reactions 10-1, 10-2, and 10-3. This produces 12 moles of NADPH, the reoxidation of which requires 6 moles of oxygen and forms 6 moles of H_2O (Chapter 12). In this procedure 6 moles of pentose phosphate and 6 moles of CO_2 will be formed (reaction 10-9).

$$6 \text{ hexose-PO}_4 + 6O_2 \longrightarrow 6 \text{ pentose-PO}_4 + 6CO_2 + 6H_2O \quad (10\text{-}9)$$

Next consider that 4 moles of the pentose phosphate react according to reactions 10-7 and 10-8 to produce 2 moles each of tetrose phosphate and hexose phosphate (reaction 10-10).

$$4 \text{ pentose-PO}_4 \longrightarrow 2 \text{ hexose-PO}_4 + 2 \text{ tetrose-PO}_4 \quad (10\text{-}10)$$

The tetrose phosphate does not accumulate, but can, in the presence of transketolase, react with 2 moles of pentose phosphate to form 2 moles of hexose phosphate and two of triose phosphate (reaction 10-11).

$$2 \text{ tetrose-PO}_4 + 2 \text{ pentose-PO}_4 \longrightarrow 2 \text{ hexose-PO}_4 + 2 \text{ triose-PO}_4 \quad (10\text{-}11)$$

Next one of the two triose phosphates can isomerize to dihydroxyace- tone phosphate and condense with the other triose phosphate to form 1 mole of hexose diphosphate; this in turn can hydrolyze to form one hexose phosphate and 1 mole of inorganic phosphate (reaction 10-12).

$$2 \text{ triose-PO}_4 + H_2O \longrightarrow 1 \text{ hexose-PO}_4 + H_3PO_4 \quad (10\text{-}12)$$

The sum of reactions 10-9, 10-10, 10-11, and 10-12 is reaction 10-13.

$$\boxed{\text{hexose-PO}_4 + 6O_2 \longrightarrow 6CO_2 + 5H_2O + H_3PO_4} \qquad (10\text{-}13)$$

Although reaction 10-13 implies the complete oxidation of a molecule of hexose phosphate (for instance, glucose-6-phosphate) to six molecules of CO_2, it is clear that each of the CO_2 molecules came from the C-1 carbon atoms of six different molecules of glucose-6-phosphate. These and other combinations may be prepared if the student is sufficiently adept mathematically, but other aspects of the pentose cycle are of greater significance.

It should be stressed that degradation of glucose-6-phosphate by way of the pentose phosphate pathway is an *aerobic* process, because $NADP^+$ is the oxidizing agent which is reduced in the initial steps of the cycle. In contrast to glycolysis, where a mechanism exists for the reoxidation of the reduced pyridine nucleotide within the framework of the glycolytic scheme itself, there is no similar reaction in the pentose phosphate pathway. In spite of the fact that there are other means within the cell for coupling the reoxidation of NADPH to some oxidized substrate, the major route for reoxidation is the cytochrome electron transport system that utilizes oxygen as the ultimate oxidizing agent. This system is described in detail in Chapter 12.

Rapidly accumulating evidence suggests that NADPH, in contrast to NADH, may have a special role in biosynthetic processes within the cell. Whenever a biosynthetic step involves a reduction, the pyridine nucleotide utilized, with few exceptions, is NADPH. NADPH, unlike NADH, is specifically utilized in the biosynthesis of long-chain fatty acids, for example. NADPH is the reducing agent employed in the reduction of glucose to sorbitol, the reduction of dihydrofolic acid to tetrahydrofolic acid, and the reduction of glucuronic acid to L-gulonic acid. In addition, NADPH is used in the reductive carboxylation of pyruvic acid to malic acid by the malic enzyme. Finally, NADPH plays a unique role in hydroxylation reactions involved in the formation of unsaturated fatty acids, the conversion of phenylalanine to tyrosine, and the formation of certain steroids. The occurrence of these reactions coupled with the observation that the $NADPH/NADP^+$ ratio in many tissues is greater then 5 does indeed argue for a special role of NADPH in biosynthetic reactions.

To the extent that NADPH does play this role in biosynthesis, it will be necessary to have some means for producing the reduced nucleotide. The pentose phosphate pathway could fulfill such a need. The pentose phosphate pathway clearly also provides a means for interrelating the metabolism of hexoses, pentoses, heptoses, and tetroses. Since all reactions in the pathway except 10-2 and 10-3 are reversible, it is possible to produce pentoses from hexose and triose phosphate (a reversal of reactions 10-11, 10-8, and 10-7). The pathway hence provides a nonoxidative as well as an oxidative route for producing ribose and other pentoses from the hexoses commonly encountered in metabolism. The pentose phosphate pathway is moreover intimately involved with the interconversion of carbon compounds produced in the initial stages of photosynthesis (Chapter 17).

Some measure of the extent to which the glycolytic pathway or the pentose phosphate pathway functions in the metabolism of glucose can be obtained with glucose samples labeled in either the C-1 or the C-6 carbon atoms. An examination of glycolysis shows that in this scheme carbons C-1 and C-6 of glucose are both converted to the methyl group of pyruvic acid and are subsequently metabolized in the same way. On the other hand, the C-1 and C-6 carbon atoms of glucose are handled quite differently in the pentose phosphate pathway. Measurements of this sort have shown that in mammalian muscle the glycolytic cycle functions almost exclusively, whereas in leucocytes and mammary gland tissue the pentose pathway may be more active. The role of the pentose pathway in photosynthesis has already been referred to; the leaves of higher plants do indeed metabolize glucose largely by this pathway. In plants there is also evidence that the predominant pathway in young, meristematic tissue is that of glycolysis and that the pentose phosphate pathway achieves more significance as the tissue matures.

REFERENCES

1. B. Axelrod in *Metabolic Pathways*, Edited by D. M. Greenberg, Academic Press, New York, 2nd edition, 1960, Vol. 1, Chapter 5.

   A recent comprehensive review of the subject of the pentose phosphate pathway with a large number of references to the original literature.

2. John M. Lowenstein, *Journal of Theoretical Biology, 1*, 98(1961).

   This brief article clearly discusses the possible roles of the oxidized and reduced pyridine nucleotides in biosynthetic reactions.

Eleven

The Tricarboxylic Acid Cycle

Introduction

The failure of lactic acid to accumulate in excised muscles which had been exposed to air and stimulated was mentioned in Chapter 9. Since glycogen is utilized in such muscles, the failure indicated a further metabolic degradation of lactic acid in this tissue. Other organic acids were also known to be metabolized in muscle; by 1920 Thunberg had shown that some forty compounds underwent oxidation by air in the presence of tissue homogenates. Some of the most rapidly oxidized were succinic, fumaric, malic, and citric acids. A more complex relation was also implied by the studies of Szent-Gyorgi, who reported that some of these acids appeared to catalyze the oxidation of unknown substrates in the homogenates. Thus an amount of fumarate that should have resulted in the uptake of 20 μl of O_2, if it were completely oxidized by the homogenate of pigeon breast muscle to which it was added, instead showed seven times that amount of oxygen consumption.

With the elaboration of the glycolytic sequence in yeast and muscle it appeared that the compounds which were being oxidized further to CO_2 and H_2O by animal tissues were pyruvate and lactate. Szent-Gyorgi subsequently showed that minced pigeon breast muscle did oxidize pyruvic acid to completion. The biochemists Keilin, Martius, Knoop, Baumann, Ochoa, and Lipmann have also contributed to our understanding of the metabolic pathway which accomplishes the aerobic oxidation of pyruvate and lactate.

The most important single contributor was the distinguished English biochemist Sir Hans Krebs. His extensive studies allowed him to postulate in 1937 the cycle of reactions which accounted for the oxidation of pyruvic acid to CO_2 and water. Although some slight modification has occurred since then, the scheme as shown on the inside of the back cover of this book is essentially that proposed by Krebs in 1937. His contributions to the problem were of such magnitude that the cycle is frequently referred to as the Krebs cycle. Krebs himself prefers to call it the *tricarboxylic acid cycle*. In 1953 he was awarded the Nobel Prize in medicine for his important discoveries.

Before considering the cycle in detail it is necessary to point out that the further oxidation of pyruvate or lactate by a living organism is of considerable significance from the standpoint of energy production. The free-energy change for the complete oxidation of glucose to CO_2 and H_2O has been given as -686 kcal.

$$C_6H_{12}O_6 + 6O_2 \longrightarrow 6CO_2 + 6H_2O \qquad (11\text{-}1)$$

$$\Delta F' = -686,000 \text{ cal (pH 7.0)}$$

In Chapter 9 we indicated that the $\Delta F'$ for the formation of lactic acid from glucose was about -47 kcal.

$$C_6H_{12}O_6 \longrightarrow 2CH_3CHOHCOOH \qquad (11\text{-}2)$$

$$\Delta F' = -47,000 \text{ cal (pH 7.0)}$$

Clearly only about 7 per cent of the available energy of the glucose molecule has been released when lactic acid is formed in glycolysis and about $-639,000$ cal remain to be released when the 2 moles of lactate from the original glucose molecule are oxidized to completion. Thus, the $\Delta F'$ per mole of lactate can be estimated as $-319,500$ cal.

$$CH_3CHOHCOOH + 3O_2 \longrightarrow 3CO_2 + 3H_2O$$

$$\Delta F' = -319,500 \text{ cal (pH 7.0)}$$

The student should also appreciate that the aerobic oxidation of glucose to CO_2 and H_2O by the living organism does not necessarily involve the formation of lactic acid as an intermediate step. Instead, the key compound produced in glycolysis, which can be either reduced to lactic acid or instead be oxidized completely to CO_2 and H_2O, is pyruvic acid. By 1935, Szent-Gyorgi had shown that pyruvate could be oxidized to completion by a muscle mince provided catalytic quantities of dicarboxylic acids such as succinate, malate, and oxalacetate were added. The individual reactions of the sequence that accomplishes this oxidation will now be considered.

Formation of Acetyl-CoA

It may be seen that pyruvic acid itself is not an intermediate in the tricarboxylic acid cycle. The α-keto acid is first converted to acetyl-CoA by one of the most complex reactions involved in the intermediary metabolism of carbohydrates. The conversion of pyruvate to acetyl-CoA is catalyzed by the enzyme complex known as *pyruvic oxidase*.

$$CH_3-\underset{\underset{O}{\|}}{C}-COOH + CoA-SH + NAD^+ \xrightarrow[\text{TPP}]{\overset{\text{lipoic acid}}{\overset{\text{Mg}^{2+}}{}}} CH_3-\underset{\underset{O}{\|}}{C}-S-CoA + NADH + H^+ + CO_2 \quad (11\text{-}3)$$

This reaction, which is an oxidative decarboxylation, involves five cofactors: Coenzyme A, NAD^+, lipoic acid, Mg^{2+}, and thiamine pyrophosphate (TPP). The details of the reaction are clearer if the process is separated into individual steps.

The α-keto acid is first decarboxylated in the presence of Mg^{2+}, TPP, and the enzyme complex. As pointed out in Chapter 8, TPP is capable of forming a carbanion which in turn can react with pyruvic acid. The addition product can undergo rearrangement resulting in decarboxylation and formation of an acylol-thiamine complex which participates in the next stage of the reaction.

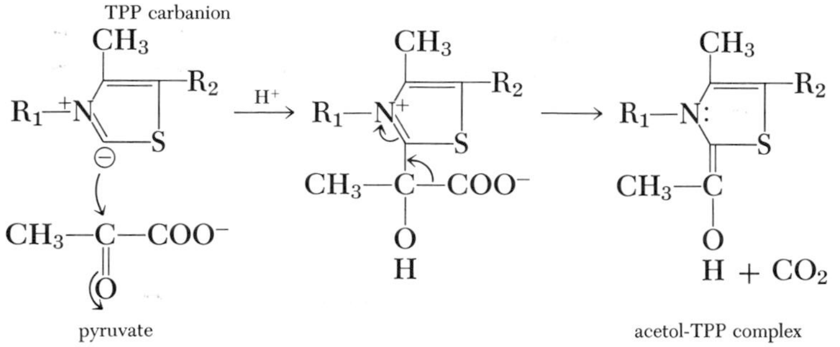

$$(11\text{-}4)$$

pyruvate   acetol-TPP complex

In the next step the acetol-TPP complex reacts with oxidized lipoic acid to form an addition product which rearranges and dissociates to regenerate the carbanion of TPP and an acetyl-lipoic acid complex.

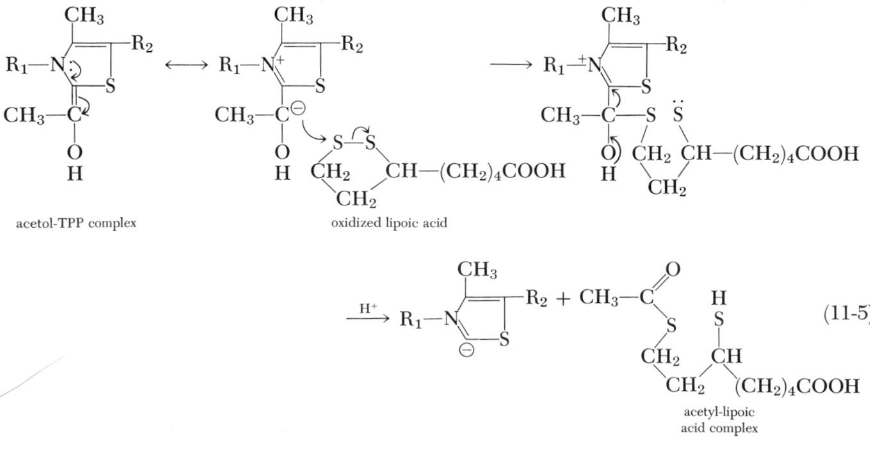

acetol-TPP complex   oxidized lipoic acid

$$(11\text{-}5)$$

acetyl-lipoic
acid complex

Note that as a result of this reaction a high-energy thioester (of reduced lipoic acid) has been formed and oxidized lipoic acid has been reduced.

Next the acetyl moiety is transferred to coenzyme A to form acetyl-CoA.

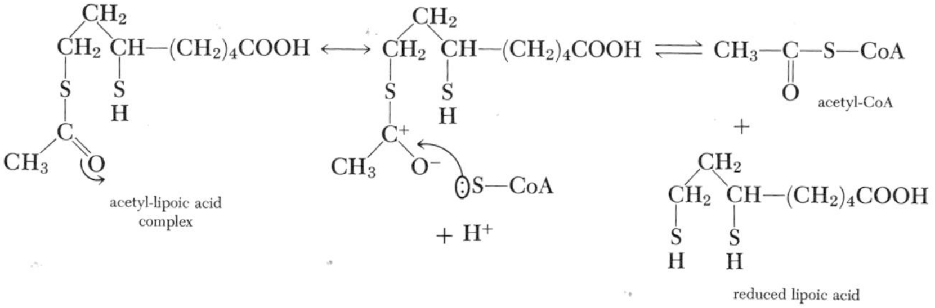

$$(11\text{-}6)$$

In the final sequence of reactions catalyzed by the pyruvic oxidase complex, the reduced lipoic acid is reoxidized by NAD^+. The sum of reactions 11-4, 11-5, 11-6, and 11-7 is reaction 11-3. The individual

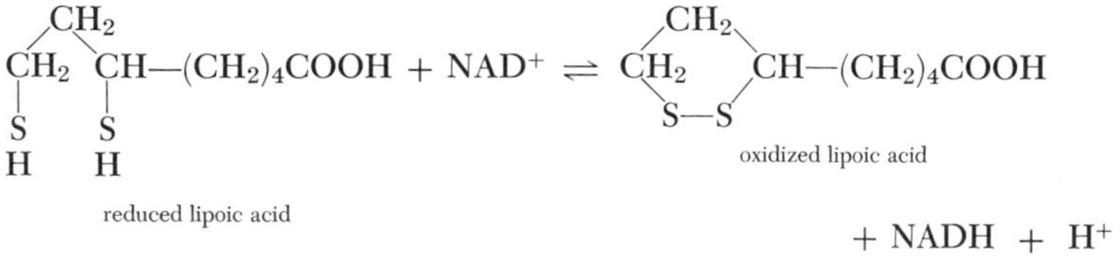

$$(11\text{-}7)$$

reactions are believed to be reversible save for the initial decarboxylation. Arsenite is an effective inhibitor of reaction 11-3 because of its specific reaction with dithiols, of which reduced lipoic acid is an example.

Reactions of the Tricarboxylic Acid Cycle

CONDENSING ENZYME

It is convenient to initiate our description of the enzymes of the cycle with the enzyme that catalyzes the entry of acetyl-CoA into the cycle.

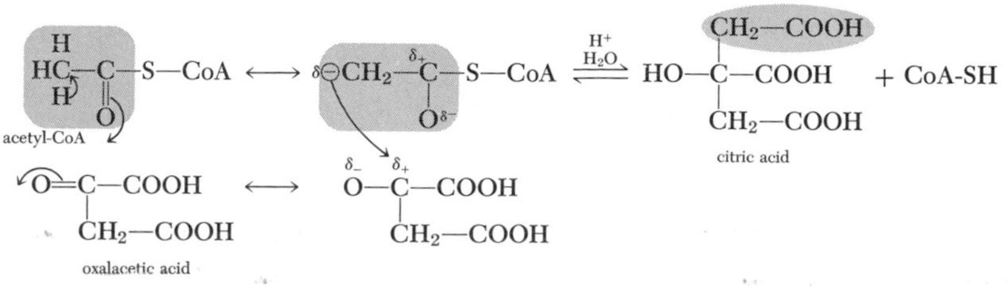

$$(11\text{-}8)$$

Note in the diagram the formation of CoA-SH and the loss of the thioester during the course of the reaction; this forces the equilibrium far to the right. The equilibrium constant for the reaction is 3.2×10^5. The two carbon atoms which originate from the acetyl-CoA are shaded in this and subsequent reactions. The enzyme which catalyzes this reaction has been crystallized from pig heart. Although crystalline, it still contains isocitric dehydrogenase. This is an important example of the impurity of some crystalline proteins.

ACONITASE

The reaction of interest catalyzed by aconitase is the isomerization of citric acid to isocitric acid.

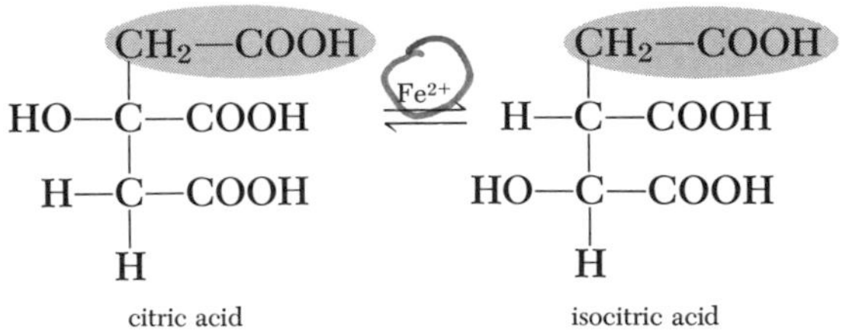

$$
\begin{array}{ccc}
\text{CH}_2\text{—COOH} & & \text{CH}_2\text{—COOH} \\
\text{HO—C—COOH} & \underset{\text{Fe}^{2+}}{\rightleftharpoons} & \text{H—C—COOH} \\
\text{H—C—COOH} & & \text{HO—C—COOH} \\
\text{H} & & \text{H} \\
\text{citric acid} & & \text{isocitric acid}
\end{array}
\qquad (11\text{-}9)
$$

This enzyme, which requires Fe^{2+}, also catalyzes an isomerization between citric acid, isocitric acid, and a third acid, *cis*-aconitic acid. Indeed *cis*-aconitic acid is frequently indicated as an intermediate in the conversion of citric to isocitric acid. Recent work by Speyer and Dickman of the University of Utah indicates however that the carbonium ion of a tricarboxylic acid is the true intermediate and that this ion is in ready equilibrium with all three tricarboxylic acids interconverted by aconitase. The requirement for Fe^{2+} ion by the enzyme suggests that its role is in the formation of the carbonium ion by promoting the dissociation of the hydroxyl group (see p. 205).

Note that when isocitric acid is formed from citric acid (reaction 11-9) the symmetric molecule citric acid is acted upon in an asymmetric manner by the enzyme aconitase. That is, the hydroxyl group is located on a carbon atom derived initially from oxalacetate rather than the methyl group of acetyl-CoA. Ogston, the English biochemist, explained this asymmetry of action by his three-point attachment theory; this theory is discussed in detail in Chapter 7.

ISOCITRIC DEHYDROGENASE

This enzyme catalyzes the oxidative decarboxylation of isocitric acid to α-ketoglutaric acid and CO_2 in the presence of Mn^{2+}, a pyridine

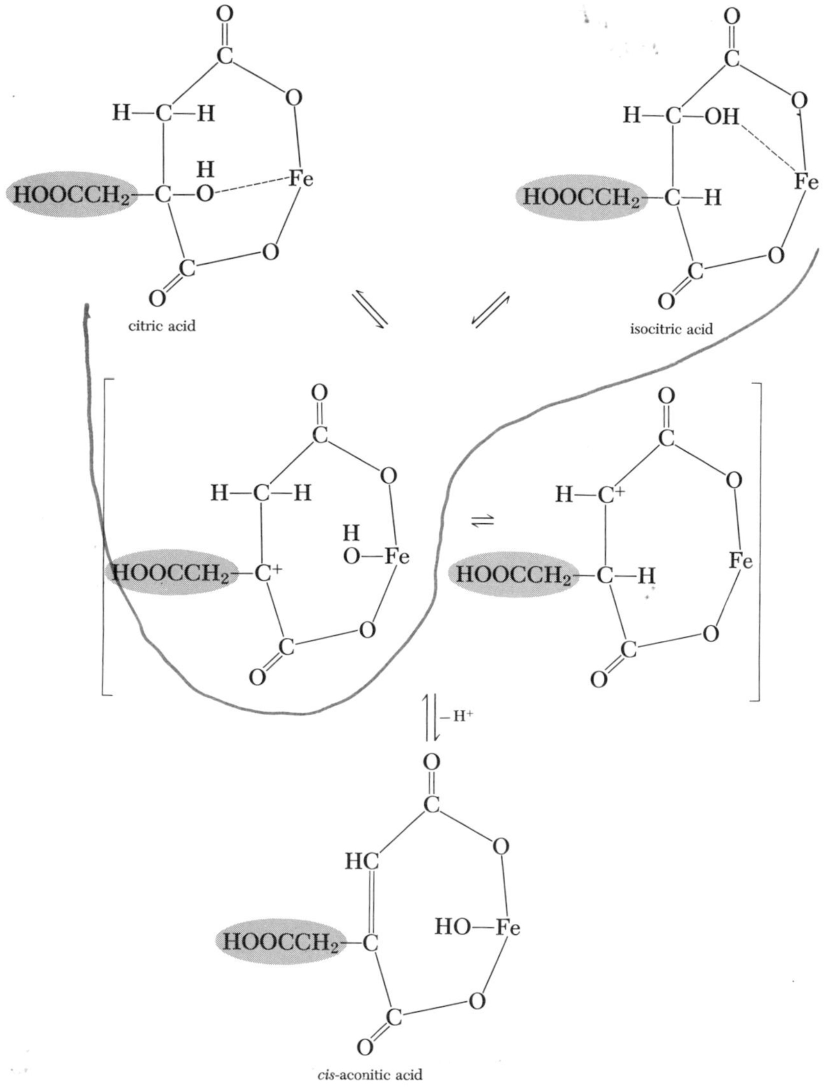

citric acid

isocitric acid

cis-aconitic acid

nucleotide is the oxidizing agent.   It would be reasonable to consider this reaction as the result of an oxidation initially which produces oxalosuccinate and then a decarboxylation of this β-keto acid to CO_2 and α-ketoglutarate.

The evidence nevertheless indicates that oxalosuccinate, if formed, is firmly bound to the surface of the enzyme and is not released as a free intermediate in either the oxidative decarboxylation of isocitrate or the reverse reaction, the reductive carboxylation of α-ketoglutarate.   For

$$H-\underset{\underset{H}{\overset{|}{O}}}{\overset{|}{C}}-\underset{\overset{|}{C}-COOH}{\overset{CH_2COOH}{\overset{|}{\underset{}{}}}} + NADP^+ \rightleftharpoons NADPH + H^+ + \left[H-\underset{\overset{\|}{O}}{\overset{|}{C}}-\underset{COOH}{\overset{CH_2COOH}{\overset{|}{\underset{}{}}}}\right] \rightleftharpoons \underset{\overset{\|}{O}}{HCH}\underset{C-COOH}{\overset{CH_2COOH}{\overset{}{\underset{}{}}}} + CO_2 \qquad (11\text{-}10)$$

isocitric acid   oxalosuccinic acid   α-ketoglutaric acid

this reason, the name *isocitric enzyme* has been proposed to indicate the two activities.   The soluble enzyme found in the cytoplasm of animal liver requires $NADP^+$.   A NAD^+ specific enzyme found in heart, kidney, and skeletal muscle is associated exclusively with the mitochondria. The enzyme in yeast is NAD^+-specific.

α-KETOGLUTARIC OXIDASE

The next step of the tricarboxylic acid cycle involves the formation of succinyl-CoA by the oxidative decarboxylation of α-ketoglutaric acid. This reaction is catalyzed by the *α-ketoglutaric acid oxidase* complex which requires TPP, Mg^{2+}, NAD^+, lipoic acid, and CoA-SH as cofactors.   The mechanism is analogous to that of the pyruvic acid oxidase. The overall process can be written as the sum of individual reactions in a manner entirely analogous to the partial reactions written for reaction 11-3.

$$\underset{\overset{\|}{O}}{\overset{|}{\underset{C-COOH}{\overset{CH_2}{\overset{CH_2COOH}{}}}}} + NAD^+ + CoA-SH \xrightarrow[\text{lipoic acid}]{\text{TPP, } Mg^{2+}} \underset{\overset{\|}{O}}{\overset{|}{\underset{C-S-CoA}{\overset{CH_2}{\overset{CH_2COOH}{}}}}} + NADH + H^+ + CO_2 \qquad (11\text{-}11)$$

α-ketoglutaric acid   succinyl-CoA

The reaction as a whole is not readily reversible, apparently because of the decarboxylation step.

As before, arsenite is an effective inhibitor of the oxidation of this α-keto acid.

SUCCINIC THIOKINASE

In the preceding reaction the high-energy bond of a thioester has been formed as the result of an oxidative decarboxylation.   The enzyme *succinic thiokinase* catalyzes the formation of a high-energy phosphate structure at the expense of the thioester.

Since reaction 11-12 involves the formation of a new high-energy phosphate structure and the utilization of a thioester, the total number

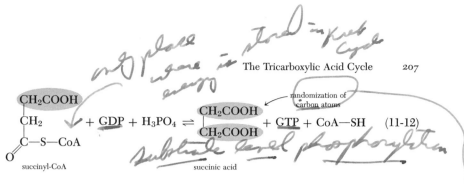

$$CH_2COOH \text{—} CH_2 \text{—} \underset{O}{\overset{||}{C}}\text{—S—CoA} + GDP + H_3PO_4 \rightleftharpoons CH_2COOH\text{—}CH_2COOH + GTP + CoA\text{—SH} \qquad (11\text{-}12)$$

succinyl-CoA   succinic acid

of high-energy structures on each side of the reaction is equal.   Therefore the reaction is readily reversible; the K_{eq} is 3.7.   The GTP formed in reaction 11-12 can in turn react with ADP to form ATP and GDP (reaction 11-13).   Since the pyrophosphate linkages in GTP and ATP have approximately the same $\Delta F'$ of hydrolysis, reaction 11-13 is readily reversible with an K_{eq} of about 1.

$$GTP + ADP \rightleftharpoons GDP + ATP \qquad (11\text{-}13)$$

SUCCINIC DEHYDROGENASE

This enzyme catalyzes the removal of two hydrogen atoms from succinic acid to form fumaric acid.

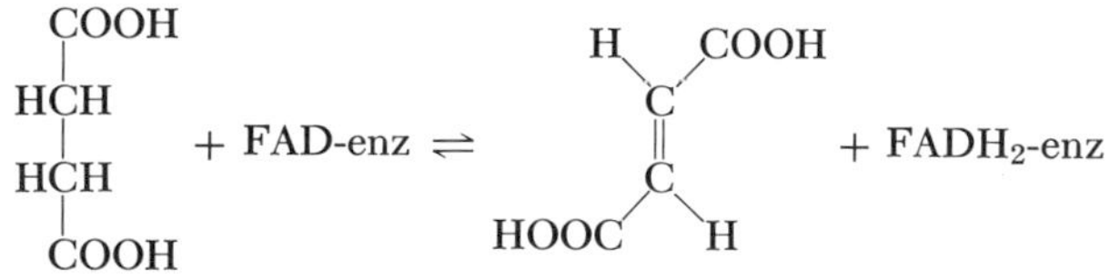

$$\begin{array}{c} COOH \\ | \\ HCH \\ | \\ HCH \\ | \\ COOH \end{array} + \text{FAD-enz} \rightleftharpoons \begin{array}{c} H\quad COOH \\ \diagdown \diagup \\ C \\ || \\ C \\ \diagup \diagdown \\ HOOC\quad H \end{array} + \text{FADH}_2\text{-enz} \qquad (11\text{-}14)$$

succinic acid   fumaric acid

The immediate acceptor (oxidizing agent) of the electrons is a flavin coenzyme (FAD) which, in contrast to other flavin enzymes, is bound to succinic dehydrogenase through a peptide linkage.   Succinic dehydrogenase is firmly associated with the insoluble structure of the cell and is rendered soluble only in the presence of surface active agents such as dodecyl sulfate or Triton X-100.   The "solubilized" preparations from beef heart and yeast contain 1 mole of flavin per mole of enzyme (mol wt of 200,000) and four atoms of nonheme iron. Succinic dehydrogenase is competitively inhibited by malonic acid, a fact which was most useful to those who were concerned initially with working out the details of the tricarboxylic acid cycle.

FUMARASE

The next reaction is the addition of H_2O to fumaric acid to form L-malic acid.

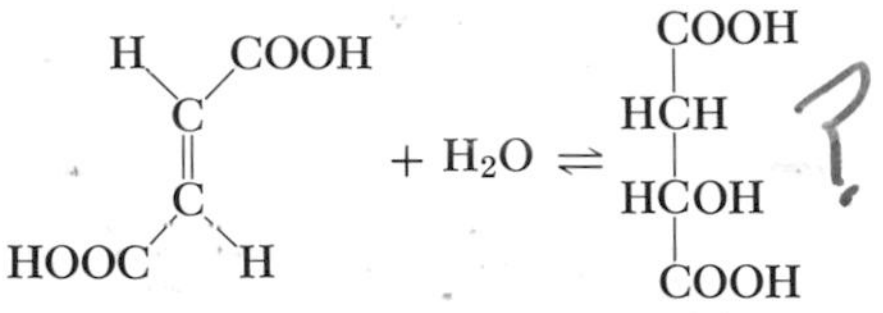

$$\text{fumaric acid} + H_2O \rightleftharpoons \text{L-malic acid} \qquad (11\text{-}15)$$

fumaric acid   L-malic acid

The equilibrium for this reaction is about 4.5. The enzyme that catalyzes the reaction, *fumarase*, has been crystallized (mol wt of 200,000) from pig heart.

MALIC DEHYDROGENASE

The tricarboxylic cycle is completed when the oxidation of L-malic acid to oxalacetic acid is accomplished by the enzyme *malic dehydrogenase*. The reaction is the fourth oxidation-reduction reaction to be encountered in the cycle; the oxidizing agent for the enzyme from pig heart is NAD^+.

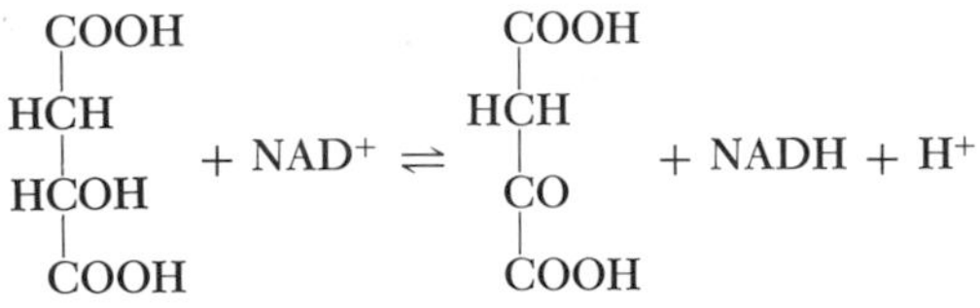

$$\text{L-malic acid} + NAD^+ \rightleftharpoons \text{oxalacetic acid} + NADH + H^+ \qquad (11\text{-}16)$$

L-malic acid   oxalacetic acid

At pH 7.0 the equilibrium constant is 1.3×10^{-5}; thus the equilibrium is very much to the left. The further reaction of acetyl-CoA with oxalacetate in the condensation reaction (reaction 11-8) is strongly exergonic, however, in the direction of citrate synthesis. This tends to drive the conversion of malate to oxalacetate by displacing the equilibrium through the continuous removal of oxalacetate.

FEATURES OF THE TRICARBOXYLIC ACID CYCLE

It is important to stress that the tricarboxylic acid cycle constitutes a device for oxidizing a molecule of acetate (in the form of acetyl-CoA) completely to CO_2 and H_2O. The acetyl-CoA may be derived from a variety of sources. The procedure whereby it can be obtained from pyruvate and thus indirectly from carbohydrate precursors has been described. In later chapters the production of acetyl-CoA during the degradation of lipids and certain amino acids will be described.

An analysis of the reactions in the tricarboxylic acid cycle shows that the types of reactions involved are not unusual. Reactions 11-14 and

11-16 are oxidation-reduction reactions in which a flavin and a pyridine nucleotide function respectively. Reaction 11-10 is an oxidative decarboxylation which utilizes a pyridine nucleotide and produces CO_2 and an α-keto acid. Reaction 11-11 is also an oxidative decarboxylation which involves a pyridine nucleotide and leads to CO_2 and a thioester. It is apparent that two carbon atoms are released as CO_2 in these last two reactions; these are replaced in reaction 11-8 where two carbon atoms are contributed in the form of acetyl-CoA.

The balanced reaction for the complete oxidation of pyruvate to CO_2 and H_2O may be written

$$CH_3-\underset{\underset{O}{\|}}{C}-COOH + 2\tfrac{1}{2}O_2 \longrightarrow 3CO_2 + 2H_2O \qquad (11\text{-}17)$$

The $\Delta F'$ for this reaction is approximately $-273,000$ cal/mole at pH 7.0.

It is informative to consider the stoichiometry of this reaction in detail. If we start with a molecule of pyruvic acid and trace its oxidation to acetyl-CoA and the subsequent oxidation of the thioester through one turn of the tricarboxylic acid cycle, we see that the following reactions are involved:

(a) There are five oxidation steps (reactions 11-3, 11-10, 11-11, 11-14, and 11-16). In each of these reactions two electrons are removed from the substrate; the subsequent reduction of O_2 by these electron pairs results in the utilization of five atoms or two and a half molecules of oxygen.

(b) When the five pairs of electrons are used to reduce O_2, 5 moles of H_2O are formed.

$$\tfrac{1}{2}O_2 + 2H^+ + 2 \text{ electrons} \longrightarrow H_2O$$

Three moles of H_2O are utilized in the oxidation of pyruvate (reactions 11-8, 11-12, and 11-15). Hence the overall reaction involves the net production of only two molecules of H_2O.

(c) Finally, three molecules of CO_2, representing the equivalent of the three carbon atoms in pyruvate, are released in reactions 11-3, 11-10, and 11-11.

All the reactions of the tricarboxylic acid cycle are reversible except the oxidative decarboxylation of α-ketoglutarate (see p. 206). As pointed out earlier, this reaction is entirely analogous to the irreversible oxidative decarboxylation of pyruvic acid. This then means that the cycle cannot be made to proceed in a reverse direction although individual sections are reversible (from oxalacetate to succinate or from α-ketoglutarate to citrate, for example). Similarly acetyl-CoA and CO_2 cannot be converted to pyruvate by a reversal of reaction 11-3.

The Use of Inhibitors

Several compounds are known to serve as inhibitors of specific reactions of the tricarboxylic acid cycle. One of these, malonic acid, was instrumental in establishing the cyclical nature of the sequence of reactions. In the presence of 0.01M malonate the oxidation of succinate by succinic dehydrogenase is strongly inhibited. Therefore in a muscle mince which can oxidize acids of the cycle but to which has been added 0.01M malonate the reaction will proceed only until succinate is formed, and this acid will accumulate.

The effect of malonate on the oxidation of pyruvate is important to understand. As described earlier, the addition of certain dicarboxylic and tricarboxylic acids to muscle homogenates stimulated the respiration of these tissues. Subsequently it was shown that the oxidation of pyruvic acid by a muscle homogenate was catalyzed by the addition of the di- or tri-carboxylic acid intermediates of the cycle to the system. On oxidation these acids give rise to oxalacetate which in turn condenses with the acetyl-CoA formed from pyruvate. Only a catalytic amount of the cycle intermediate is required, however, since once present it can traverse the cycle many times, with each passage disposing of a molecule of acetyl-CoA. This is the way the cycle functions normally in intact tissue.

It is clear that succinic dehydrogenase in the presence of malonate cannot oxidize succinate to fumarate; succinate will hence accumulate. Under these conditions the utilization of acetyl-CoA can proceed only if there is a supply of oxalacetate with which it can condense. Clearly then, fumarate, malate, and oxalacetate are the only compounds which can provide for the utilization of acetyl-CoA, since they are the intermediates in the cycle after succinic dehydrogenase which can be converted to oxalacetate. Moreover, they must be added in *stoichiometric amounts* equivalent to the acetyl-CoA which is to be utilized. The addition of the tricarboxylic acids or α-ketoglutaric acid in a malonate-inhibited system is of no help since they can only be converted to oxalacetate through succinic dehydrogenase.

In experimental practice it is the utilization of pyruvate rather than acetyl-CoA which is examined. The oxidation of pyruvate proceeds until the catalytic quantity of coenzyme A in the reaction mixture is converted to acetyl-CoA; the oxidation of any additional pyruvate cannot occur until additional coenzyme A is made available. In these reactions the thiol compound is only released from the acetyl moiety on the condensation which oxalacetate; hence pyruvate oxidation is also indirectly influenced by the supply of oxalacetate.

Another inhibitor of one of the enzymes of the tricarboxylic acid cycle is fluorocitrate, which inhibits aconitase. Fluorocitrate is an interesting inhibitor because it can be *synthesized* within the living cell and at that point accomplish its inhibitory action. Certain plants in South Africa are known to be toxic because they contain monofluoro-acetic acid (FCH_2COOH). This compound, which has been used as a rodentocide, is acted on by the condensing enzyme to form fluorocitrate apparently because the condensing enzyme is able to utilize fluoroacetyl-CoA as a substrate instead of acetyl-CoA. Once the fluorocitrate is formed, however, it strongly inhibits aconitase, and large quantities of citric acid accumulate in the tissues of poisoned animals.

Evidence for Occurrence of the Tricarboxylic Acid Cycle

The tricarboxylic acid cycle enzymes are specifically located in the mitochondria, small subcellular particles (See Chapter 12, p. 224) which oxidize the intermediates of the cycle at a rapid rate. As described in the next chapter, the enzymes associated with electron transport and oxidative phosphorylation are also found in the mitochondria where they are closely associated with the enzymes of the tricarboxylic acid cycle.

If the question of the occurrence of the cycle in an unstudied tissue is raised, the ability of properly isolated mitochondria to carry out the following reactions should be examined: The intermediates of the cycle should be oxidized by the particles; the oxidation of pyruvic acid should be strongly stimulated by the addition of catalytic quantities of di- and tricarboxylic acids; the oxidation of succinate should be inhibited by malonate; and the oxidation of pyruvate in such an inhibited system should require stoichiometric quantities of dicarboxylic acids. It should be possible to detect the enzymes in the mitochondria and, if the particles are not isolated with considerable care, it may be necessary to add back certain of the cofactors required (for instance, NAD^+ or $NADP^+$ and Mg^{2+}). Although all these observations can be made with mitochondria, it is important to stress that the initial observations on animal tissues were made with homogenates.

Occurrence of the Tricarboxylic Acid Cycle

When criteria like those described in the preceding section are applied to many different living organisms, it is apparent that the tricarboxylic acid cycle is widely distributed in nature. The evidence indicates that the cycle occurs in the respiring tissues of animals ranging from the protozoa to mammals. The cycle also occurs in higher plants, where it accomplishes the oxidation of pyruvic acid to CO_2 and H_2O. In the case of micro-organisms the situation is more complex. If a given yeast or mold carries out the aerobic oxidation of acetate to CO_2 and H_2O, it is quite likely that the sequence of reactions responsible is the tricarboxylic acid cycle. The difficulty of course is that the aerobic oxidation of acetate is not a reaction common to all micro-organisms.

The major amount of the carbohydrate fermented by yeasts under anaerobic conditions results in alcohol formation; many strains of bacteria produce large amounts of acetate as the result of carbohydrate degradation, and in many molds citric acid is an end product of the utilization of carbohydrate, ethanol, or acetate. It is clear that the tricarboxylic acid cycle alone cannot account for the net formation of citrate from acetate. The question then is: In molds that form citrate and in other micro-organisms where there is no evidence for the formation of acetate (alcoholic fermentation) or its utilization, do the enzymes of tricarboxylic acid exist and have a role? The best evidence is that the enzymes not only occur in these organisms but that the tricarboxylic acid cycle functions in whole or in part and that, in the latter case, there is a new role for the cycle. This role is the biosynthesis of essential cell constituents, especially amino acids. The means by which intermediates of the tricarboxylic acid cycle can be converted to certain amino acids is discussed in more detail in Chapter 15.

CO_2 Fixation Reactions

Several reactions encountered in living organisms are classed as "CO_2 fixation" reactions. The initial observations that stimulated the identification of these reactions were made by Wood and Werkman in 1936. They reported that when propionic acid bacteria fermented glycerol to propionic and succinic acids *more* carbon was found in the products than had been added as glycerol. Carbon dioxide was moreover proved to be the source of the extra carbon atoms or the carbon that was "fixed." Today it is recognized that CO_2 serves as a reactant in several CO_2 fixation reactions; three of these result in the formation of a dicarboxylic acid. The enzymes catalyzing the reactions are found in animals, higher plants and micro-organisms.

The *malic enzyme* catalyzes the reversible formation of L-malate from CO_2 and pyruvic acid, and the equilibrium constant of the reaction at pH 7 is 1.6. Thus it is readily reversible. The high concentration of NADPH relative to $NADP^+$ which is observed in many cells would favor the formation of malate, however.

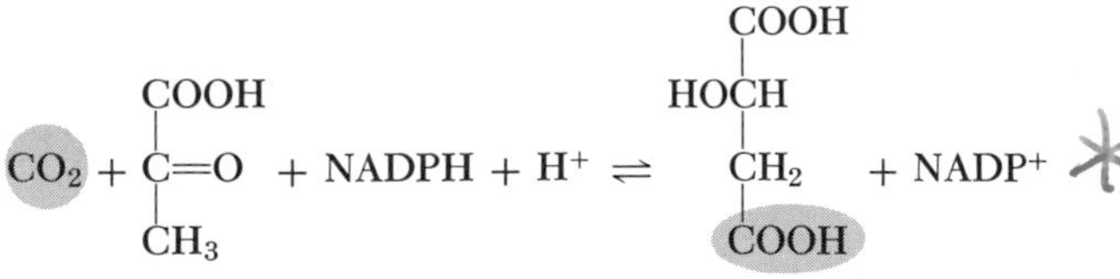

$$CO_2 + \begin{array}{c} COOH \\ | \\ C{=}O \\ | \\ CH_3 \end{array} + NADPH + H^+ \rightleftharpoons \begin{array}{c} COOH \\ | \\ HOCH \\ | \\ CH_2 \\ | \\ COOH \end{array} + NADP^+ \qquad (11\text{-}18)$$

pyruvic acid   L-malic acid

Another enzyme, *phosphoenol pyruvic carboxykinase,* catalyzes the reaction shown next. This reaction is also readily reversible and constitutes a means for forming a dicarboxylic acid from CO_2 and a three-carbon precursor.

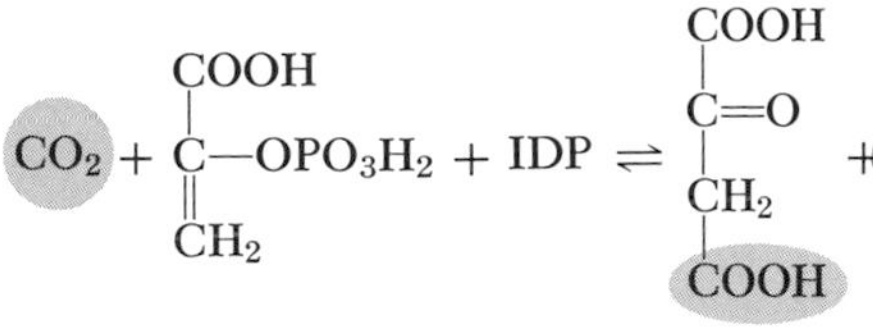

$$CO_2 + \begin{array}{c} COOH \\ | \\ C{-}OPO_3H_2 \\ || \\ CH_2 \end{array} + IDP \rightleftharpoons \begin{array}{c} COOH \\ | \\ C{=}O \\ | \\ CH_2 \\ | \\ COOH \end{array} + ITP \qquad (11\text{-}19)$$

phosphoenol-   oxalacetic
pyruvic acid   acid

These two enzymes are widely distributed in nature. From left to right the reactions constitute an important link between the intermediates of glycolysis and the tricarboxylic acid cycle. The carboxykinase indeed provides a mechanism for the formation of oxalacetate, which is needed for operation of the tricarboxylic acid cycle and which can serve as a precursor of certain amino acids. From right to left phosphoenol pyruvic carboxykinase provides a means for synthesizing phosphoenol pyruvate from oxalacetate, a reaction more easily accomplished than the reversal of the reaction of glycolysis catalyzed by pyruvic kinase.

Another CO_2 fixation reaction is that catalyzed by the enzyme phosphoenol pyruvic carboxylase, which is found in spinach leaves and

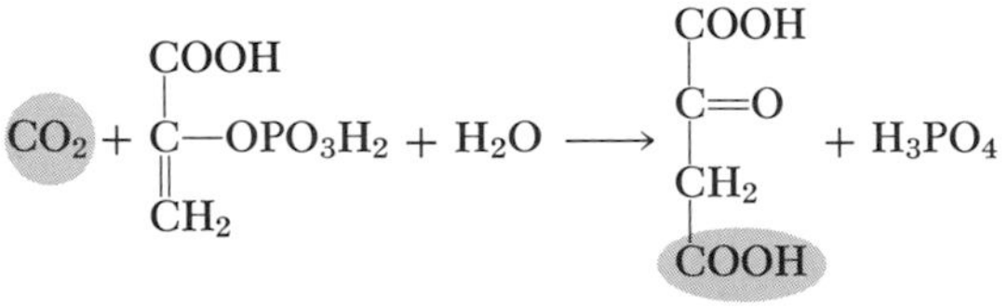

$$CO_2 + \begin{array}{c} COOH \\ | \\ C{-}OPO_3H_2 \\ || \\ CH_2 \end{array} + H_2O \longrightarrow \begin{array}{c} COOH \\ | \\ C{=}O \\ | \\ CH_2 \\ | \\ COOH \end{array} + H_3PO_4 \qquad (11\text{-}20)$$

phosphoenol-   oxalacetic
pyruvic acid   acid

wheat germ. This reaction, unlike the two preceding ones, is irreversible; apparently a fraction of the energy of the enolic phosphate is utilized in the formation of the C—C bond and the remainder is liberated as heat resulting in an irreversible reaction. This is in contrast to reaction 11-19 where the majority of the energy is conserved in the formation of a pyrophosphate linkage.

A fourth CO_2 fixation reaction is catalyzed by propionyl-CoA carboxylase. Unlike the first three, this reaction involves the thioesters of the organic acids.

$$CO_2 + CH_3CH_2{-}\overset{\overset{O}{\|}}{C}{-}S{-}CoA + ATP + H_2O \rightarrow CH_3{-}\underset{\underset{COOH}{|}}{\overset{\overset{H}{|}}{C}}{-}\overset{\overset{O}{\|}}{C}{-}S{-}CoA + ADP + H_3PO_4 \quad (11\text{-}21)$$

Still another extremely important reaction involving CO_2 fixation is the reaction catalyzed by carboxydismutase. This reaction plays a key role in the path of CO_2 in photosynthesis and is described in detail in Chapter 17.

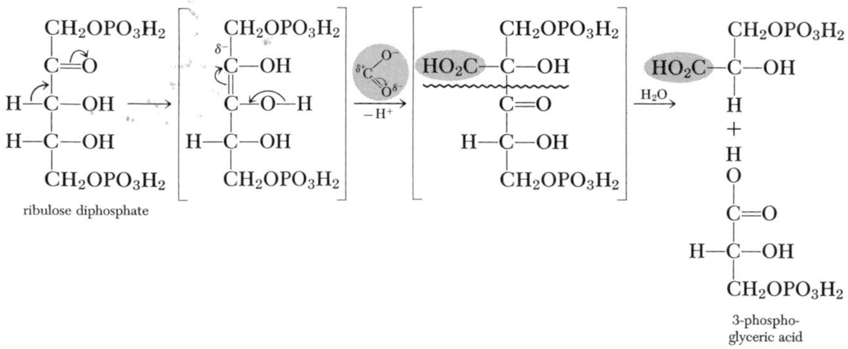

$$(11\text{-}22)$$

ribulose diphosphate

3-phospho-
glyceric acid

REFERENCES

1. H. A. Krebs and J. M. Lowenstein in *Metabolic Pathways*, edited by D. M. Greenberg, Academic Press, New York, 2nd edition; 1960, Vol. 1, Chapter 4.

    An authoritative and thoroughly readable review of recent developments in the tricarboxylic acid cycle.

2. H. A. Krebs and H. L. Kornberg, *Ergebnisse der Physiologie, biologischen Chemie und experimentellen Pharmakologie, 49,* 212 (1957).

    A masterful survey of the energy transformations encountered in the tricarboxylic acid cycle. Strongly recommended for the advanced student in biochemistry.

Twelve

Electron Transport and

Oxidative Phosphorylation

Introduction

In the preceding chapter the oxidation of pyruvate and acetyl-CoA was described. Although the oxidation is frequently called the aerobic phase of carbohydrate metabolism, the title is misleading since both pyruvate and acetyl-CoA can also be obtained from noncarbohydrate sources. In addition, the term *aerobic* is not strictly precise when the reactions are described as on the inside of the back cover, since the immediate oxidizing agents are pyridine and flavin nucleotides rather than oxygen. As in the glycolytic sequence, the amount of pyridine or flavin nucleotides in the cell is limited, and the reaction ceases when the supply of oxidized nucleotides is exhausted. Hence, in order for the oxidation of organic substrates to continue, the reduced pyridine and flavin nucleotides must be reoxidized. In the intact cell, in tissue homogenates, or in mitochondria containing the enzymes that catalyze the oxidation of pyruvate by means of the tricarboxylic acid cycle, molecular oxygen serves as the ultimate oxidizing agent and accomplishes the oxidation of NADH and $FADH_2$. The enzymes that catalyze this process will now be described.

Composition of the Electron Transport Chain

When a molecule of malic acid, for example, is oxidized by mitochondria, the series of oxidation-reduction reactions shown in our diagram occurs. This is a simplified version of the electron transport chain in which pyridine nucleotides, flavins, cytochromes, and molecular O_2 are indicated as components. Each of these components will be described in detail shortly.

The notation of *curved arrows* was effectively used by Baldwin to in-

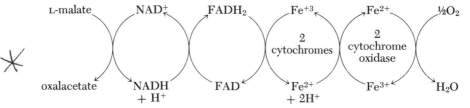

dicate the flow of electrons in the coupled oxidation-reduction reaction; thus the first pair of arrows indicate the oxidation of malic acid by NAD^+, a reaction catalyzed by malic dehydrogenase. The subsequent

$$
\begin{array}{c}
\text{COOH} \\
| \\
\text{HOCH} \\
| \\
\text{CH}_2 \\
| \\
\text{COOH}
\end{array}
+ \text{NAD}^+ \rightleftharpoons
\begin{array}{c}
\text{COOH} \\
| \\
\text{C=O} \\
| \\
\text{CH}_2 \\
| \\
\text{COOH}
\end{array}
+ \text{NADH} + \text{H}^+ \qquad (12\text{-}1)
$$

L-malate   oxalacetate

pair of arrows pointing upward indicates the reoxidation of NADH by FAD, a reaction which occurs in the presence of a specific flavoprotein. By continuing through the chain of carriers as shown, the oxidation of an organic substrate (L-malic acid) is accomplished at the expense of the reduction of molecular oxygen.

Pyridine Nucleotides

The pyridine nucleotides have been described in detail in Chapter 8. It should be reemphasized that in the presence of the appropriate dehydrogenase the equivalent of two hydrogen atoms is removed from the substrate of the dehydrogenase. In turn the oxidized pyridine nucleotide accepts the equivalent of two electrons and one proton in becoming reduced; the other hydrogen is released in solution as a proton.

$$
\begin{array}{c}
\text{COOH} \\
| \\
\text{HOCH} \\
| \\
\text{HCH} \\
| \\
\text{COOH}
\end{array}
+ \text{NAD}^+ \rightleftharpoons
\begin{array}{c}
\text{COOH} \\
| \\
\text{C=O} \\
| \\
\text{HCH} \\
| \\
\text{COOH}
\end{array}
+ \text{NADH} + \text{H}^+ \qquad (12\text{-}2)
$$

L-malate   NAD⁺   oxalacetate   NADH

Four of the five enzymes involved in the oxidation of pyruvic acid by means of the tricarboxylic acid cycle utilize pyridine nucleotides as oxidizing agents.   In the two oxidative decarboxylations (pyruvic oxidase and α-ketoglutaric oxidase) a molecule of lipoic acid is reduced initially and this compound in turn is reoxidized by NAD^+.

Although the reaction catalyzed by the soluble malic dehydrogenase is readily reversible, the diagram on p. 216 indicates that the oxidation of malate proceeds in only one direction.   Since NADH may be readily reoxidized by the electron transport scheme, the oxidation of malate (and not the reduction of oxalacetate) is favored.

Flavin Coenzymes

The next step in the electron transport chain is the reduction of a flavin coenzyme by the reduced pyridine nucleotide.

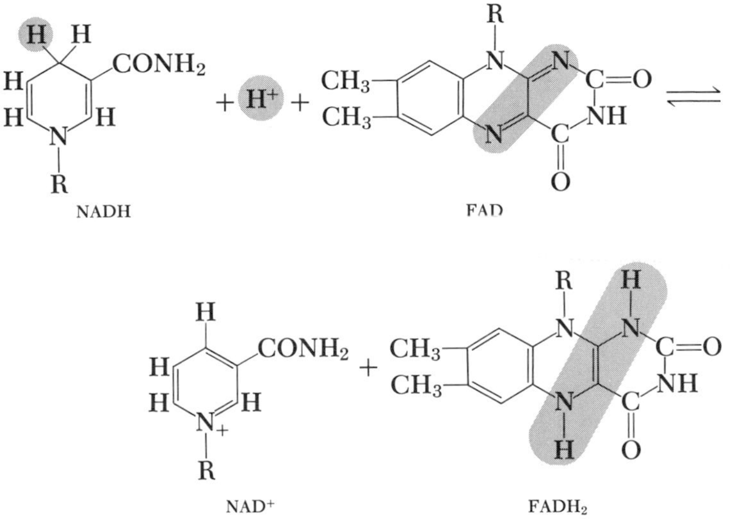

(12-3)

In the case of succinic dehydrogenase a flavin coenzyme firmly associated with the dehydrogenase is reduced and a pyridine nucleotide is not involved.   The reaction involves the removal of two hydrogen atoms from the succinate molecule and the addition of the equivalent to the oxidized flavin.

In recent years a number of flavin enzymes have been shown to be metalloenzymes, that is, enzymes with which metals such as iron, manganese, or molybdenum may be associated in addition to the protein and flavin components.   In the case of iron the ability of the electron transport chain to function is impaired if the metal is converted to a complex by the addition of iron-binding agents such as o-phenanthroline. The metal appears to function between the flavin coenzyme and the next components in the chain, the cytochromes.

There is also good evidence that still another carrier molecule may exist between the metalloflavin enzyme and the cytochromes. In mitochondria a quinone of the structure we show may be found.

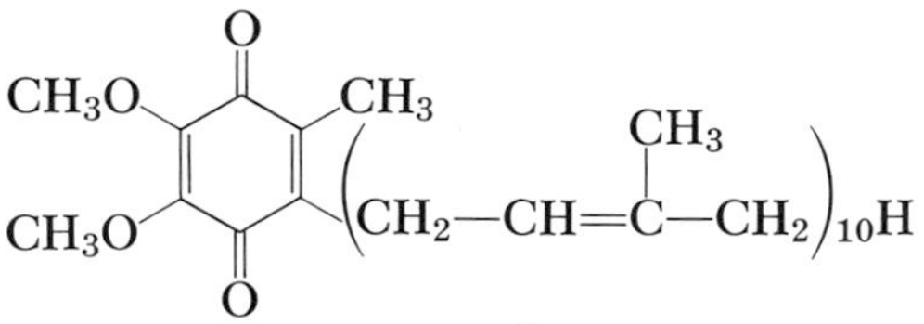

coenzyme Q_{10}

The length of the side chain varies with the source of the mitochondria; in animal tissues the quinone possesses ten isoprenoid units in its side chain and is called coenzyme Q_{10}. If the quinone is extracted from the mitochondria, the transport of electrons from substrates to oxygen is inhibited; the activity is restored when the quinone is added back. Because it is easily reduced and oxidized it may serve as an additional carrier between the flavin coenzymes and the cytochromes.

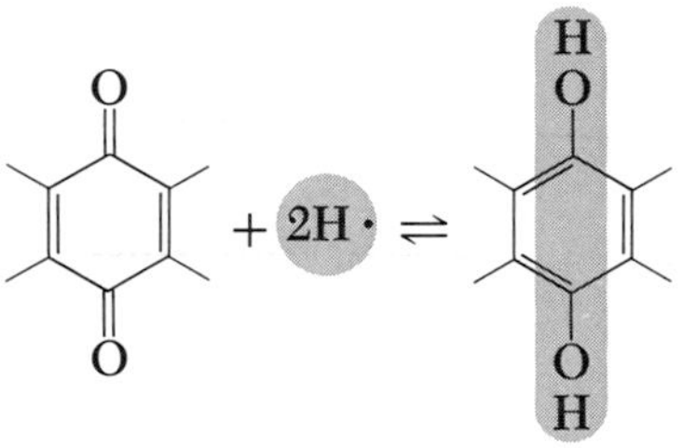

oxidized quinone   hydroquinone
or reduced quinone

The Cytochromes

These respiratory carriers were among the earliest components of the electron transport chain to be studied. The classical experiments of D. Keilin in England in 1926–27 demonstrated that these cell pigments (cyto-chromes) were found in almost all living tissues and implied an essential role for these substances in cellular respiration. Indeed Keilin's studies showed that there were at least three cytochromes, to which he assigned the letters a, b, and c. The research on the cytochromes was facilitated by the fact that they absorb light of different wavelengths in a characteristic manner. The absorption spectra of oxidized and reduced cytochrome c are shown in Figure 12-1. This cytochrome is readily made soluble and has been studied extensively; it

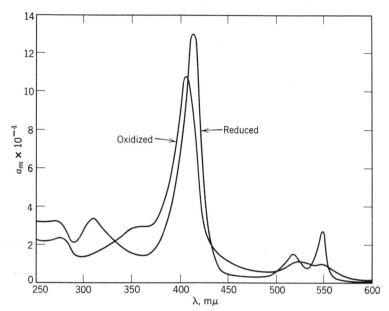

Fig. 12-1. Absorption spectra of oxidized and reduced cytochrome *c*. Data of E. Margoliash, reproduced from D. Keilin and E. C. Slater, *British Medical Bulletin*, 9, 89 (1953), The British Council, London.

has been crystallized from horse heart (mol wt 12,900) as well as yeast, wheat germ, and tuna.

The absorption spectra together with other properties of the cytochromes indicate that these compounds are conjugated proteins having an iron porphyrin as a prosthetic group. The structure of the prosthetic group for cytochrome *c* is shown; it is a derivative of iron-protoporphyrin IX (see Chapter 15), and it is bound through thioether linkages with cysteine residues in the protein component. The iron porphryins associated with cytochromes a and b are known to be different because of differences in their absorption spectra; this has subsequently been confirmed by chemical studies on the structure of the porphyrins. Although the porphyrin of cytochrome b is also related to protoporphyrin IX, the precise nature of the porphyrin of cytochrome a is not yet known. Most of the cytochromes that have been identified can be assigned to the a, b, or c type. They also appear to be associated with the insoluble particles in the cell, mainly the mitochondria in animals and higher plants.

The cytochromes form complexes with substances such as HCN, CO, and H_2S; these complexes were first identified by their characteristic absorption spectra. It is the combination of carbon monoxide with the ferrous iron of cytochrome a_3 (cytochrome oxidase) which accounts for the extreme toxicity of this compound to biological organisms.

The studies on soluble cytochrome c confirmed what Keilin had originally observed in intact tissues, that the cytochromes are capable of being alternately reduced and oxidized. The iron of the oxidized cytochromes is ferric iron; it is reduced to ferrous iron by the incorporation of one electron into the valence shell of the iron atom. Indeed, it is this property that allows the cytochromes to function as carriers in the electron transport process. As indicated on p. 216, cytochromes are reduced when the flavins are reoxidized. Since each reduced flavin molecule can furnish two electrons for the reduction of the iron pigment, *two* molecules of cytochrome are required to react with one molecule of reduced flavin.

$$FADH_2 + 2 \text{ cytochrome-}(Fe^{3+}) \longrightarrow FAD + 2 \text{ cytochrome-}(Fe^{2+}) + 2H^+ \quad (12\text{-}4)$$

The reaction is balanced by the release of two protons into the medium.

As indicated earlier, there are at least three cytochromes of the a, b, and c types in the mitochondria of every cell. In addition, a cytochrome called c_1, which is closely related to the easily solubilized cytochrome c, occurs in these particles. The available evidence indicates that in the intact mitochondria the cytochromes react in a sequence, with cytochrome b the first to be reduced, then cytochrome c_1, cytochrome c, and finally cytochrome a. The possibility that coenzyme Q_{10} and atoms of nonheme iron may react between the cytochromes and the flavin coenzyme is indicated in the diagram (p. 221).

In discussing the cytochromes some extra attention should be given to cytochrome a_3, or *cytochrome oxidase*. This iron-porphyrin protein is firmly associated with the insoluble portion of the cell, and investigation of its properties has been quite difficult. Reduced cytochrome a_3

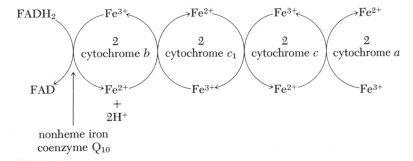

has the ability to transfer electrons to molecular oxygen and thereby reduce the latter to water. Cytochrome oxidase thus constitutes the last carrier in the chain of electron transport and is referred to as the *terminal oxidase* of the cytochrome chain. Without implying anything about the mechanism of this complex reaction, we may write it as:

$$2\text{ cytochrome } a_3\text{-}(Fe^{2+}) + 2H^+ + \tfrac{1}{2}O_2 \longrightarrow 2\text{ cytochrome } a_3\text{-}(Fe^{3+}) + H_2O \quad (12\text{-}5)$$

Two molecules of reduced cytochrome a_3 are again required to furnish the two electrons necessary for reduction of one oxygen atom, and two protons are required to balance the reaction.

To summarize, the complexity of the electron transport chain was not fully recognized from the earlier studies. A soluble enzyme preparation, which was called NADH-cytochrome c reductase, catalyzed the reduction of oxidized cytochrome c by NADH and was shown to contain a flavin coenzyme, FAD. As a result of studies on the electron transport chain in mitochondria the components necessary for reduction of cytochrome c by NADH are now known to include FAD, nonheme iron, a quinone, cytochrome b, and cytochrome c_1. Similarly, cytochrome oxidase was the name assigned to an insoluble enzyme preparation which catalyzed the reoxidation of reduced cytochrome c by molecular O_2. In the mitochondrion this reaction involves the interaction of both cytochrome a and cytochrome a_3 and recent studies suggest that copper ions may also participate.

Oxidative Phosphorylation

A major purpose of the degradation of carbon substrates by a living organism is the production of energy for the development and growth of that organism. In the anaerobic degradation of sugars to lactic acid, some of the energy available in the sugar molecule was conserved in the formation of energy-rich phosphate compounds, which are made available to the organism. As pointed out in Chapter 11, however, over 90 per cent of the energy available in glucose is released when pyruvate is oxidized to CO_2 and H_2O through the reactions of the tricarboxylic acid cycle.   In that process there was only one energy-rich compound, namely succinyl-CoA, synthesized by reactions involving the substrates of the cycle itself; in the presence of succinic thiokinase, this thioester was utilized to convert GDP to GTP.

When the production of energy-rich compounds in biological organisms was investigated in more detail, two different types of phosphorylation process were recognized.   In one of the processes, phosphorylated or thioester forms of the substrate were produced initially and subsequently utilized to produce ATP.   Examples of these are the reactions of glycolysis in which phosphoenol pyruvic acid and 1,3-diphosphoglyceric acid are formed and react with ADP to form ATP, as well as the reaction catalyzed by succinic thiokinase in the Krebs cycle. These phosphorylation processes have been referred to as *substrate level phosphorylations* and are to be distinguished from the phosphorylations associated with electron transport usually referred to as *oxidative phosphorylation*.

In 1937, workers in Russia and in the United States observed that phosphorylation occurred during the oxidation of pyruvic acid by muscle homogenates.   Although the subsequent fate of the pyruvate molecule was not clear at that time, oxygen was consumed by the homogenate, and inorganic phosphate was esterified as hexose phosphates.   If the reaction were inhibited by cyanide or by the removal of O_2, both the phosphorylation and the oxidation ceased.   Thus the synthesis of a sugar phosphate bond was dependent on a biological oxidation in which molecular oxygen was consumed.

Several important advances occurred which simplified the study of oxidative phosphorylation.   First, the process was shown to be confined to the mitochondria of higher plant and animal cells; in bacteria, smaller structural units of the cell appeared to be responsible.   Second, the only phosphorylation reaction that could be identified was the incorporation of inorganic phosphate into ADP to form ATP.

$$ADP + H_3PO_4 \longrightarrow ATP + H_2O$$

This is clearly a reaction which requires energy; the $\Delta F'$ is approximately $+8000$ cal/mole (under physiological concentrations the $\Delta F'$ may be $+12,000$ cal/mole).

Third, the composition of the electron transport chain of mitochondria was investigated in some detail; and fourth, the oxidation of NADH by O_2 in the presence of mitochondria was shown to lead to formation of ATP by the esterification of inorganic phosphate.   The importance of this extremely significant observation by Lehninger, then (in 1949) of the University of Chicago, should be emphasized.

If NADH is added to a reaction mixture containing ADP, inorganic phosphate, Mg^{2+}, and animal or plant mitochondria which have been properly prepared, the NADH will be oxidized to NAD^+ and one atom of O_2 will be reduced.   This occurs because, as described earlier, mitochondria contain the intact electron transport chain.   Simultaneously with this oxidation, inorganic phosphate will react with ADP to form ATP.   Under ideal conditions, between 2 and 3 moles of ATP will be formed per atom of O_2 consumed.   Since the mitochondria contain ATP-ase and also can catalyze side reactions which utilize ATP, it is believed that 3 moles of ATP are formed per mole of NADH oxidized or atom of oxygen consumed.   This may be represented schematically as:

$$\text{NADH} + \text{H}^+ + \tfrac{1}{2}\text{O}_2 + 3\text{ADP} + 3\text{H}_3\text{PO}_4 \longrightarrow \text{NAD}^+ + 3\text{ATP} + 4\text{H}_2\text{O} \quad (12\text{-}6)$$

The mechanism of oxidative phosphorylation is not well understood; indeed, it is a field of extremely active research.   Presumably phosphorylated intermediates of an unknown nature are involved; probably phosphorylated derivatives of NADH, FAD, and the cytochromes are not involved.   Although the nature of the intermediates is not known, it is established that the phosphorylations occur as a pair of electrons makes its way along the electron transport chain.   For example, one phosphorylation occurs when reduced cytochrome c is oxidized by molecular oxygen; the other two phosphorylations occur when a pair of electrons makes its way from NADH to cytochrome c.   This may be represented as follows, with the simplified electron transport chain diagrammed on p. 216.

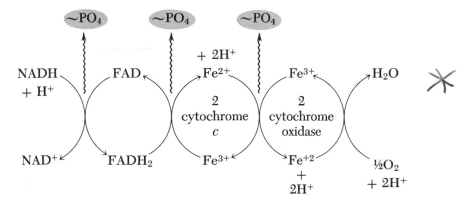

The mitochondrion that contains the enzymes for electron transport has frequently been referred to as a biochemical machine.   It is a complex machine because it also contains the enzymes of the tricarboxylic acid cycle, the enzymes for oxidative phosphorylation, the enzymes for fatty acid oxidation, as well as enzymes for the formation of certain

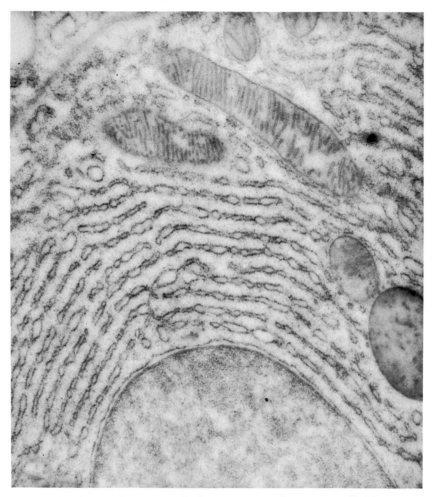

Fig. 12-2(a). Electron photomicrograph of a cross section of an exocrine cell of the pancreas of a guinea pig. (Courtesy of G. E. Palade.)

specific cell materials.   Although it thus appears to have a complex organization, the mitochondrion must represent a simplification over the whole cell in which it occurs.   Mitochondria (Fig. 12-2) are rod- or spherical-shaped bodies found in all animal and plant cells.   Their isolation is described in Appendix 2.

There is good evidence to believe that the mitochondrion is a complete biochemical unit.   The intermediates of the tricarboxylic acid cycle and fatty acid oxidation are, for the most part, oxidized by intact mitochondria without the addition of any of the cofactors known to be involved, that is, NAD^+, $NADP^+$, Mg^{2+}, Mn^{2+}, or FAD.   Similarly the

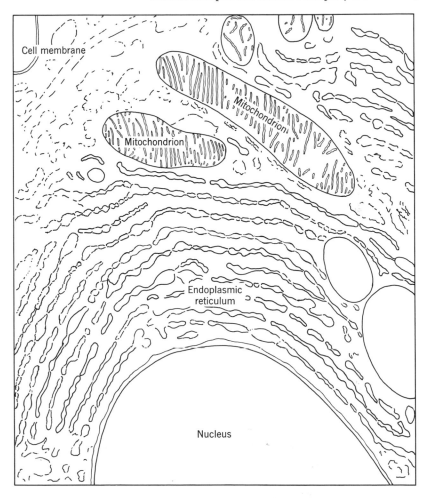

Fig. 12-2(b). Artist's sketch of the electron photomicrograph of an exocrine cell identifying the various subcellular components.

several cytochromes which are functional in the electron transport scheme are present in intact mitochondria and do not need to be added. Indeed, all that is required is molecular O_2, ADP, and inorganic phosphate.   The requirement for the latter two compounds results from the fact that the process of oxidative phosphorylation is *obligatorily linked* to electron transport in intact mitochondria.   If phosphorylation cannot occur because there is a lack of ADP or inorganic phosphate, the oxidation of intermediates of the tricarboxylic acid cycle by intact mitochondria will be inhibited.

Studies on the physical structure of the mitochondrion indicate that it has an external double membrane which surrounds an organized group of internal structures known as cristae. The walls of the cristae have double membranes, and the entire structure presents the picture of a highly organized unit. There is evidence to indicate that different sub-units of mitochondria may be obtained by specific fractionation procedures and that each subunit may have specific enzymatic properties, particularly in relation to the electron transport scheme. Thus the concept of an organized structure within the mitochondrion itself is supported by this observation.

In Chapter 6 the $\Delta F'$ for the oxidation of one mole of NADH by molecular O_2 was calculated as approximately $-52,000$ cal from the oxidation-reduction potentials of $NAD^+/NADH$ and O_2/H_2O. Since the oxidation of NADH by O_2 through the cytochrome electron transport system leads to the formation of three high-energy phosphate bonds, the efficiency of the process of energy conservation may be calculated as $-24,000$ (3×-8000) divided by $-52,000$, or 46 per cent. If, as is indicated under physiological conditions, the $\Delta F'$ for formation of ATP is $+12,000$ cal, the efficiency of energy conservation will be approximately 70 per cent.

Table 12-1. Formation of Energy-Rich Phosphate During the Oxidation of Pyruvate by the Tricarboxylic Acid Cycle

Enzyme or Process	Reaction	Energy-Rich Phosphate Produced
Pyruvic oxidase	Pyruvate + NAD^+ + CoASH $\longrightarrow$ acetyl-CoA + NADH + H^+ + CO_2	0
Electron transport	NADH + H^+ + $\frac{1}{2}O_2$ $\longrightarrow$ NAD^+ + H_2O	3
Isocitric enzyme	Isocitrate + $NADP^+$ $\longrightarrow$ α-keto-glutarate + CO_2 + NADPH + H^+	0
Electron transport	NADPH + H^+ + $\frac{1}{2}O_2$ $\longrightarrow$ $NADP^+$ + H_2O	3
α-Ketoglutaric oxidase	α-Ketoglutarate + NAD^+ + CoASH $\longrightarrow$ succinyl-CoA + NADH + H^+ + CO_2	0
Electron transport	NADH + H^+ + $\frac{1}{2}O_2$ $\longrightarrow$ NAD^+ + H_2O	3
Succinic thiokinase	Succinyl-CoA + GDP + H_3PO_4 $\longrightarrow$ succinate + GTP + CoASH	1
Succinic dehydrogenase	Succinate + FAD $\longrightarrow$ fumarate + FAD-H_2	0
Electron transport	FADH$_2$ + $\frac{1}{2}O_2$ $\longrightarrow$ FAD + H_2O	2
Malic dehydrogenase	Malate + NAD^+ $\longrightarrow$ oxalacetate + NADH + H^+	0
Electron transport	NADH + H^+ + $\frac{1}{2}O_2$ $\longrightarrow$ NAD^+ + H_2O	3
		Sum: 15

* = oxidative phosphorylation
✓ = substrate level

It is now possible to understand why the oxidation of pyruvic acid to CO_2 and H_2O by means of the tricarboxylic acid cycle leads to the esterification of inorganic phosphate. The oxidation steps in the process lead to the production of reduced pyridine and flavin coenzymes; when these are reoxidized by means of the electron transport system of the mitochondria, the process of oxidative phosphorylation leads to the production of ATP from ADP and inorganic phosphate.

Table 12-1 list the different reactions which result in the formation of energy-rich phosphate compounds; the total number of high-energy phosphate bonds synthesized per mole of pyruvate oxidized is 15. Since the oxidation of pyruvate to CO_2 and H_2O results in a free-energy change of $-273,000$ cal (Chapter 11), the efficiency of energy conservation in this process is at least $-120,000$ (-8000×15) divided by $-273,000$, or 44 per cent.

In line with this calculation, it is possible to estimate the total number of high-energy phosphate bonds which may be synthesized when glucose is oxidized to CO_2 and H_2O aerobically. The conversion of 1 mole of glucose to 2 moles of pyruvic acid forms 2 high-energy phosphates as a result of substrate level phosphorylation in the glycolytic sequence. The further oxidation of the 2 moles of pyruvic acid in the tricarboxylic acid cycle forms 30 high-energy phosphates. In addition, there are 6 more high-energy phosphates to be added to the 32 just listed. When glucose is converted to 2 molecules of pyruvate without the latter being reduced to lactic acid, 2 molecules of NADH remain to be disposed of; if these are not utilized in the reduction of pyruvate to lactate, they must be oxidized by means of the cytochrome pathway. The oxidation of 2 molecules of NADH by this route will result in the formation of 6 high-energy phosphates. The total, then, for the aerobic oxidation of glucose to CO_2 and H_2O is 38 high-energy bonds.

As discussed previously, the $\Delta F'$ for the oxidation of glucose by O_2 to CO_2 and H_2O has been estimated from calorimetric data.

$$C_6H_{12}O_6 + 6O_2 \longrightarrow 6CO_2 + 6H_2O \qquad (12\text{-}7)$$

$$\Delta F' = -686,000 \text{ cal (pH 7.0)}$$

If there were no mechanism for trapping any of this energy, it would be released to the environment as heat, for the entropy term (see Chapter 6) is negligible. The cell can conserve a large portion of this energy, however, by coupling the energy released to the synthesis of the energy-rich ATP from ADP and H_3PO_4. Since 38 moles of ATP can be formed during the oxidation of glucose, this represents a total of 38×-8000 or $-304,000$ cal. The amount of energy that would be liberated as heat in reaction 12-7 is hence reduced by this amount, and the overall oxidation and phosphorylation may now be written as:

$$C_6H_{12}O_6 + 6O_2 + 38ADP + 38H_3PO_4 \longrightarrow$$

$$6CO_2 + 38ATP + 44H_2O \qquad (12\text{-}8)$$

$$\Delta F' = -382,000 \text{ cal (pH 7.0)}$$

The conservation of $-304,000$ cal as energy-rich phosphate represents an efficiency of conservation of $-304,000$ divided by $-686,000$ or 44 per cent. The trapping of this amount of energy is a noteworthy achievement for the living cell.

The enzymes of electron transport and oxidative phosphorylation have no prejudices regarding the origin of reduced pyridine and flavin coenzymes. In the last consideration only the NADH and $FADH_2$ which resulted from the oxidation of pyruvate and carbohydrate precursors were discussed. The NADH and $FADH_2$ produced in the oxidative degradation of fatty acids or amino acids may also be oxidized by the cytochrome electron transport chain, and of course this results in the production of high-energy phosphate. Indeed the oxidative deamination of glutamic acid catalyzed by glutamic dehydrogenase produces NADH, which in turn can yield high-energy phosphate on reoxidation by molecular oxygen. Similarly the oxidation of one molecule of palmitic acid to CO_2 and H_2O may be expected to produce 130 energy-rich phosphate bonds (Chapter 13).

Summary of Energy Metabolism

At this point it is informative to review the three stages of energy metabolism. The first of these stages, the *production* of energy-rich phosphate bonds, has been extensively described. This consists of the processes of substrate level phosphorylation, encountered in glycolysis, and oxidative phosphorylation, associated with electron transport. In these processes either an energy-rich phosphate compound or a thioester is produced initially, which in closely related reactions results in the formation of ATP.

The second stage of energy metabolism is the *storage* of energy-rich phosphate bonds. In higher animals the role of creatine phosphate has already been mentioned; in a period of ATP production, this triphosphate reacts with creatine in the presence of creatine kinase to produce creatine phosphate and ADP. In fact, this is an important means for regenerating ADP, which then can once more accept high-energy phosphate to form more ATP. A similar relation exists in many invertebrates, where arginine can be phosphorylated to produce arginine phosphate as a stored form of energy-rich phosphate. In the Australian meal-

$$
\underset{\substack{\text{creatine}}}{\underset{\displaystyle CH_3-N-CH_2COOH}{\overset{\displaystyle H_2N}{\diagdown}\ C=NH}} \ + \ ATP \ \rightleftharpoons \ \underset{\substack{\text{creatine phosphate}}}{\underset{\displaystyle CH_3-N-CH_2COOH}{\overset{\displaystyle HO-P^+-N}{\diagdown}\ C=NH}} \ + \ ADP
$$

worm still another guanidinium compound, lombricine, serves as a phosphagen for storage of energy-rich phosphate structures.

The third stage of energy metabolism is the *utilization* of the energy-rich compounds. Perhaps the most common example, which has already been described, is the use of ATP in biosynthetic reactions. Thus ATP is utilized in the phosphorylation of glucose or fructose-6-phosphate in the presence of the appropriate kinases. The formation of thioesters of fatty acids is another example of biosynthesis at the expense of high-energy phosphate. The synthesis of amides, peptides, and proteins, are still other examples.

High-energy compounds, usually the compound ATP, play essential roles as the energy sources for other important processes. The process of muscular contraction and the performance of work by muscle tissues depend on a steady source of ATP. When work is done by a contracting muscle, ATP is utilized; when the supply of ATP is exhausted, the work ceases. Other processes such as osmotic work utilize ATP as the energy source. In the kidneys water is removed against a salt gradient; in the stomach HCl is secreted at a concentration of $0.2M$; in higher plants, ions are accumulated from extremely dilute concentrations in the soil medium and transferred into the concentrated vacuole. All these processes represent the expenditure of energy by living cells in the form of ATP. The production of light by the firefly—an example of bioluminescence—is another process requiring ATP as an energy source.

REFERENCES

1. B. Chance and G. R. Williams in *Advances in Enzymology*, edited by F. F. Nord, Interscience Publishers, New York, 1956, Vol. 17, p. 65.

2. A. L. Lehninger in *The Harvey Lectures*, Series XLIX, 1955, p. 176.

    Two authorities in the field have reviewed the subject of oxidative phosphorylation and electron transport. References to the older literature will be found in these two works together with possible mechanisms of oxidative phosphorylation.

3. E. E. Conn in *Comparative Biochemistry*, edited by M. Florkin and H. S. Mason, Academic Press, New York, 1960, Vol. 1, Chapter 10.

    The comparative aspects of electron transport and oxidative phosphorylation are described here.

Thirteen

Lipid Metabolism

Introduction

Lipids are stored in large amounts as neutral, highly insoluble triglycerides; they can be rapidly mobilized and degraded to meet the cell's demands for energy. The complete combustion of a typical fatty acid, palmitic acid, represents a large decrease in free energy:

$$C_{16}H_{32}O_2 + 23O_2 \longrightarrow 16CO_2 + 16H_2O$$

$$\Delta F' = -2,338,000 \text{ cal/mole}$$

The decrease is due to the oxidation of the highly reduced hydrocarbon radical attached to the carboxyl group of the fatty acid. Of all the common foodstuffs, only the long-chain fatty acids possess this important chemical feature. Thus lipids have quantitatively the best caloric value of all foods.

Lipids also function as important insulators of delicate internal organs. Nerve tissue, cell membranes, and membranes of subcellular particles such as mitochondria, microsomes, and nuclei have neutral lipids or complex derivatives as essential components. In addition, the vital electron transport system in mitochondria and the intricate structures found in chloroplasts, the sites of photosynthesis, contain lipid derivatives in their basic architecture.

As we have indicated, the chief storage form of available energy in the animal cell is the lipid molecule. When the caloric intake exceeds utilization, excess food is invariably stored as fat; the body cannot store any other form of food in such large amounts. Carbohydrates are converted to glycogen, for example, but the capacity of the body to store this polysaccharide as a potential source of energy is strictly limited. In a normal liver the average amount of glycogen is 5–6 per cent of the total weight, and in skeletal muscle the glycogen content averages only 0.4–0.6 per cent. Blood glucose, a source of glycogen units, is present at a level of 60–100 mg per 100 ml of whole blood. Only under pathological conditions are these values drastically altered. The normal animal therefore very carefully regulates, by hormonal and metabolic controls, the carbohydrate concentration in its various tissues, and this class of compound can serve only to a limited extent as a storage form of energy.

Proteins, the third major class of foodstuffs, differ considerably from carbohydrates and fats in their biological function; they serve as a source of twenty-odd amino acids required for *de novo* protein synthesis and as a source of the carbon skeletons essential for the synthesis of purines, pyrimidines, and other nitrogenous compounds. In an adult organism in which active growth has ceased, moreover, nitrogen output is more or less geared to nitrogen intake, and the organism shows no tendency to store surplus proteins from the diet.

History

With these interrelations of foodstuffs in mind, we shall find an examination of the development of the modern concepts of lipid metabolism fruitful.

As early as 1882, Shotten fed the sodium salts of fatty acids to animals and examined the urine for fatty acid derivatives. The higher members of the fatty acids were completely oxidized, but the animals excreted large amounts of acetic acid when they were fed acetic acid. In 1904, Knoop conceived the now classical idea of introducing the phenyl structure, which was not easily changed in the body, into the terminal methyl groups of the fatty acids. In this manner the degradation products of the fatty acid could be easily identified in the urine.

Phenyl derivatives of fatty acids containing from one to five carbon atoms were administered to dogs, and the excretion products in the urine were examined. Knoop discovered that the phenyl derivatives of the even-numbered fatty acids always led to the excretion of phenylacetic acid (actually the glycine conjugate, phenylaceturic acid) whereas the phenyl derivatives of the odd-numbered fatty acids were degraded to benzoic acid (that is, to the glycine conjugate, hippuric acid). From

odd:

$$\text{C}_6\text{H}_5\text{—C}\vdash\text{C—C}\vdash\text{C—COOH} \rightarrow\rightarrow \text{C}_6\text{H}_5\text{—COOH} + 2\text{``C}_2\text{''}$$

benzoic acid

even:

$$\text{C}_6\text{H}_5\text{—C—C}\vdash\text{C—C}\vdash\text{C—COOH} \rightarrow\rightarrow \text{C}_6\text{H}_5\text{—C—COOH} + 2\text{``C}_2\text{''}$$

phenylacetic acid

these results Knoop postulated that a successive removal of C_2 units could readily explain the experimental observations. Termed the *β-oxidation* theory, this postulate has played a dominant role in lipid metabolism. The success of his experimental approach was also a strong impetus to apply stable and radioisotopes to similar biochemical problems.

Knoop's classic experiments stimulated much work in the field, but the science of modern biochemistry had not developed sufficiently to handle the complex problem of fatty acid oxidation. Then, in 1943, Munoz and Leloir of Argentina showed that homogenized guinea pig liver could oxidize butyric acid, provided that adenosine 5′-phosphate, inorganic phosphate, magnesium ion, cytochrome c, and succinic acid were present. When radioactive carbon (C^{14}) was discovered by Kamen soon after World War II and new fractionation procedures for cell homogenates were developed by the Belgian scientist Albert Claude, the solution to Knoop's 1904 observations was at hand. The following observations, listed chronologically, proved of great importance to the ultimate solution:

(a) In 1944, Weinhouse incubated octanoic acid-1-C^{14} with rat liver slices and isolated acetoacetic acid with C^{14}-label in both the carboxyl and the carbonyl carbons of the acid. This observation strongly suggested that the even-chain fatty acids were degraded to a C_2 unit that could then combine with another C_2 unit to form acetoacetic acid.

(b) In 1950, Lehninger and Kennedy of the University of Chicago demonstrated that the exclusive site of fatty acid oxidation was the subcellular unit, the mitochondrion. All other subcellular fractions were inert.

(c) In 1950, Stadtman and Barker of the University of California demonstrated a completely water-soluble enzyme system from *Clostridium kluvyeri* which could catalyze either the degradation or synthesis of fatty acids.

(d) The discovery of coenzyme A by Lipmann of Harvard and of acetyl-coenzyme A by Lynen at Munich opened wide the door to the rapid solution of the problem of fatty acid degradation.

The "C_2" unit

Lynen isolated acetyl-coenzyme A (acetyl-CoA) from a yeast suspension which was oxidizing ethanol aerobically. With the elucidation of the structure of acetyl-CoA, the unique chemistry of the "C_2" unit became evident. The structure is depicted as and represents a class of

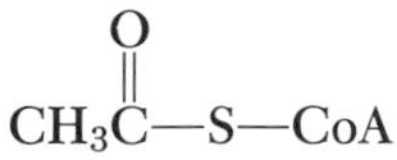

$$CH_3\overset{O}{\underset{\|}{C}}-S-CoA$$

compounds known as the thioesters. As discussed in Chapters 6 and 8, thioesters are known as energy-rich compounds because they have a relatively large negative $\Delta F'$ of hydrolysis. Some of their unique properties are now described.

Thioesters differ from oxygen esters in several important ways. Oxygen esters can exist in two forms that are stabilized by resonance:

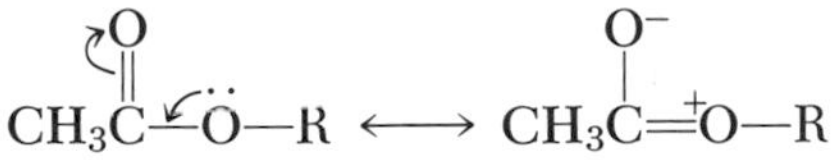

$$CH_3\overset{O}{\underset{}{C}}-O-R \longleftrightarrow CH_3\overset{O^-}{\underset{}{C}}{=}\overset{+}{O}-R$$

oxygen ester: resonance stabilized

The sulfur of a thioester does not readily release its electrons for double-bond formation, and cannot exist in the resonance-stabilized form found with the oxygen esters. Instead, because both the carboxyl oxygen and the sulfur atom are electronegative, thioesters possess considerable carbonyl character and may be depicted as in our diagram.

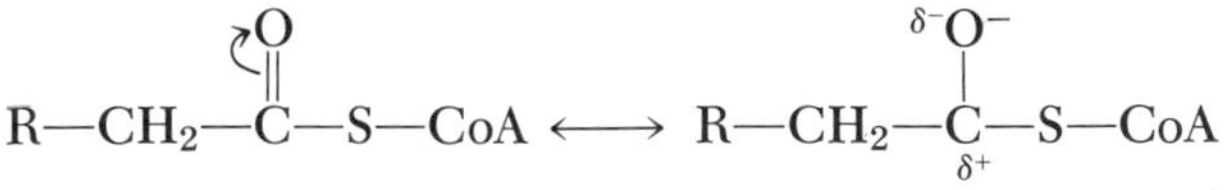

$$R-CH_2-\overset{O}{\underset{\|}{C}}-S-CoA \longleftrightarrow R-CH_2-\overset{\delta^-O^-}{\underset{\delta+}{C}}-S-CoA$$

Since the carbonyl carbon possesses a fractional positive charge (δ^+), one of the hydrogens in the α-methylene carbon will tend to dissociate as a proton leading to a potential carbanion in which the α-carbon has a fractional negative charge (δ^-). We see in the diagram that acetyl-

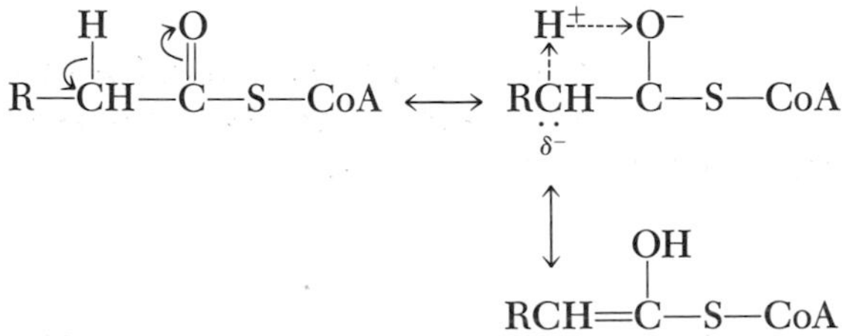

$$R-\overset{H}{\underset{}{CH}}-\overset{O}{\underset{}{C}}-S-CoA \longleftrightarrow R\overset{H^\pm\cdots\to O^-}{\underset{\delta^-}{CH}}-\overset{}{C}-S-CoA$$

$$\downarrow \quad OH$$

$$RCH{=}\overset{OH}{\underset{}{C}}-S-CoA$$

CoA has a unique structure in that a *nucleophile* such as H_2O, $R-S:^-$, or the α-carbon of acetyl-CoA can attack the site of the fractional positive charge. In addition, an *electrophile* such as CO_2 or the carbonyl carbon of acetyl-CoA can also approach the site of the negative charge with its pair of unshared electrons. With these basic facts

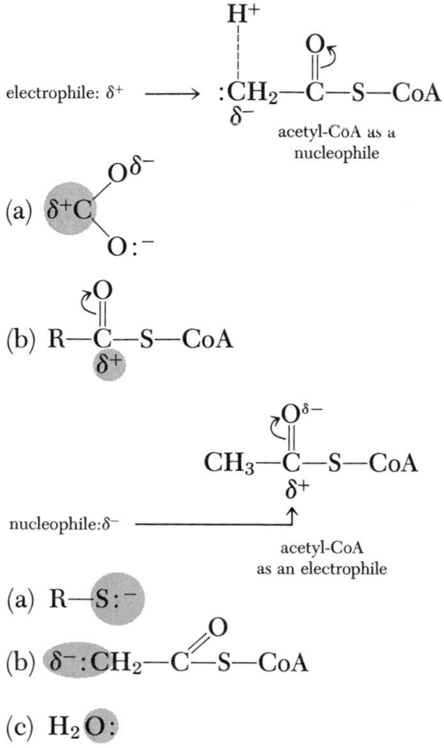

$$\text{electrophile: } \delta^+ \longrightarrow \begin{array}{c} H^+ \\ | \\ :CH_2-\overset{\displaystyle O}{\underset{\displaystyle \delta^-}{\overset{\|}{C}}}-S-CoA \end{array}$$

acetyl-CoA as a
nucleophile

(a) $\delta^+C\begin{array}{c} O^{\delta-} \\ \diagup \\ \diagdown \\ O:^- \end{array}$

(b) $R-\overset{\displaystyle O}{\underset{\displaystyle \delta^+}{\overset{\|}{C}}}-S-CoA$

$$CH_3-\overset{\displaystyle O^{\delta-}}{\underset{\displaystyle \delta^+}{\overset{\|}{C}}}-S-CoA$$

nucleophile:δ^- ⟶↑

acetyl-CoA
as an electrophile

(a) $R-S:^-$

(b) $\delta^-:CH_2-\overset{\displaystyle O}{\overset{\diagup}{C}}-S-CoA$

(c) $H_2O:$

in mind we are now prepared to examine the modern concept of β-oxidation.

β-Oxidation scheme

In 1952, Green in Wisconsin and Lynen in Munich announced the separation, isolation, and purification of the five enzymes responsible for the β-oxidation of fatty acids. They are:

Thiokinase
   type reaction:

$$R-COOH + ATP + CoA-SH \xrightarrow{Mg^{2+}} R-\overset{\displaystyle O}{\overset{\|}{C}}-S-CoA + AMP + P-P$$

Acyl dehydrogenase
   type reaction:

$$RCH_2CH_2\overset{\displaystyle O}{\overset{\|}{C}}-S-CoA + FAD \rightleftharpoons \underset{\beta}{R}CH\overset{trans}{=}\underset{\alpha}{CH}-\overset{\displaystyle O}{\overset{\|}{C}}-S-CoA + FADH_2$$

Enoyl hydrase
  type reaction:

$$RCH{=}CH\overset{\displaystyle O}{\overset{\|}{C}}{-}S{-}CoA + H_2O \rightleftharpoons RCHOHCH_2{-}\overset{\displaystyle O}{\overset{\|}{C}}{-}S{-}CoA$$

L(+)-β-hydroxyl acyl-CoA

β-Hydroxyacyl dehydrogenase
  type reaction:

$$RCHOHCH_2\overset{\displaystyle O}{\overset{\|}{C}}{-}S{-}CoA + NAD^+ \rightleftharpoons RCOCH_2\overset{\displaystyle O}{\overset{\|}{C}}{-}S{-}CoA + NADH + H^+$$

β-keto acyl-CoA

β-Ketoacyl thiolase
  type reaction:

$$R{-}\overset{\displaystyle O}{\underset{\displaystyle O}{\overset{\|}{\underset{\|}{C}}}}{-}CH_2{-}\overset{\displaystyle O}{\overset{\|}{C}}{-}S{-}CoA + CoA{-}SH \rightleftharpoons R{-}\overset{\displaystyle O}{\underset{\displaystyle O}{\overset{\|}{\underset{\|}{C}}}}{-}S{-}CoA + CH_3{-}\overset{\displaystyle O}{\overset{\|}{C}}{-}S{-}CoA$$

Here R is the saturated aliphatic chain of the fatty acids. These five reactions are integrated into the helical scheme (Figure 13-1). Each turn of the cycle removes a two-carbon unit.

There are several important features of Fig. 13-1 that should be emphasized:

(a) Only the CoA derivatives of the fatty acids serve as substrates for the enzymes.

(b) The free energy of hydrolysis of the thioester is of the order of -8000 cal, which places this type of ester in the group of high-energy or energy-rich compounds. The driving potential built into the thio-ester bond confers on these compounds some of their unique properties.

(c) Only one molecule of ATP is required to activate a fatty acid for its complete degradation to acetyl-CoA regardless of the number of carbon atoms in its hydrocarbon chain. In other words, whether we wish to oxidize either a C_4 acid or a C_{16} acid, only one equivalent of ATP is needed for activation. This makes for great economy and efficiency in the oxidation of fatty acids.

(d) Several derivatives of vitamins such as riboflavin, pantothenic acid, nicotinamide, adenine nucleotide, and trace metals such as Mn^{2+} or Mg^{2+} play essential roles in fatty acid oxidation. If there were a deficiency in any one of these substances, serious blocks would occur in the degradation of fatty acids.

(e) All enzymes associated with the β-oxidation system are localized

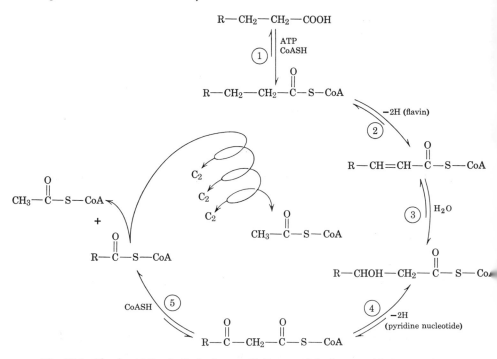

Fig. 13-1. The β-oxidation helical scheme. (1) Fatty acid thiokinases. (2) Fatty acyl-CoA dehydrogenases. (3) Enoyl hydrase. (4) β-hydroxyacyl dehydrogenase. (5) β-ketoacyl thiolase.

in the mitochondrial particle, in which are also found the enzymes of the tricarboxylic acid cycle, electron transport and oxidative phosphorylation. This arrangement is of fundamental importance to the efficient release and conservation of the potential energy stored in the long-chain fatty acid. When acetyl-CoA is produced in the breakdown of fatty acids it may be subsequently oxidized to CO_2 and H_2O by means of the tricarboxylic acid cycle.

(f) The oxidative system can be found in many insect, animal, bacterial, and plant tissues. The universality of the system implies the importance of the sequence as a means of degrading fatty acids.

Energetics of β-oxidation

In the total combustion of palmitic acid, considerable energy is released.

$$C_{16}H_{32}O_2 + 23O_2 \longrightarrow 16CO_2 + 16H_2O$$

$$\Delta F' = -2{,}338{,}000 \text{ cal/mole}$$

How much of this potential energy is actually made available to the cell? When palmitic acid is degraded enzymically, one energy-rich bond of ATP is required for the primary activation, and eight energy-rich thioester bonds are formed. Each time the helical cycle (Figure 13-1) is traversed, 1 mole of FAD-H_2 and 1 of NADH are formed; they may be reoxidized by the electron transport chain. Since, in the final turn of the helix, 2 moles of acetyl-CoA are produced, the helical scheme must be traversed only *seven* times to degrade palmitic acid completely. In this process 7 moles each of reduced flavin and pyridine nucleotide are formed. The sequence can be divided into two steps:

Step 1:

$$\text{palmitic acid} \longrightarrow \text{8 acetyl-S-CoA} + \text{14 electron pairs}$$
$$\text{7 electron pairs} \longrightarrow \text{flavin system} \times 2 = \text{14 energy-rich bonds}$$
$$\text{7 electron pairs} \longrightarrow \text{NAD}^+ \text{ system} \times 3 = \text{21 energy-rich bonds}$$
$$\text{Total} = 35$$
$$\text{Net} = 35 - 1$$
$$= \text{34 energy-rich bonds}$$

Step 2:

$$8 \text{ acetyl-CoA} + 16O_2 \xrightarrow{\text{TCA cycle}} 16CO_2 + 8H_2O + 8CoA\text{-SH}$$

If we assume that for each oxygen atom consumed three energy-rich bonds are formed during oxidative phosphorylation, then

$$32 \times 3 = 96 \text{ energy-rich bonds}$$

Thus step 1 (34 bonds) and step 2 (96 bonds) = 130 energy-rich bonds;

$$\frac{130 \times 8000 \times 100}{2,338,000} = 48 \text{ per cent}$$

Thus in the complete oxidation of palmitic acid to CO_2 and H_2O, 48 per cent of the available energy can theoretically be conserved in a form (ATP) that is utilized by the cell for work. The remaining energy is lost, probably as heat. It hence becomes clear why, as a food, fat is an effective source of available energy. In this calculation we neglect the combustion of glycerol, the other component of a triglyceride.

Synthesis of Fatty Acids

Ever since Knoop postulated his β-oxidation sequence in 1904, biochemists have been intrigued with the idea of *β-multiple condensation* of the same C_2 units, obtained from the oxidation of a fatty acid, for the synthesis of even-chain fatty acids. The answer to this problem had to wait for the complete definition of the degradative sequence.

In 1954, Stansly and Beinert of the University of Wisconsin, employing the five enzymes of β-oxidation and acetyl-CoA, performed the crucial experiment to test the β-multiple condensation theory. Their results indicated that shorter-chain fatty acids were not built up to either palmitic or stearic acid by enzymes of the β-oxidation sequence. Earlier, Brady and Gurin of the University of Pennsylvania had described homogenates that had the capacity to synthesize fatty acids from acetate. Therefore, acetate could be converted to long-chain fatty acids. The dilemma of how acetate units were joined together to form fatty acids was solved in 1959, when several workers showed that the actual condensing unit was not acetyl-CoA but rather malonyl-CoA. Synthesizing extracts in plant, animal, and bacterial systems required CO_2. These systems were extremely sensitive to avidin, a fact strongly suggesting a catalytic role for biotin. A specific biotinyl-acetyl-CoA carboxylase catalyzes the synthesis of malonyl-CoA from acetyl-CoA and ties in the role of CO_2 in fatty acid synthesis.

$$CO_2 + ATP + \text{biotin—enz} \longrightarrow CO_2\text{–biotin—enz} + ADP + H_3PO_4 \quad (13\text{-}1)$$

$$CO_2\text{–biotin—enz} + \text{acetyl-CoA} \longrightarrow \text{malonyl-CoA} + \text{biotin—enz} \quad (13\text{-}2)$$

Lynen in 1961 noted that the malonyl residue from malonyl-CoA is transferred to the synthetase complex to form a malonyl-enzyme complex. A saturated acyl-CoA then condenses with the malonyl-enzyme complex to form a β-ketoacyl-enzyme complex and CO_2. Reduction, dehydration, and a second reduction occur with the substrates bound to the enzyme surface. In the final step the saturated acyl-enzyme complex can be transferred to CoA-SH to form a saturated acyl-CoA and a free enzyme complex, which in turn is ready to repeat the synthetic process.

The unusual aspect of fatty acid synthesis is that the purification data and the physical properties of the enzyme system involved point to a single stable complex which consists of six different enzymes arranged around a functional sulfhydryl unit. This group apparently binds the intermediates through a thioester linkage to the active sites of the synthetase unit. The orderly additions of C_2 units to form even-chain fatty acids are depicted in our diagram. This arrangement explains the earlier observations by investigators of the lack of free intermediates in fatty acid synthesis, the absence of β-oxidation enzymes in the synthetase unit, and the lack of activity of the free-thioester intermediates of β-oxidation in the synthesizing system. Table 13-1 summarizes the differences between the synthesizing system and the β-oxidation system.

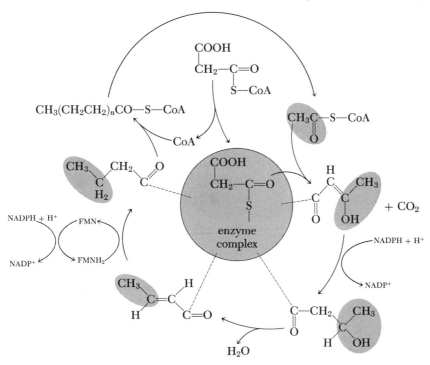

fatty acid synthetase complex

The overall reaction for fatty acid synthesis may then be written as:

$$CH_3\underset{O}{\overset{\|}{C}}\text{-S-CoA} + n \text{ malonyl-CoA} + n \text{ NADPH} + n \text{ FMNH}_2 \longrightarrow$$

$$CH_3(CH_2)_n\underset{O}{\overset{\|}{C}}\text{-S-CoA} + n \text{ NADP}^+ + n \text{ FMN} + n \text{ CO}_2 \quad (13\text{-}3)$$

Why should the initial reaction catalyzed by the synthetase unit differ so greatly from the fifth reaction in the β-oxidation sequence? A consideration of the K_{eq} for the thiolase reaction in the β-oxidation sequence provides important information. The equilibrium for the thiolase reaction is

$$\frac{(\text{acetyl-CoA})^2}{(\text{acetoacetyl-CoA})(\text{CoASH})} = 10^5$$

The equilibrium is therefore greatly in favor of the breakdown of acetoacetyl-CoA. In other words, if we have 1000 molecules of acetyl-CoA, we can calculate the number of molecules of acetoacetyl-CoA that

Table 13-1.   Comparison of the Differences between the Reactions of β-Oxidation and Fatty Acid Synthesis

Reaction	β-Oxidation Sequence Substrate	Synthesis Substrate
$C + C \rightleftharpoons \overset{}{\underset{}{}}C-C\overset{}{\underset{}{}}$ carbon-carbon bond formation	Acetyl-CoA	Malonyl-CoA
$C=O \rightleftharpoons C\overset{OH}{\underset{H}{}}$ reduction of carbonyl	NAD$^+$ L($+$)-hydroxy-Acyl	NADP$^+$ D($-$)-hydroxy-Acyl
$-\overset{H}{\underset{H}{\overset{O}{C}}}-CH_2- \rightleftharpoons C=C$ dehydration	L($+$)-hydroxy-Acyl	D($-$)-hydroxy-Acyl
$CH=CH \rightleftharpoons -CH_2-CH_2-$ reduction of double bond	FAD	FMN
Sulfhydryl Component	CoA-SH	Enzyme-SH

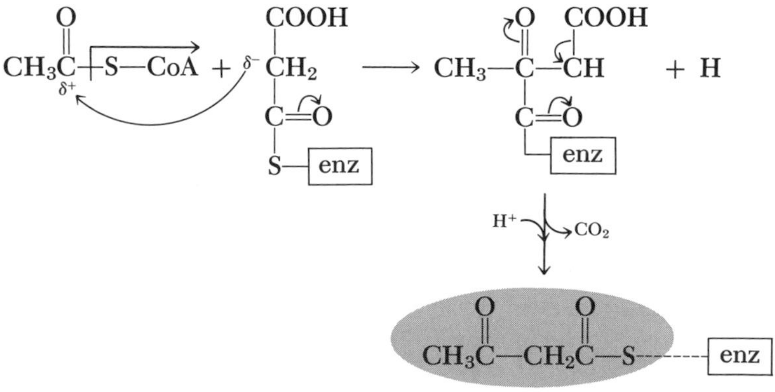

would be in equilibrium.   Starting with 1003 molecules of acetyl-CoA, only 3 molecules of acetoacetyl-CoA (0.3 per cent) would be synthesized.   This is a highly unfavorable equilibrium for the initial step in synthesis.   With malonyl-CoA as the condensing unit, we have a very favorable condition, in that a decarboxylation occurs as the condensation takes place.   The loss of CO_2 as a gas therefore "drives" the reaction in the direction of synthesis, and thus the origin of carbon atoms in palmitic acid is as follows:

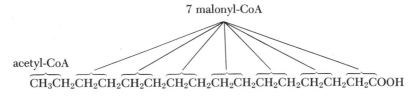

7 malonyl-CoA

acetyl-CoA

$CH_3CH_2CH_2CH_2CH_2CH_2CH_2CH_2CH_2CH_2CH_2CH_2CH_2CH_2CH_2COOH$

Biosynthesis of Unsaturated Fatty Acids

Although much is known about the biosynthesis of saturated fatty acids, there are few data on the synthesis of unsaturated fatty acids.

In the late 1930's, the work of Schoenheimer at Columbia University indicated that stearic acid was converted to oleic acid in rats:

$$stearic \rightleftharpoons oleic + 2H$$

No enzymic evidence was provided until 1959, however, when Bloch at Harvard demonstrated the following reaction in extracts of aerobically grown yeast:

$$stearyl\text{-}CoA + NADPH + H^+ + O_2 \longrightarrow oleyl\text{-}CoA + H_2O + NADP^+$$

Bloch has recently provided evidence that in anaerobic organisms where oxygen is unavailable a different pathway exists for the synthesis of unsaturated fatty acids. Decanoic acid, probably as a thioester, can condense with malonyl-CoA and after decarboxylation, reduction, and dehydration, the double-bond system so formed is maintained as such as more malonyl-CoA units are condensed to the unsaturated acyl-CoA ester:

$$CH_3(CH_2)_6CH_2CH_2CO\text{—}S\text{—}CoA \xrightarrow{\text{malonyl—CoA}} \rightarrow \rightarrow CH_3(CH_2)_6CH_2CH_2COCH_2CO\text{—}S\text{—}CoA$$

decanoyl—CoA CO_2 $\downarrow 2H$

$$CH_3(CH_2)_6CH_2CH_2CHOHCH_2CO\text{—}S\text{—}CoA$$

$$\downarrow -H_2O$$

$$CH_3(CH_2)_6CH_2CH=CHCH_2CO\text{—}S\text{—}CoA$$

$$\downarrow$$
$$\downarrow 3 \text{ malonyl-CoA}$$
$$\downarrow$$

$$CH_3(CH_2)_7CH=CH(CH_2)_7COOH$$

oleic acid

Mead at the University of California has shown that in animal tissues the unsaturated fatty acids—oleic, linoleic, and linolenic—are not inter-convertible with each other but instead form distinct and independent families of compounds. The changes involve a dehydrogenation, addition of a C_2 unit, and another dehydrogenation. The reaction of dehydrogenation is always toward the carboxyl group. The relationship may be described as follows:

the oleic family

$$CH_3(CH_2)_7CH=CH(CH_2)_7COOH \longrightarrow CH_3(CH_2)_7(CH=CHCH_2)_3(CH_2)_2COOH$$

oleic acid   5,8,11-eicosatrienoic acid

the linoleic family

$$CH_3(CH_2)_4CH=CHCH_2CH=CH(CH_2)_7COOH \longrightarrow$$

linoleic acid

$$CH_3(CH_2)_4(CH=CHCH_2)_4(CH_2)_2COOH$$

arachidonic acid

the linolenic family

$$CH_3CH_2(CH=CHCH_2)_3(CH_2)_6COOH \longrightarrow CH_3CH_2(CH=CHCH_2)_6CH_2COOH$$

linolenic   4,7,10,13,16,19 docosahexaenoic acid

Phospholipids

The phosphatidyl derivatives of choline, aminoethanol, and serine form important complex derivatives in the cell. They are found associated with important structural units of cell membranes and nerve fibers. Their synthesis has been carefully analyzed, chiefly by Kennedy of Harvard University, who found that the important nucleotide derivative involved in biosynthesis is cytidine diphosphocholine (CDPC).

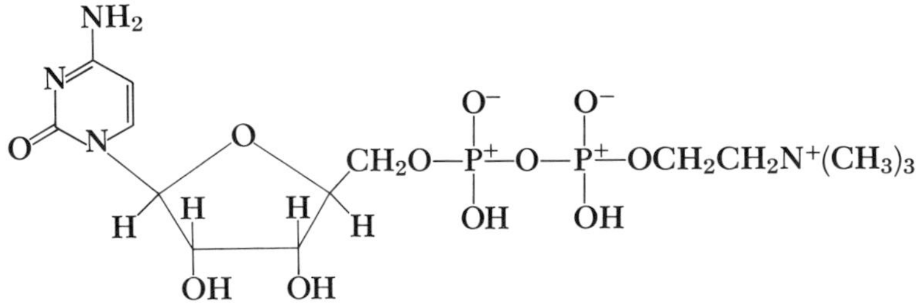

cytidine diphosphocholine

If we examine the structure of phosphatidyl choline (lecithin), we note that its basic units are long-chain fatty acids ($—OCOR_1$ and $—OCOR_2$), glycerol, phosphate, and choline. How are they assembled?

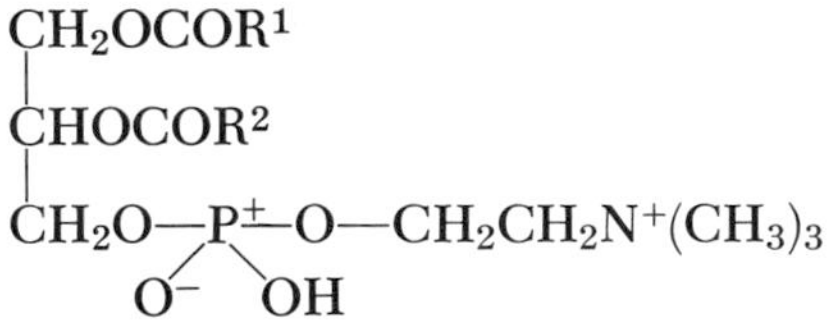

$$CH_2OCOR^1$$
$$CHOCOR^2$$
$$CH_2O—P^{\pm}—O—CH_2CH_2N^+(CH_3)_3$$
$$\qquad\quad O^- \quad OH$$

lecithin

In the cell an orderly sequence of events, all catalyzed by specific enzymes, bring the separate units together. The first reaction is the phosphorylation of choline.

$$\text{choline} + \text{ATP} \longrightarrow \text{phosphorylcholine} + \text{ADP}$$

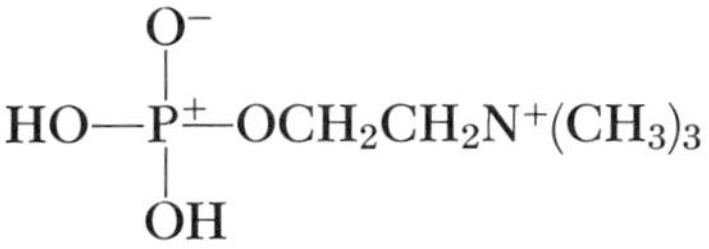

$$O^-$$
$$HO—P^{\pm}—OCH_2CH_2N^+(CH_3)_3$$
$$OH$$

Phosphorylcholine then reacts with CTP to form CDPC.

$$\text{CTP} + \text{phosphorylcholine} \longrightarrow \text{CMP} \cdot \text{PC} + \text{P—P}$$
(CDPC)

In the meantime glycerol is phosphorylated and then acylated to yield the important intermediate, phosphatidic acid.

$$\text{glycerol} + \text{ATP} \rightarrow \text{L-}\alpha\text{-glycerophosphate} + \text{ADP}$$

$$CH_2OCOR$$
$$\text{L-}\alpha\text{-glycerophosphate} + 2RCO—S—CoA \rightarrow CHOCOR \qquad + 2CoA\text{-}SH$$
$$CH_2O—^{\pm}P—OH$$
$$\qquad\quad O^- \quad OH$$

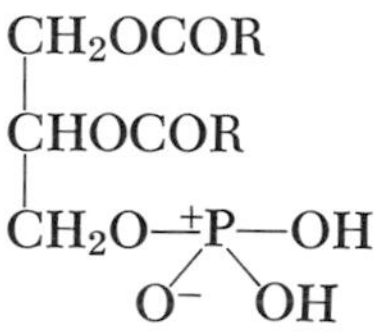

L-α-phosphatidic acid

L-α-Phosphatidic acid is a central intermediate for both phospholipid biosynthesis and triglyceride synthesis. A control of these two factors could play an important role in channeling the synthesis to triglycerides or to phospholipids.   The final assembling of the units is accomplished as in the diagram.

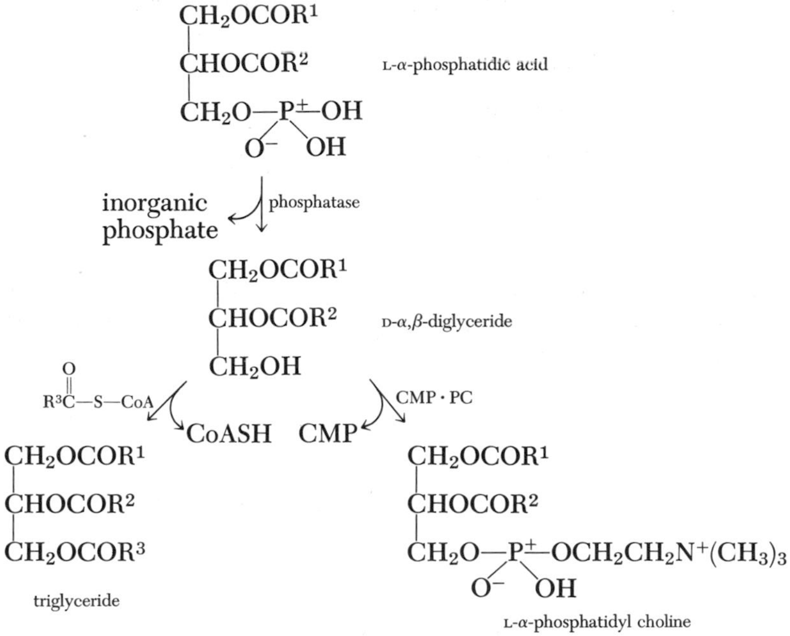

$$CH_2OCOR^1$$
$$CHOCOR^2 \qquad \text{L-α-phosphatidic acid}$$
$$CH_2O—P^{\pm}—OH$$
$$O^- \quad OH$$

inorganic   phosphatase
phosphate

$$CH_2OCOR^1$$
$$CHOCOR^2 \qquad \text{D-α,β-diglyceride}$$
$$CH_2OH$$

$$\overset{O}{\underset{\|}{R^3C}}—S—CoA \qquad \qquad CMP \cdot PC$$

CoASH   CMP

$$CH_2OCOR^1 \qquad\qquad\qquad CH_2OCOR^1$$
$$CHOCOR^2 \qquad\qquad\qquad CHOCOR^2$$
$$CH_2OCOR^3 \qquad\qquad\qquad CH_2O—P^{\pm}—OCH_2CH_2N^+(CH_3)_3$$
$$\qquad\qquad\qquad\qquad\qquad\qquad O^- \quad OH$$

triglyceride   L-α-phosphatidyl choline

Physiological Role of Phospholipids

It is a curious fact that the nuclear, mitochondrial, and microsomal fractions of the cell have an unusually high quantity of phosphatides. Thus 70–90 per cent of the total lipid of these fractions are related to phosphatides.   Some biochemists suggest that the phosphatides, in particular phosphatidyl choline, may play a role in insulating a series of enzymes in an organized lipid-protein matrix in the mitochondrion. The enzymes may include those in electron transfer and oxidative phosphorylation.   Of considerable interest is the observation that in chloroplasts, the sites for photosynthesis in leaf tissue, the major complex lipid component is a galactosylglycerol lipid:

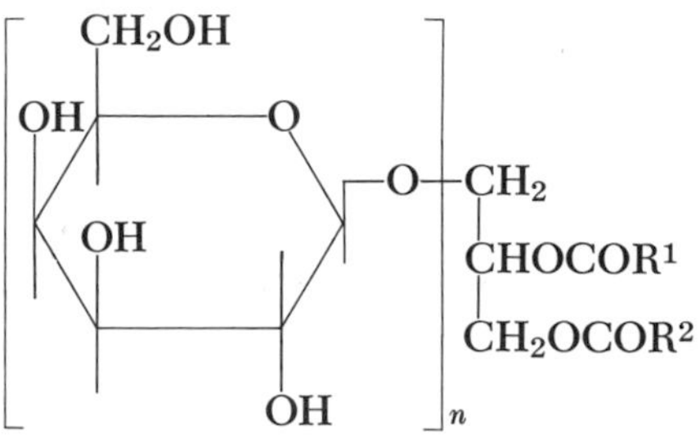

$$\begin{array}{c} CH_2OH \\ OH \qquad O \\ \qquad\qquad O—CH_2 \\ OH \qquad\qquad CHOCOR^1 \\ \qquad\qquad CH_2OCOR^2 \\ OH \end{array}_n$$

where n may be 1 or 2. Little if any triglyceride is found, although phospholipids do occur in some amounts. The role of this neutral glycolipid in the chloroplast structure may again be related to possible insulating properties required in a photochemical event.

Because of their anionic properties, phospholipids may also play a role in cation transport and permeability. Secretion of protein from such organs as the pancreas may also be tied into the lipoidal-ionic properties of phospholipids. Phospholipids have been implicated in blood coagulation; they are found associated in the principle lipid components of the myelin sheath of nerve fiber, and hence they possibly play an important role in nerve conduction. The unique polar and nonpolar properties of phosphatides make their elucidation in physiological activities a challenging goal.

Conversion of Fat to Carbohydrate—the Glyoxylate Cycle

Although it is a common observation that carbohydrates are readily converted to fats in animal tissue, there is no evidence to suggest that the reverse, namely the conversion of fats to carbohydrates, occurs. In plant tissues, however, highly fat-containing seeds rapidly convert their fat deposits to sucrose on germination.

Until recently the mechanism of conversion of fat to carbohydrates was not known. In 1957, H. L. Kornberg of Oxford University noticed that when a bacterial organism, a *Pseudomonad* strain, was exposed for 3 seconds to acetate-C^{14}, malate and citrate were highly labeled whereas the other tricarboxylic acid cycle intermediates had considerably lower labeling. It became obvious that there were two points of entry into the tricarboxylic acid cycle. One is the reaction catalyzed by the condensing enzyme (reaction 13-4).

$$\text{acetyl-CoA} + \text{oxaloacetate} \longrightarrow \text{citrate} + \text{CoASH} \qquad (13\text{-}4)$$

The second is the reaction catalyzed by the enzyme *malic synthetase* (reaction 13-5). The glyoxylate needed for reaction 13-5 is supplied by

$$\underset{\text{acetyl-CoA}}{CH_3-\overset{\overset{\displaystyle O}{\|}}{C}-S-CoA} + \underset{\text{glyoxylate}}{CHO-COOH} \rightleftarrows \underset{\underset{\text{L-malate}}{}}{H-\overset{\displaystyle CH_2COOH}{\underset{\overset{\displaystyle O}{\underset{\displaystyle H}{|}}}{\overset{|}{C}}}-COOH} + CoASH$$

$$(13\text{-}5)$$

the breakdown of isocitrate by the enzyme isocitritase (reaction 13-6). The combined efforts of reactions 13-5, 13-6, with members of the tri-

$$\begin{matrix} CH_2COOH \\ | \\ HCCOOH \\ | \\ H-C-COOH \\ | \\ O \\ H \\ \text{isocitrate} \end{matrix} \longrightarrow \begin{matrix} CH_2COOH \\ | \\ CH_2COOH \\ \text{succinate} \end{matrix} + CHO-COOH \quad\quad (13\text{-}6) \\ \text{glyoxylate}$$

carboxylic acid cycle give the so-called glyoxylate cycle, depicted in Figure 13-2.

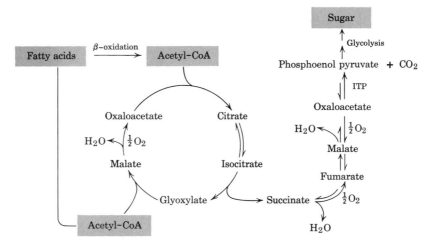

Fig. 13-2. Glyoxylate cycle. Conversion of fatty acids to sugar.

One turn of the cycle results in:

$$2 \text{ acetate} + \tfrac{1}{2}O_2 \longrightarrow \text{succinate} + H_2O \quad\quad (13\text{-}7)$$

Thus two acetate molecules are consumed to form one molecule of a dicarboxylic acid which may then be converted through phosphoenol pyruvate to mono- or disaccharides by a reversal of glycolysis.

The two key enzymes, malate synthetase (reaction 13-5) and isocitritase (reaction 13-6) occur in many micro-organisms and in high concentrations in germinating seeds that have a high oil content. As soon as the fat deposits have been depleted in these seeds, the activity of the two enzymes disappears. Another point of considerable interest is that seeds which depend on starch rather than fat as a source of energy during the process of germination do not possess the glyoxylate cycle. There is suggestive evidence that malic synthetase and isocitritase are examples of inducible enzymes in higher plants.

Since animal tissues do not contain detectable amounts of malic synthetase and isocitritase, it becomes obvious why animals are unable to convert fats to carbohydrates.

REFERENCES

1. *Lipide Metabolism,* edited by Konrad Bloch, John Wiley and Sons, New York, 1960.
   A useful albeit uneven series of chapters on the subject of lipid metabolism by experts in the field.
2. P. K. Stumpf, Lipid Metabolism, *Annual Review of Biochemistry,* Annual Review, Inc., Palo Alto, Calif., 1960, Vol. 29, p. 261.
   A review of the literature up to 1960.   Students should consult more recent volumes of this series for review chapters on lipid metabolism.
3. J. W. Cornforth, *Journal of Lipid Research, 1,* 3–28(1959).
   A brilliant application of modern organic chemistry to problems of lipid metabolism.
4. F. Lynen, *Federation Proceedings, 20,* 941(1962).
   A provocative article by a leader in the field concerning the mechanism of synthesis of saturated fatty acids.

Fourteen

Synthesis of Nucleic Acids
and Their Components

Pyrimidine Synthesis

In the 1940's, work with isotopes showed that the atoms in the pyrimidine ring originate from relatively simple precursors.

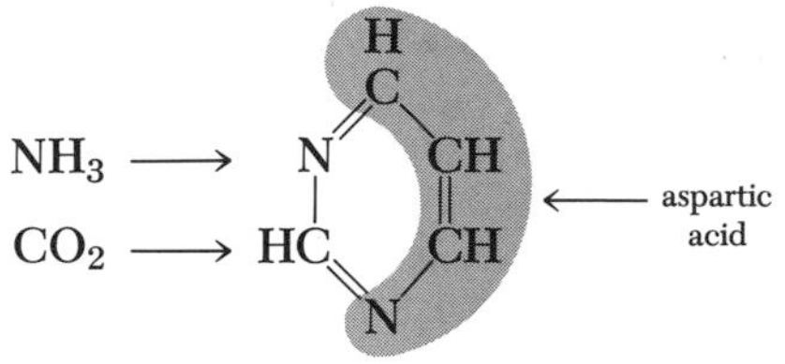

$$NH_3 \longrightarrow$$
$$CO_2 \longrightarrow$$
$$\longleftarrow \text{aspartic acid}$$

The assembling of NH_3, CO_2, and aspartic acid into the ring is rather involved, however. The basic outline is illustrated in Figure 14-1.

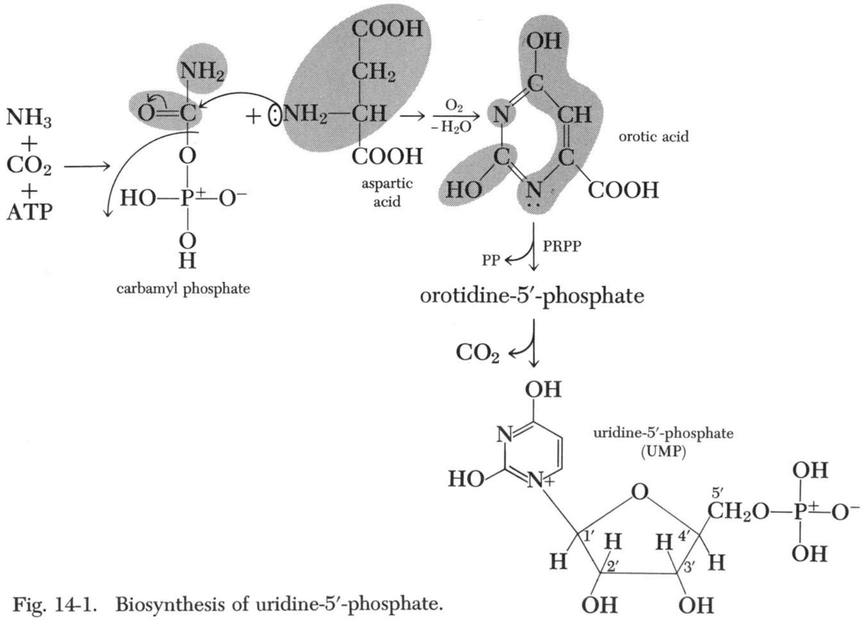

Fig. 14-1. Biosynthesis of uridine-5'-phosphate.

Orotic acid couples with 5'-phosphoryl-ribosyl pyrophosphate (PRPP) to form the ribonucleotide, orotidine-5'-phosphate.

Note that the ring nitrogen atom of orotic acid acts as a nucleophile and displaces the pyrophosphate moiety of PRPP to form the glycosidic bond. Pyrophosphate (PP) is an ideal leaving group (see Appendix 2 for the definition of a leaving group). PRPP is an important biochemical since it is the active unit employed to form ribonucleotide structures. As illustrated in the next diagram, it is formed by the transfer of a pyrophosphate from ATP to ribose-5'-phosphate.

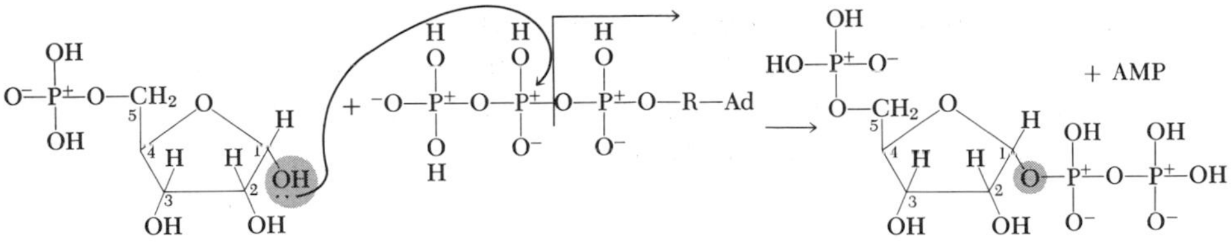

ribose-5'-phosphate   ATP   5'-phosphorylribosyl-1-pyrophosphate (PRPP)

Orotidine-5'-phosphate is decarboxylated to yield uridine-5'-phosphate (UMP); this compound in turn is converted to the triphosphate by ATP and then aminated by NH_3 to cytidine triphosphate.

$$\boxed{UMP} \xrightarrow{ATP} \boxed{UTP} \xrightarrow{NH_3} \boxed{CTP}$$

There is also good evidence that in some tissues the following reactions account for the formation of thymidine-5'-phosphate and deoxycytidine-5'-phosphate.

$$UMP \xrightarrow{Vitamin\ B_{12}} deoxy\text{-}UMP \xrightarrow{methylene\text{-}N^{5-10}\ FH_4} \boxed{TMP} + FH_2$$

thymidine-5'-phosphate

$$CMP \xrightarrow{vitamin\ B_{12}} \boxed{deoxy\text{-}CMP}$$

In summary, the synthesis of the pyrimidines involves the formation of orotic acid, the formation of its ribonucleotide, and its decarboxylation to uridine-5'-phosphate. Minor modifications of the ring or a reduction of the hydroxyl group on the 2'-position in the ribosyl portion of UMP result in the entire range of pyrimidine nucleotides needed as precursors for nucleic acid synthesis.

Purine Synthesis

Isotopic precursor studies indicate that the basic purine ring is derived from aspartic acid, glycine, glutamine, formic acid, and CO_2.

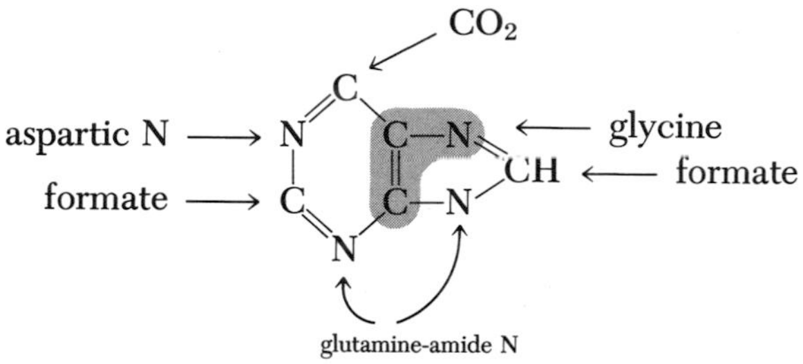

Through a rather involved series of reactions, the cell takes the initial substrates to the key intermediate, *inosinic acid*, from which all the other purines involved in DNA or RNA synthesis are synthesized. Let us examine the synthesis of inosinic acid and its interconversions. The salient points of the pathway are outlined in Figure 14-2.

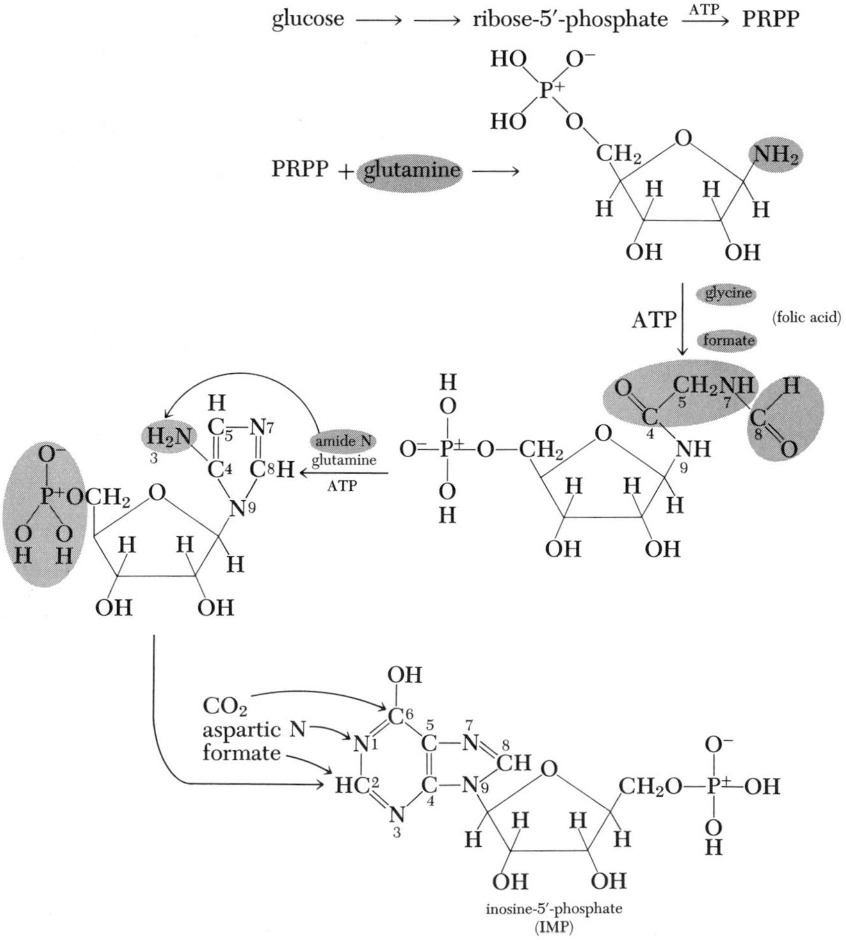

Fig. 14-2. Biosynthesis of inosinic acid.

Inosinic acid can now be converted to the remaining purine derivatives by the reactions shown in the following diagram.

$$IMP \xrightarrow[\text{GTP}]{\text{aspartic}} \boxed{\text{adenosine-5'-phosphate}}$$

$$IMP \xrightarrow{\text{NAD}^+} \text{xanthosine-5'-phosphate}$$
$$\downarrow \text{NH}_3$$
$$\boxed{\text{guanosine-5'-phosphate}}$$

Note that in the synthesis of both pyrimidine and purine nucleotides the construction of the ring unit proceeds with the early insertion of the sugar phosphate. Similarly in both cases two key nucleotides, uridine-5'-phosphate and inosine-5'-phosphate, are formed. From these all the other derivatives are made. In both cases tetrahydrofolic acid participates in formate transfer. The reduction of the 2'-hydroxyl group of the ribosyl moiety to form deoxynucleotide derivatives involves vitamin B_{12}, and the formation of a methyl group on thymidine-5'-phosphate again requires the methylene ring derivative of FH_4. (See Chapter 8 for the roles of vitamin B_{12} and folic acid.)

The relationship of these nucleotides to DNA and RNA synthesis is outlined in Figure 14-3.

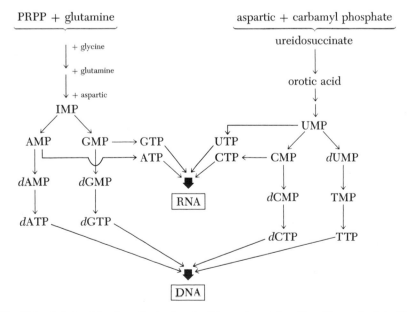

Fig. 14-3. Relationship of synthesis of nucleotides and nucleic acids. The prefix d signifies deoxy-; thus AMP contains the ribosyl moiety but dAMP contains a deoxyribosyl moiety.

Synthesis of Nucleic Acids

RIBONUCLEIC ACID

In 1955, Ochoa at New York University observed in a variety of bacterial extracts a polynucleotide phosphorylase that catalyzes the condensation of purine and pyrimidine nucleoside *diphosphates* to a polymer and inorganic phosphate:

$$n\ ppB \xrightarrow{\text{Mg}^{2+}} (pB)_n + n\ p$$

In this reaction B represents either a purine or a pyrimidine ribonucleoside and p stands for phosphate. The reaction is readily reversible.

The addition of inorganic phosphate to a polyribonucleotide will phosphorylyze the polymer to ribonucleoside-5′-diphosphates. The polymer can be formed from ADP, IDP, CDP, UDP, and GDP to yield poly-A, poly-I, poly-C, poly-U, and poly-G respectively. A mixture of nucleoside diphosphates will give a mixed polynucleotide. The synthesized polymer is completely susceptible to RNA-ase, indicating 3′,5′-diphosphate ester linkages. It is interesting that a lag period in the synthesis of poly-A from ADP can be eliminated by adding a small amount of poly-A to the system; this observation indicates the need for a primer. The same requirement holds for the synthesis of the other polymers.

Although polynucleotide phosphorylase synthesizes RNA, another enzyme with remarkable properties has recently been described by Hurwitz of New York University and by Weiss of the University of Chicago. Called RNA polymerase, the enzyme has been obtained from extracts of *E. coli* and catalyzes the incorporation of ribonucleoside *triphosphates* into RNA. The enzyme requires the presence of UTP, ATP, GTP, and CTP, all of which are incorporated. Of great interest is the observation that DNA is required since the incorporation of the nucleotides is completely dependent on the presence of DNA. We have noted in Chapter 5 the relationship of opposing bases in a two stranded DNA molecule. Thus, adenine is always matched by thymine, and guanine by cytosine. The same relationship holds for the RNA synthesis controlled by DNA. Thus, the amount of adenine in the DNA primer is matched by an equivalent amount of uracil in the newly created RNA (uracil of course substitutes for thymine in RNA), the amount of thymine in DNA by an equal amount of adenine in RNA, etc. Hurwitz observed that if DNA obtained from calf thymus with a $\dfrac{A + T}{G + C}$ ratio of 1.3 is added as a primer to the reaction mixture, the newly synthesized RNA would have a $\dfrac{A + U}{G + C}$ ratio of 1.3; with a DNA ratio from *E. coli* of 1, the newly formed RNA ratio would be 1! Thus, the base ratio in the newly produced RNA is determined by the base ratio of the DNA added.

In contrast to Ochoa's system, the nucleoside triphosphates rather than the nucleoside diphosphates are the substrates, and the primer required is DNA rather than RNA. Not only is DNA required for the polymerization; it also directs the *sequence* of ribonucleotides in the product. Finally, pyrophosphate rather than inorganic phosphate is formed in the polymerization of the units.

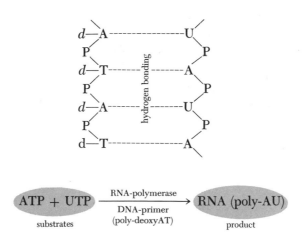

We may also note that RNA-polymerase is localized in the nucleus of the cell, a fact that suggests its role in the mediation of information transfer from DNA to RNA.

It is believed that the genetic carrier, DNA, is directing the synthesis by RNA polymerase of a special RNA molecule, called messenger RNA, the sequence of whose bases is controlled by DNA. A more detailed account of the role of messenger RNA in protein synthesis is found in Chapter 15 and of its role in the biosynthesis of enzymes and their control in Chapter 21.

DEOXYRIBONUCLEIC ACID

In 1956, Arthur Kornberg of Stanford University described the *de novo* synthesis of DNA by a highly purified DNA polymerase from *E. Coli*. The system requires a DNA primer and four deoxyribonucleoside triphosphates—deoxyadenosine-5′-triphosphate, deoxycytidine-5′-triphosphate, deoxyguanosine-5'-triphosphate and thymidine-5'-triphosphate.

$$n\ ppp\text{-}d\text{B} \xrightarrow{\text{Mg}^{2+}} (p\text{-}d\,\text{B})_n + n\ pp$$

where dB represents the base deoxyriboside.

$$\text{Thus:}\quad \left.\begin{array}{l} n\ d\text{ATP} \\ n\ d\text{GTP} \\ n\ d\text{CTP} \\ n\ \text{TTP} \end{array}\right\} + \text{DNA} \longrightarrow \text{DNA}\!\!\left.\begin{array}{l} d\text{AMP} \\ d\text{GMP} \\ d\text{CMP} \\ \text{TMP} \end{array}\right\} + 4n\ pp$$

The newly synthesized DNA has a base composition of $\dfrac{\text{A} + \text{T}}{\text{G} + \text{C}}$, which corresponds very closely to that of its primer. The polymerase takes direction from the primer template and faithfully reproduces the base pattern of the primer. In addition, when a synthetic DNA polymer consisting of only A and T bases (poly-dAT) is employed as the primer, the product contains only deoxyadenylic and deoxythymidylic acids, even when the four deoxyribonucleoside triphosphates are present. Thus the polymerase employing poly-dAT as a template rejects deoxyguanidylic and deoxycytidylic triphosphates and uses only the deoxyadenylic and deoxythymidylic triphosphates as substrates.

The newly formed polymer has the double helix structure conforming to the Watson-Crick model and its polydeoxyribonucleotide chains are joined by 3',5' diester bonds. Figure 14-3 summarizes the information presently available for the synthesis of RNA and DNA. The role of DNA is discussed further in Chapters 15, 20, and 21.

REFERENCES

1. Van R. Potter, *Nucleic Acid Outlines, Vol. I, Structure and Metabolism*, Burgess Publishing Company, Minneapolis, 1960.
   The student is once more referred to this excellent book for a full discussion of the synthesis of nucleic acids and their components.

Fifteen

Metabolism of Amino Acids

and Proteins

Introduction

As is so often the case, the knowledge of the intermediary metabolism of amino acids and proteins has its foundations in early nutritional investigations. Osborne and Mendel demonstrated in 1914 that the growing rat required tryptophan and lysine in its diet. Subsequently W. C. Rose of the University of Illinois showed that eight other amino acids were required by the rat for growth and development. World War II provided the stimulus and the research funds for identifying the amino acids required by man in experiments which involved the feeding of gram quantities of highly purified amino acids to male volunteers. These experiments, which were performed by keeping the subjects in *nitrogen equilibrium*, demonstrated that lysine, tryptophan, phenylalanine, threonine, valine, methionine, leucine, and isoleucine were *indispensable.*

An individual (man or other animal) is said to be in nitrogen equilibrium when the nitrogen consumed per day in the diet is equal to the amount of nitrogen excreted. The former is easily measured, especially if the diet is a synthetic one consisting of a mixture of amino acids; the nitrogen excreted is that found in the urine and feces. An *adult* animal can be maintained in nitrogen equilibrium provided an amount of nitrogen is supplied which is adequate to meet its minimum metabolic needs. This nitrogen, however, cannot be furnished simply as NH_3 but must be provided in the form of the indispensable amino acids. If one of these amino acids is omitted from the diet, the animal will degrade tissue proteins to meet its requirements and will go into negative nitrogen balance. That is, the nitrogen excreted in the urine and feces exceeds that in the diet. When the omitted amino acid is restored to the diet the individual attains equilibrium again.

Fevers and wasting diseases place an individual in negative nitrogen balance as does inadequate dietary nitrogen. On the other hand a growing animal which is continually increasing the amount of its body protein will be in positive nitrogen balance; that is, it takes in more nitrogen than it excretes.

There are two important consequences of the nutritional work on the indispensable amino acids we have described; first, it is clear that the animal cannot make these amino acids, at least in the amounts it requires. We may ask then whether the animal lacks the ability to make the carbon skeleton of the indispensible amino acid. The answer apparently is yes, for if an animal which is being furnished a diet which is deficient in phenylalanine, for example, is supplied with phenyl-pyruvic acid, the keto analog of phenylalanine, and extra nitrogen in the form of the other indispensable amino acids, it goes into equilibrium. These results are interpreted as meaning that the problem is not one of supplying nitrogen but rather one of synthesis of the carbon skeleton. In the case of phenylalanine, the difficulty is in the synthesis of the aromatic ring the amino acid possesses. Thus it may be concluded that certain types of carbon skeleton are not readily synthesized by higher animals.

Since only about half of the naturally occurring amino acids are indispensable to animals, it is clear that animals can synthesize the remaining amino acids; they are known as *dispensable* amino acids. Synthesis involves not only the manufacture of the carbon skeleton; it also includes the transfer of nitrogen atoms from dietary amino acids to complete the dispensable amino acid. Although much is known about the detailed metabolism of each of the twenty amino acids, we only have space to treat those reactions which apply, in general, to all the amino acids. In considering these reactions it will be apparent how the carbon skeletons of the dispensable amino acids can be synthesized, as will the manner in which the nitrogen atoms of the dispensable amino acids are acquired.

Deamination Reactions

One way in which the nitrogen on one amino acid can be made available for the synthesis of other amino acids is by deamination reactions in which NH_3 is produced. The deamination reactions most amino acids undergo can be classified as either *oxidative* or *nonoxidative*. The oxidative deamination reactions in turn can be divided into two groups; (a) those catalyzed by enzymes which require a pyridine nucleotide as coenzyme, and (b) those catalyzed by flavoproteins. The most important example of the first group is the enzyme glutamic acid dehydrogenase.

Glutamic dehydrogenase is widely distributed in nature.   It has been crystallyzed from beef liver and shown to contain zinc.   The enzyme has been purified from higher plants and is found in most micro-organisms.   The reaction catalyzed is:

$$
\begin{array}{c}
\text{COOH} \\
| \\
\text{NH}_2\text{CH} \\
| \\
\text{HCH} \\
| \\
\text{HCH} \\
| \\
\text{COOH}
\end{array}
+ \text{NAD}^+ + \text{H}_2\text{O} \rightleftharpoons
\begin{array}{c}
\text{COOH} \\
| \\
\text{C}=\text{O} \\
| \\
\text{CH}_2 \\
| \\
\text{CH}_2 \\
| \\
\text{COOH}
\end{array}
+ \text{NADH} + \text{H}^+ + \text{NH}_3 \qquad (15\text{-}1)
$$

L-glutamic acid   α-ketoglutaric acid

Although the enzyme was originally believed to be specific for L-glutamic acid, other L-amino acids (L-leucine, L-valine) can also be oxidized by the crystalline enzyme.   Since the maximum rates of oxidation with these amino acids are much less, however, the reaction with L-glutamic acid appears to be the most significant.   Both the pyridine nucleotides can serve as coenzymes for the animal and plant enzymes.   The most important feature of the enzyme, nevertheless, is that the reaction it catalyzes is readily reversible.   In the presence of NADH, NH₃, α-ketoglutarate, and the enzyme, the amino acid L-glutamic acid is formed. Hence this reaction provides a bridge between an intermediate of the tricarboxylic acid cycle and glutamic acid.   The ready participation of glutamic acid in transamination (see the reaction below) also emphasizes the role of glutamic dehydrogenase in the nitrogen metabolism of the organism.

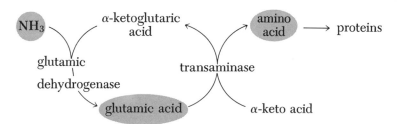

The introduction of ammonia into an organic molecule to form an amino group which may then be transferred by appropriate reactions is the chief function of glutamic dehydrogenase in many organisms, and in particular in the higher plants.

An alanine dehydrogenase which catalyzes the oxidative deamination of L-alanine in a reaction analagous to that catalyzed by glutamic dehydrogenase has recently been described in bacteria.

$$CH_3-\underset{\underset{H}{|}}{\overset{\overset{NH_2}{|}}{C}}-COOH + NAD^+ + H_2O \rightleftharpoons CH_3-\overset{\overset{O}{\|}}{C}-COOH + NADH + H^+ + NH_3 \quad (15\text{-}2)$$

The enzyme appears to be specific for NAD^+.

Oxidative deamination reactions are catalyzed by a group of flavin enzymes known as amino acid oxidases. In 1935, Krebs showed that kidney and liver slices catalyzed the formation of NH_3 from different amino acids and that oxygen was consumed. Subsequently, both enantiomorphs of racemic mixtures of amino acids were shown to be acted on by the slices, and the enzyme which catalyzed the oxidative deamination of the D-isomer to be soluble. The details of the reaction were elucidated with a partially purified D-amino oxidase prepared from sheep kidney. The overall reaction is:

$$R-\underset{\underset{H}{|}}{\overset{\overset{NH_3^+}{|}}{C}}-COO^- + O_2 + H_2O \rightarrow R-\overset{\overset{O}{\|}}{C}-COO^- + NH_4^+ + H_2O_2 \quad (15\text{-}3)$$

The enzyme requires FAD as a prosthetic group, and the reaction is not readily reversible. The overall reaction may be broken down into individual steps for which there is experimental evidence. In the first, oxidation of the amino acid leads to the corresponding imino acid.

$$R-\underset{\underset{H}{|}}{\overset{\overset{NH_3^+}{|}}{C}}-COO^- + FAD \rightleftharpoons R-\underset{\underset{H}{\|}}{\overset{\overset{}{|}}{C}}-COO^- + FADH_2 + H^+ \quad (15\text{-}4)$$
$$\hspace{7.5cm} N$$

The imino acid in turn is spontaneously hydrolyzed in the presence of H_2O.

$$R-\underset{\underset{H}{\|}}{\overset{}{C}}-COO^- + H_2O + H^+ \rightleftharpoons R-\underset{\underset{O}{\|}}{\overset{}{C}}-COO^- + NH_4^+ \quad (15\text{-}5)$$
$$\hspace{1.2cm} N$$

The reduced flavin formed in turn will be reoxidized by molecular oxygen to form H_2O_2.

$$FADH_2 + O_2 \longrightarrow FAD + H_2O_2 \quad (15\text{-}6)$$

This last reaction, the oxidation of $FADH_2$ by O_2, is not reversible. Therefore, although reactions 15-4 and 15-5 are reversible, the overall reaction 15-3, which is the sum of reactions 15-4, 15-5, and 15-6, is not. In the presence of a highly purified enzyme that contains no impurities to destroy H_2O_2 the reaction proceeds further. In this case the H_2O_2 formed in reaction 15-6 reacts nonenzymically with the keto acid.

$$R-\underset{\underset{O}{\|}}{C}-COO^- + H_2O_2 \longrightarrow R-COO^- + CO_2 + H_2O$$

The L-amino acid oxidase of kidney and liver is firmly associated with the mitochondria of the cell. The activity is so low that its physiological significance is doubtful, however. D-Amino acid oxidases have been found in *Neurospora crassa,* and L-amino acid oxidase has been purified from snake venom, *Proteus vulgaris,* and *Neurospora.* This latter enzyme unlike those of animal tissues, clearly provides a means for oxidative deamination of a large number of amino acids and perhaps serves as a first step in the degradation of the amino acid to NH_3, CO_2, and H_2O in bacteria and fungi. Since the reaction is not readily reversible, the enzyme is of no significance in the biosynthesis of amino acids.

In contrast to the reactions of oxidative deamination is the process of nonoxidative deamination. One type of nonoxidative deamination is the reaction catalyzed by the α-deaminases. Aspartase, which belongs to this group of enzymes, catalyzes the following reaction.

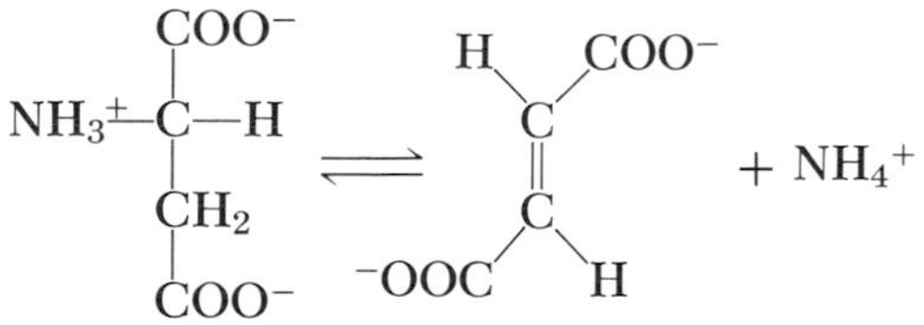

$$\underset{\text{L-aspartate}}{\underset{\overset{|}{COO^-}}{NH_3^{\pm}-\underset{\underset{COO^-}{|}}{\overset{|}{C}}-H}} \rightleftharpoons \underset{\text{fumarate}}{\overset{H}{\underset{{}^-OOC}{>}}C=C\overset{COO^-}{\underset{H}{<}}} + NH_4^+$$

The enzyme, which is specific for L-aspartic acid and fumaric acid, is found in *E. Coli* and other micro-organisms. The reaction catalyzed is readily reversible so that this reaction, as well as the one catalyzed by glutamic dehydrogenase, constitutes a method for incorporating inorganic nitrogen in the form of NH_3 into the α-amino position of an amino acid. Other α-deaminases catalyze the deamination of histidine, β-methylaspartic acid, phenylalanine, and tyrosine.

A somewhat different type of deamination is catalyzed by an enzyme in liver termed a dehydrase, which is specific for L-serine. The reaction involves the loss of NH_3 and rearrangement of the remaining atoms to yield pyruvate.

$$\underset{\text{L-serine}}{\overset{\displaystyle COO^-}{\underset{\displaystyle CH_2OH}{NH_3^{\pm}-C-H}}} \longrightarrow \underset{\text{pyruvate}}{\overset{\displaystyle COO^-}{\underset{\displaystyle CH_3}{C=O}}} + NH_4^+$$

Previously it was believed that amino acrylic acid,

$$CH_2=C(NH_2)-COOH$$

and its isomer, an imino acid, $CH_3-C(=NH)COOH$, were intermediates in this process. It has been subsequently shown that this enzyme requires pyridoxal phosphate as a coenzyme, and the Schiff's base of this coenzyme with the amino acid (see p. 146 and Chapter 8) is believed to be the intermediate. A similar deamination is catalyzed by another enzyme that acts on L-threonine. Finally, the deamination of cysteine is catalyzed by an enzyme found in animal, plants, and microorganisms. This enzyme also requires pyridoxal phosphate as a coenzyme and presumably operates by a mechanism similar to that of serine dehydrase. The overall reaction may be written.

$$\underset{\text{L-cysteine}}{\overset{\displaystyle COO^-}{\underset{\displaystyle CH_2SH}{NH_3^{\pm}-C-H}}} + H_2O \longrightarrow \underset{\text{pyruvate}}{\overset{\displaystyle COO^-}{\underset{\displaystyle CH_3}{C=O}}} + NH_4^+ + H_2S$$

Transamination

Equally important to the reversible oxidative deamination of glutamic acid are the transamination reactions, in which almost every amino acid participates. These reactions involve the transfer of the amino group from one amino acid to the carbon skeleton of another amino acid:

$$\underset{H}{\overset{NH_3^+}{R_1-C-COO^-}} + \underset{O}{\overset{}{R_2-C-COO^-}} \rightleftharpoons \underset{O}{\overset{}{R_1-C-COO^-}} + \underset{H}{\overset{NH_3^+}{R_2-C-COO^-}} \quad (15\text{-}7)$$

The significance of such reactions was first noted by the Russian workers Braunstein and Kritzmann, who observed that in the presence of animal tissue homogenates an amino acid could donate its amino group to α-ketoglutaric acid and so form L-glutamic acid. Purification of some

of the proteins involved demonstrated that quite specific enzymes could
be obtained that catalyze reactions 15-8 and 15-9.

$$
\begin{array}{ccccc}
\text{COO}^- & \text{COO}^- & \text{COO}^- & \text{COO}^- \\
| & | & | & | \\
\text{NH}_3^+\!\!-\!\text{C}\!-\!\text{H} + \text{C}=\!\text{O} \rightleftharpoons \text{C}=\!\text{O} + \text{NH}_3^+\!\!-\!\text{C}\!-\!\text{H} \\
| & | & | & | \\
\text{CH}_2 & \text{CH}_2 & \text{CH}_2 & \text{CH}_2 \\
| & | & | & | \\
\text{CH}_2 & \text{COO}^- & \text{CH}_2 & \text{COO}^- \\
| & & | & \\
\text{COO}^- & & \text{COO}^- &
\end{array}
\qquad (15\text{-}8)
$$

L-glutamate   oxalacetate   α-keglutarate   L-aspartate

$$
\begin{array}{ccccc}
\text{COO}^- & \text{COO}^- & \text{COO}^- & \text{COO}^- \\
| & | & | & | \\
\text{NH}_3^+\!\!-\!\text{C}\!-\!\text{H} + \text{C}=\!\text{O} \rightleftharpoons \text{C}=\!\text{O} + \text{NH}_3^+\!\!-\!\text{C}\!-\!\text{H} \\
| & | & | & | \\
\text{CH}_2 & \text{CH}_3 & \text{CH}_2 & \text{CH}_3 \\
| & & | & \\
\text{CH}_2 & & \text{CH}_2 & \\
| & & | & \\
\text{COO}^- & & \text{COO}^- &
\end{array}
\qquad (15\text{-}9)
$$

L-glutamate   pyruvate   α-ketoglutarate   L-alanine

As indicated, reactions 15-8 and 15-9 are readily reversible. More
recent work has shown that the first enzyme is widely distributed
in nature, and the fact that glutamic acid readily transaminates with
many keto acids indicates that other transaminases are common. Indeed, transaminase enzyme activity is perhaps the most common and
the most widely distributed enzymatic activity involving amino acids.
The fact that both aspartic and glutamic acids are active in transamination suggests that these compounds occupy a central position in amino
acid metabolism. As an example of the usefulness of transamination,
reaction 15-9 from left to right can be coupled with reaction 15-1 from
right to left. The overall reaction is:

$$
\begin{array}{cc}
\text{COO}^- & \text{COO}^- \\
| & | \\
\text{NH}_4^+ + \text{NADH} + \text{H}^+ + \text{C}=\!\text{O} \rightleftharpoons \text{NAD}^+ + \text{NH}_3^+\!\!-\!\text{C}\!-\!\text{H} + \text{H}_2\text{O} \\
| & | \\
\text{CH}_3 & \text{CH}_3
\end{array}
$$

pyruvate   L-alanine

The transaminases are known to require a derivative of vitamin B_6,
either pyridoxamine phosphate or pyridoxal phosphate, as cofactors.
The function of this coenzyme is, in the presence of the enzyme,
to form a Schiff's base with the amino acid. By subsequent electron rear-

rangements, the amino group is transferred to the coenzyme to form pyridoxamine phosphate (See Chapter 8 for the detailed mechanism).

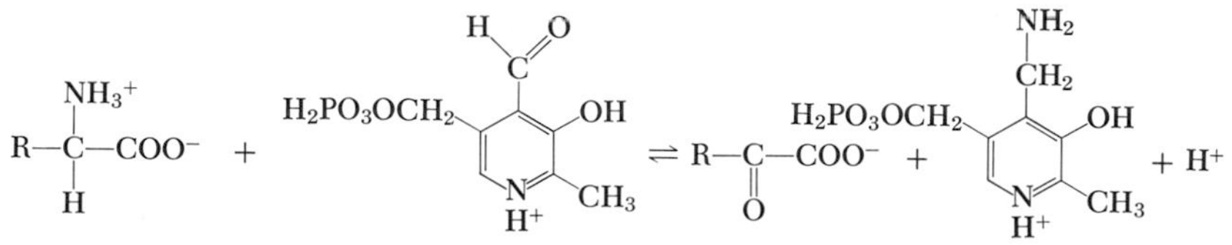

$$R-\underset{\underset{H}{|}}{\overset{\overset{NH_3^+}{|}}{C}}-COO^- \quad + \quad \text{(pyridoxal phosphate)} \quad \rightleftharpoons \quad R-\underset{\underset{O}{\|}}{C}-COO^- \quad + \quad \text{(pyridoxamine phosphate)} \quad + \quad H^+$$

The pyridoxamine phosphate can then react with the keto acid that is a reactant in the initial transamination reaction. In this process the pyridoxal phosphate is regenerated when the reaction is completed.

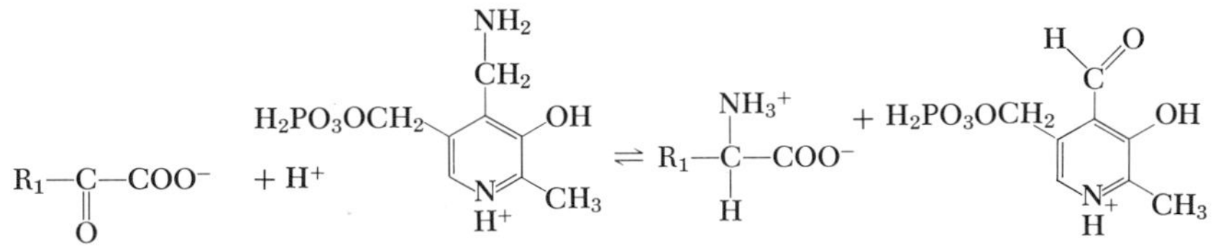

$$R_1-\underset{\underset{O}{\|}}{C}-COO^- \quad + H^+ \quad \text{(pyridoxamine phosphate)} \quad \rightleftharpoons \quad R_1-\underset{\underset{H}{|}}{\overset{\overset{NH_3^+}{|}}{C}}-COO^- \quad + \quad \text{(pyridoxal phosphate)}$$

Since the overall transamination reaction (reaction 15-7) is readily reversible, every step in the partial reactions we have shown must also be readily reversible.

Decarboxylation

The third type of general enzymatic reaction of amino acids is decarboxylation:

$$R-\underset{\underset{H}{|}}{\overset{\overset{NH_3^+}{|}}{C}}-COO^- \longrightarrow R-\underset{\underset{H}{|}}{\overset{\overset{NH_2}{|}}{C}}-H + CO_2$$

A common source of amino acid decarboxylases is bacteria, although the enzymes are widely distributed in nature. In bacteria the enzymes, which are inducible, are formed when the bacteria are grown with amino acids in the culture medium. For example, it is possible to obtain a specific decarboxylase for L-glutamic acid in *Clostridium perfringens* by growing the bacterium with this amino acid as its chief source of carbon. Because of specificity of the induction of the enzyme, dried cells of *Clostridium perfringens* grown in this way can be used as a means for specifically decarboxylating L-glutamic acid. Since CO_2

can be accurately measured manometrically this constitutes a means for quantitative analysis of L-glutamic acid.

The amino acid decarboxylases require pyridoxal phosphate as a co-factor. A Schiff's base is again an intermediate, and it is possible to write a detailed mechanism resulting in decarboxylation. Some of the amines formed as a result of decarboxylation have important physiological effects. Thus a histidine decarboxylase, found in animal tissues, can produce histamine, a substance which among other effects stimulates gastric secretion. The reaction catalyzed is:

$$\underset{\text{L-histidine}}{\underset{\underset{C \atop II}{N \quad NH}}{HC=C-CH_2-\overset{NH_3^+}{\underset{H}{C}}-COO^-}} \xrightarrow[\text{decarboxylase}]{\text{histidine}} \underset{\text{histamine}}{\underset{\underset{C \atop H}{N \quad NH}}{HC=C-CH_2-\overset{NH_2}{\underset{H}{C}}-H}} + CO_2$$

Another enzyme, tyrosine decarboxylase, will also decarboxylate 3,4-dihydroxyphenylalanine to form dopamine. This substance in turn is an intermediate in the formation of adrenalin, a vasoconstrictor which is released into the blood stream when an individual is frightened or startled. While the release of adrenalin is under other control mechanisms, the decarboxylase must function in the formation of the amine precursor.

$$\underset{\substack{\text{3,4-dihydroxyphenylalanine} \\ \text{(dopa)}}}{HO-\bigcirc-CH_2-\overset{NH_3^+}{\underset{H}{C}}-COO^-} \xrightarrow[\text{decarboxylase}]{\text{dopa}} \underset{\substack{\text{3,4-dihydroxyphenylethylamine} \\ \text{(dopamine)}}}{HO-\bigcirc-CH_2-\overset{NH_2}{\underset{H}{C}}-H} + CO_2$$

Other examples of amines which can be formed from amino acids by decarboxylase activity include γ-amino butyric acid. This substance, which is the third most abundant nitrogen compound in potato tubers, can be formed by the enzymatic decarboxylation of the α-COOH group of glutamic acid.

$$\underset{\text{L-glutamate}}{NH_3^+\!-\!\overset{\displaystyle COO^-}{\underset{\displaystyle CH_2}{\underset{\displaystyle CH_2}{\underset{\displaystyle COO^-}{\overset{|}{C}-H}}}}} \xrightarrow[\text{decarboxylase}]{\text{glutamic}} \underset{\text{γ-amino butyrate}}{NH_2\!-\!\overset{\displaystyle H}{\underset{\displaystyle CH_2}{\underset{\displaystyle CH_2}{\underset{\displaystyle COO^-}{\overset{|}{C}-H}}}}} + CO_2$$

This amine appears to be a highly important compound in the central nervous system of animals.

Porphyrin Biosynthesis

An outstanding example of amino acid metabolism is the role of glycine in the biosynthesis of the porphyrin structure.

CHEMISTRY

The biochemically important compounds chlorophyll, hemoglobin, and the cytochromes have in common a cyclic tetrapyrrole structure called a *porphyrin*. The parent structure, *porphrin*, contains four pyrrole rings linked by methine bridges (—CH=). Before considering their chemistry we shall outline a useful method for writing a porphyrin ring. Figure 15-1 elucidates the sequence. In the figure,

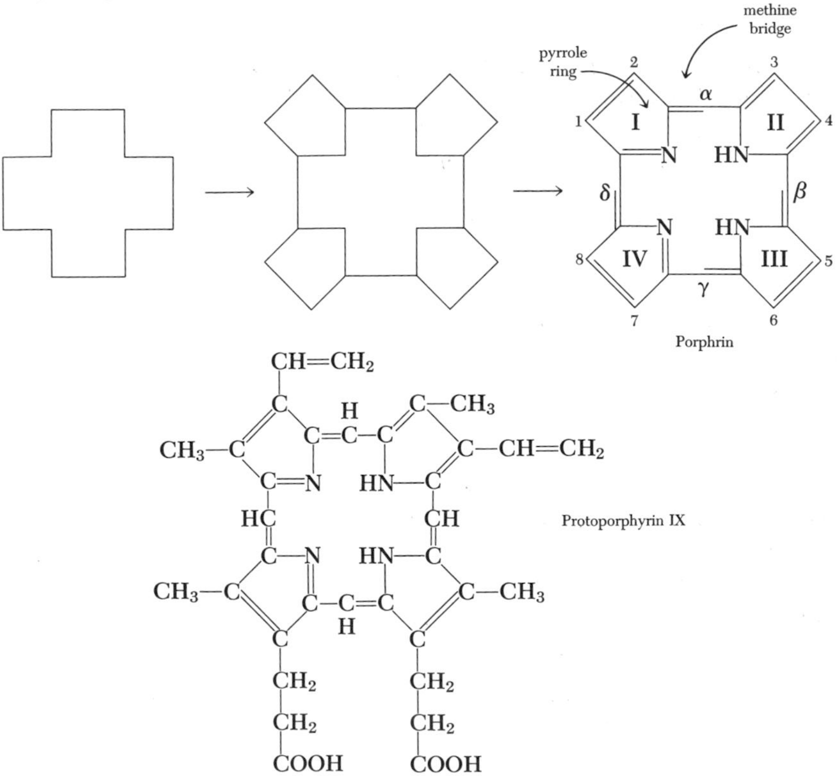

Fig. 15-1. At the top is shown the procedure for drawing a porphrin ring. First draw a symmetrical cross. Add the rings. Complete the structure to give porphrin ring. Below is shown protoporphyrin IX.

rings I, II, III, and IV are connected by methine bridges, α, β, γ, and δ. Note that the double-bond system is highly conjugated. In actual fact the double bonds are not definitely assigned, since the structure is a resonating system with several possible structures. The chlorophyll ring (see Chapter 17, p. 289 for its structure) and vitamin B_{12} (see Chapter 8, p. 151 for its structure) are modifications of the basic porphyrin structure. Protoporphyrin IX is one of fifteen possible isomers and is the most common in nature. The porphyrin ring is sterically a flat structure with a specific metal very firmly chelated by the electron pairs of the nitrogen atoms of the four pyrrole residues.

BIOSYNTHESIS

David Shemin of Columbia University and S. Granick of the Rockefeller Institute have made major contributions to the problem of biosynthesis of these important cyclic pyrrole structures. Isotopic data showed that all the carbon and nitrogen atoms of the porphyrin ring are derived from glycine and succinic acid. The biosynthetic sequence can be divided into three steps.

Step 1: Glycine and succinyl-CoA (the activated form of succinic acid) condense in the presence of a widespread enzyme to form δ-aminolevulinic acid. The enzyme requires pyridoxal phosphate.

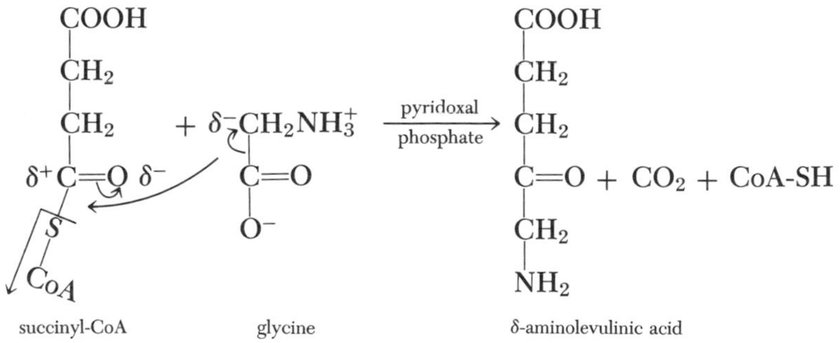

succinyl-CoA   glycine   δ-aminolevulinic acid

Step 2: The second step involves the condensation of 2 molecules of δ-aminolevulinic acid to yield the pyrrole derivative *porphobilinogen.* Note the distribution of the glycine (plain) and succinate (shaded) residues in the ring.

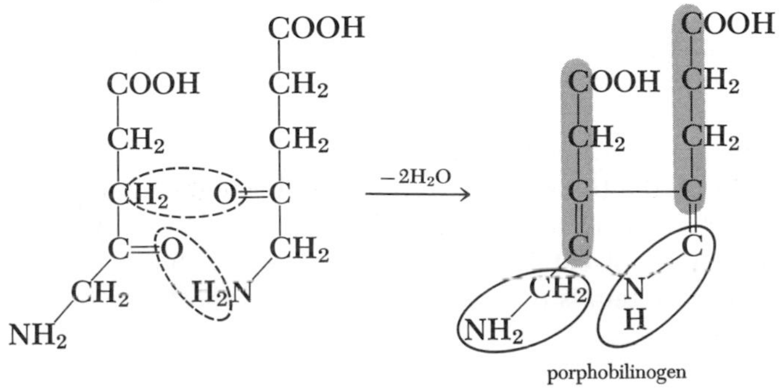

porphobilinogen

Step 3: A complicated series of condensations, isomerizations, decar-boxylations, and oxidations occur, the details of which are beyond the scope of this book. These reactions concern themselves mostly with the modifications of the side chains to give vinyl ($-CH=CH_2$), methyl, and propionic residues at the appropriate positions.

$$4 \text{ porphobilinogen} \rightarrow \rightarrow \rightarrow \text{protoporphyrin IX}$$

Protoporphyrin IX in cytochrome *c* is held to its specific protein by cysteinyl bridges and by chelation of imidazole residues (from the histidines of the protein) to the iron moiety of the porphyrin ring, as in-dicated in Figure 15-2. The role of the porphyrins is extremely impor-

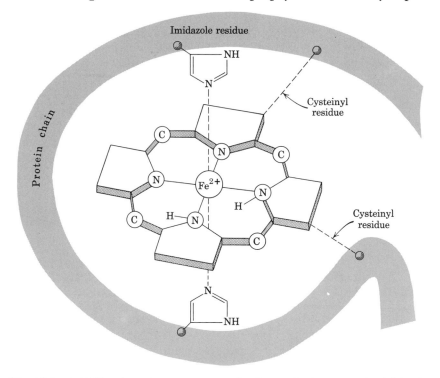

Fig. 15-2. A highly schematic representation of a flat porphyrin structure buried in the tertiary structure of a protein. Imidazole residues from histidines in the protein presumably coordinate with the iron of the porphyrin.

tant in the economy of the cell. Whenever the student reads about photosynthesis, the transport of oxygen (by hemoglobin and myoglobin), the transport of electrons to oxygen (by the cytochrome systems), or the catalytic activity of catalase and peroxidase, he should be aware that the porphyrin system is the key structure in all these functions.

Peptide Biosynthesis

Several kinds of peptide or peptide-like compounds are found in the living cell; in the late 1940's these compounds were considered as model systems for the study of protein synthesis. Thus the information concerning the biosynthesis of glutamine, hippuric acid, and glutathione was at first applied to the larger problem of protein synthesis. A brief consideration of this information is necessary to appreciate what is to follow.

HIPPURIC ACID

As soon as coenzyme A became available, it could be shown that the enzymic synthesis of hippuric acid involved the sequence we show.

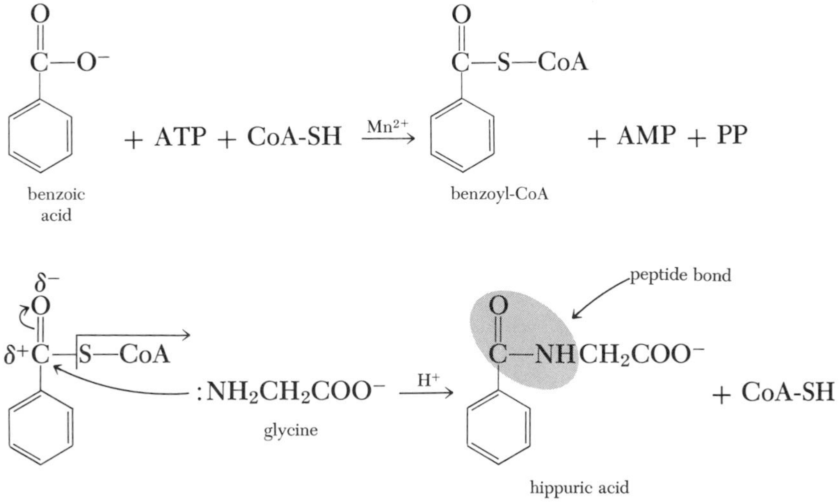

benzoic acid   + ATP + CoA-SH $\xrightarrow{\text{Mn}^{2+}}$ benzoyl-CoA   + AMP + PP

glycine $\xrightarrow{\text{H}^+}$ hippuric acid   + CoA-SH

GLUTAMINE

Glutamine is synthesized by glutamine synthetase, an enzyme found in plants, animals, and bacteria. The first step is believed to be the formation of a γ-glutamyl-phosphate-enzyme complex. In the second step ammonia, a good nucleophile, attacks the complex and displaces the phosphate group to form glutamine and inorganic phosphate. Note that only the γ-amide is formed. Isoglutamine, the compound with the α-carboxyl group amidated, is never formed. The enzyme is also highly specific, since aspartic acid cannot replace glutamic acid as a substrate. Recently it has been shown that asparagine is synthesized by a yeast system requiring aspartic acid, ATP, Mg^{2+}, and NH_3 and this enzyme will react only with aspartic acid.

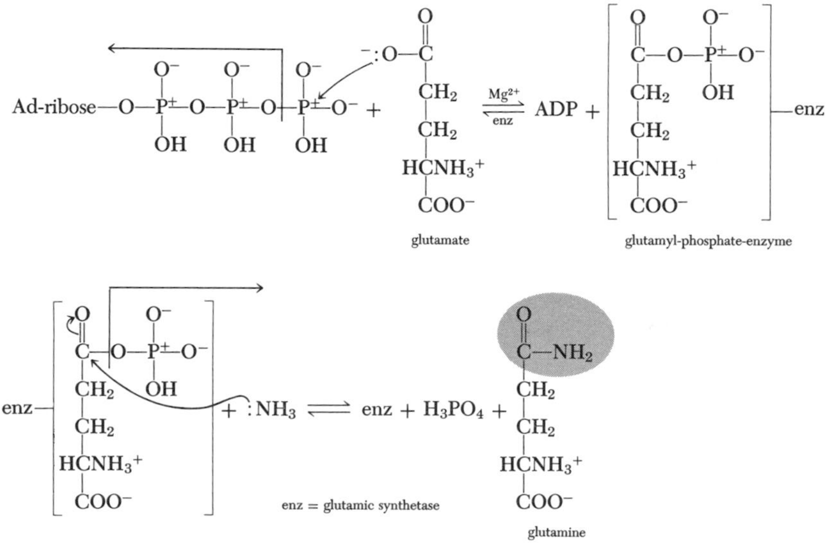

glutamate　　　　　　　　　glutamyl-phosphate-enzyme

enz = glutamic synthetase　　　　　glutamine

GLUTATHIONE

A tripeptide which occurs in yeast, plants, and animal tissues, this compound requires two discrete enzyme systems to form the two peptide bonds. The first enzyme, γ-glutamyl cysteine synthetase (a), catalyzes the condensation of glutamic acid and cysteine with the formation of the first peptide bond. Then a second enzyme, glutathione synthetase (b), adds glycine to the previously synthesized dipeptide to form the second peptide bond. In each step, the carboxyl group is presumably activated by ATP as already outlined for glutamine synthesis. Cysteine does not directly attack the γ-carboxyl group of glutamic acid since the —O^- of the carboxyl group is a poor leaving group; if a phosphate group is placed on the carboxyl carbon at the expense of ATP, then, as with glutamine synthesis, we have an excellent leaving group.

Note that CoASH is required in the synthesis of hippuric acid and that the reaction products include AMP and pyrophosphate; in the synthesis of glutamine and glutathione, ADP and inorganic phosphate are the reaction products and CoASH is not required. This indicates strongly that the peptide bond in hippuric acid is synthesized by a mechanism unlike that found in the latter two examples. Note moreover that the sequence of these simple steps is controlled by the speci-

(a)

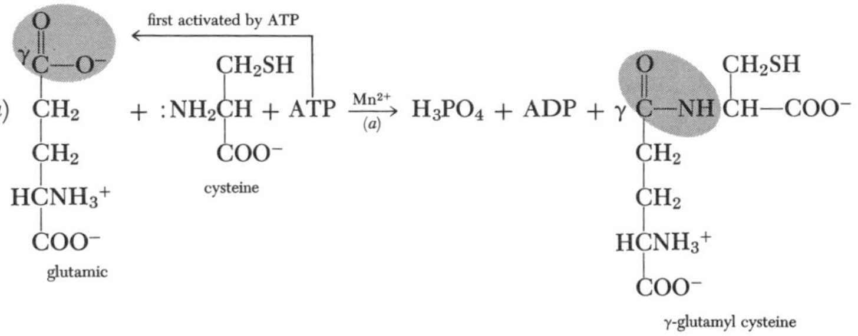

$$\gamma\overset{O}{\underset{}{C}}-O^- \quad + \; :NH_2CH + ATP \xrightarrow[(a)]{Mn^{2+}} H_3PO_4 + ADP + \gamma\overset{O}{\underset{}{C}}-NH$$

first activated by ATP

cysteine

glutamic

γ-glutamyl cysteine

(b)

first activated by ATP

glycine

γ-glutamyl-cysteinyl-
glycine or glutathione

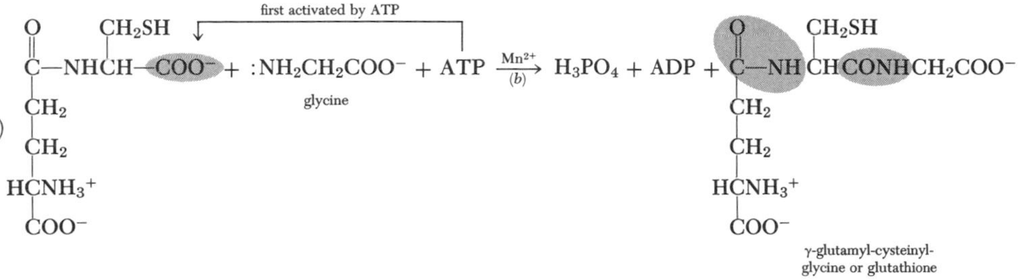

ficity of the enzymes involved. That is, in glutathione synthesis, the reverse peptide glycyl-glutamyl-cysteine is not produced because the specificities of the two enzyme systems control the order of addition. Thus, enzyme *a* catalyzes *only* reaction *a* and enzyme *b* catalyzes only reaction *b*. Hence the order of reaction is glutamic with cysteine and not glutamic with glycine.

Protein Synthesis

In examining the problem of protein synthesis we are immediately faced with the gigantic task of synthesizing a very complex molecule containing hundreds of L-amino acid residues in exactly the same sequence each time the molecule is produced. In other words, the mechanism of synthesis must have a precise coding system which automatically programs the insertion of only one specific amino acid residue in a specific position in the protein chain. The coding system, in determining the primary structure precisely, also establishes the secondary and tertiary structures of a given protein. This problem does not exist in the area of simple peptide or amide synthesis.

A vast literature has developed in the field during the last ten years. Among important contributors to this field are Hoagland, Berg, Zamecnik, Schweet, Monod, Ochoa, Nirenberg, Hurwitz, and Weiss. We cannot develop the historical aspects of this most interesting problem but will attempt to present the current concepts surrounding this field.*

The problem can be divided into four general areas: (a) amino acid activation; (b) transfer of the amino acid to a preliminary coding system, the soluble RNA (*s*-RNA); (c) the controlled synthesis of messenger RNA (*m*-RNA) by DNA; and (d) the transfer and complexing of *m*-RNA to the surface of the ribosomal protein and the condensation of the amino acid residues associated with *s*-RNA to form the primary structure of a protein at or near this *m*-RNA-ribosomal complex.

ACTIVATION OF AMINO ACID

The twenty amino acids commonly found in protein structures must undergo an initial activation step, which also involves a selection and preliminary screening of amino acids. Thus D-isomers and certain amino acids such as γ-methylene glutamic acid, β-alanine, and diamino pimelic acid, which are used for other purposes in the cell, are rejected at this stage. Each amino acid of the twenty normally found in proteins has its own specific activation enzyme system. Our diagram indicates what the step involves.

$$\underset{\text{(aa)}}{\text{ATP} + \text{amino acid}} \xrightarrow[\text{Mn}^{2+}]{\text{enzyme}} \underset{\substack{\text{amino acid-adenylate-}\\\text{enzyme complex}}}{\text{aa-AMP-enz}} + \underset{\text{pyrophosphate}}{\text{P—P}}$$

Mechanism:

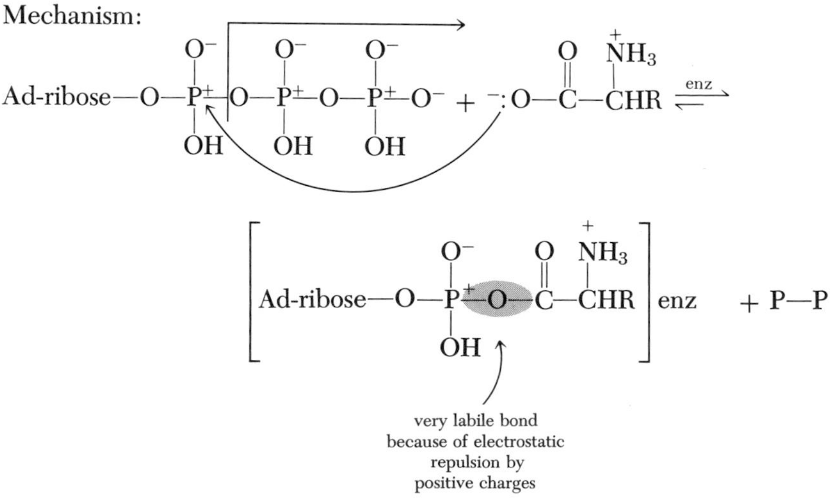

Ad-ribose—O—P—O—P—O—P—O⁻ + ⁻:O—C—CHR
enz
Ad-ribose—O—P—O—C—CHR
enz
+ P—P
very labile bond
because of electrostatic
repulsion by
positive charges

* The reader is warned that in this extremely active field the following discussion may soon be outmoded (March, 1962) and is therefore encouraged to seek for himself the current thoughts about this subject.

Amino acyl adenylates are extremely reactive and remain associated with the parent enzyme. The great lability is associated with the large positive charge on the amino group adjacent to the positive phosphorous atom resulting in a strong electrostatic repulsion and a subsequent labilization of the P—O—C bond.

TRANSFER TO A PRELIMINARY CODING SYSTEM

The amino acyl adenylate-enzyme complex now is ready to transfer the amino acid residue to a suitable coding acceptor. This important acceptor is a soluble ribonucleic acid of relatively small molecular weight. It has about 80 to 100 nucleotide residues connected to form a structure with a mol wt of about 25,000 to 30,000. There are at least twenty different ribonucleic acid acceptors (called soluble RNA or s-RNA; transfer RNA or t-RNA), each specific for its particular amino acid. Of great interest is that each s-RNA is similar to the others in that the first base, guanine, and the last three bases are identical in every s-RNA so far studied.

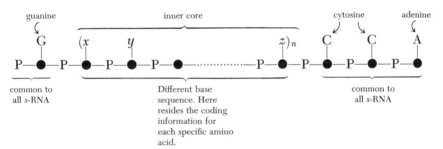

The detailed structure is shown in the next diagram. Note carefully the structure of the terminal adenine-ribose moiety (the shaded area with two vicinal hydroxy groups), since it is at this site that the amino acid-AMP-enz transfers its amino acid residue to its specific s-RNA (next page).

It is not definitely known whether the amino acid residue is on the $2'$- or $3'$-hydroxyl group of the ribosyl moiety, but regardless of which position is occupied, what appears to be an ester linkage of some stability is in actual fact a very labile amino acid residue that is readily hydrolyzed off at pH 10 at room temperature. The amino acid residue is hence energetically in a position to be readily transferred to a suitable acceptor for peptide bond formation. s-RNA is unlike m-RNA, to be discussed next, in that it is of cytoplasmic origin, smaller in molecular weight than m-RNA, and its synthesis is not under the control of DNA.

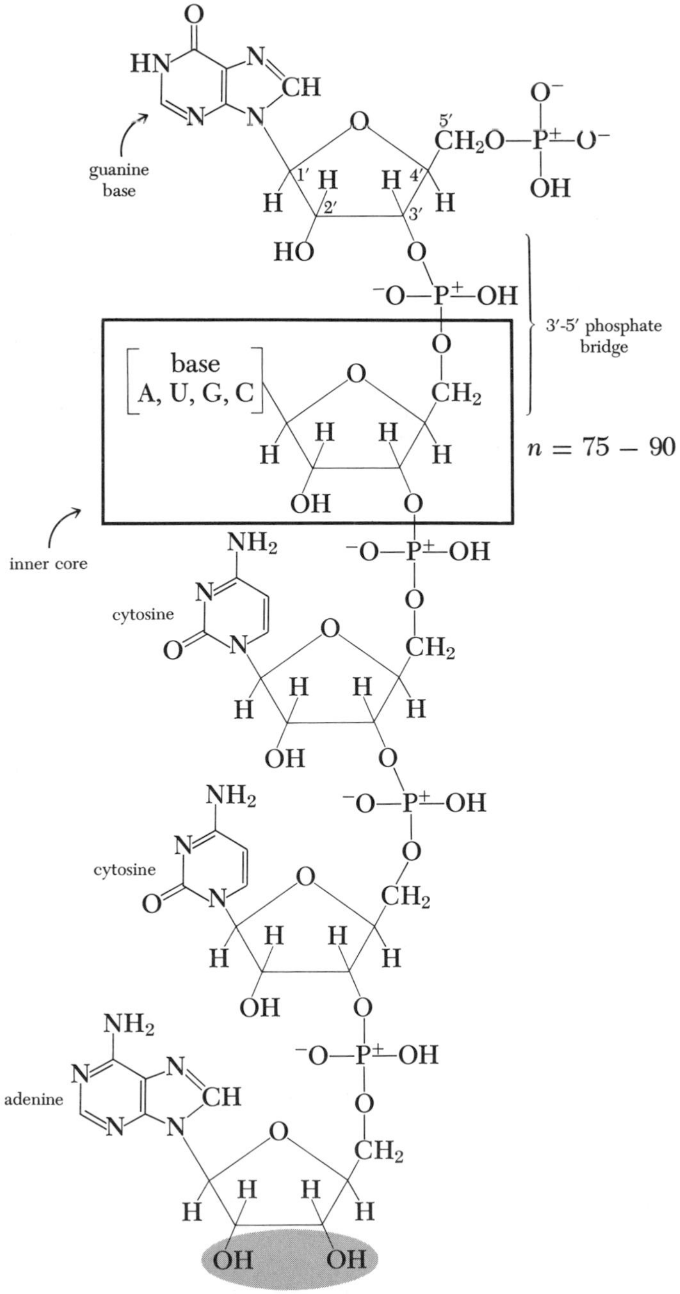
guanine base
3′-5′ phosphate bridge
base
A, U, G, C
n = 75 – 90
inner core
cytosine
cytosine
adenine

Mechanism:

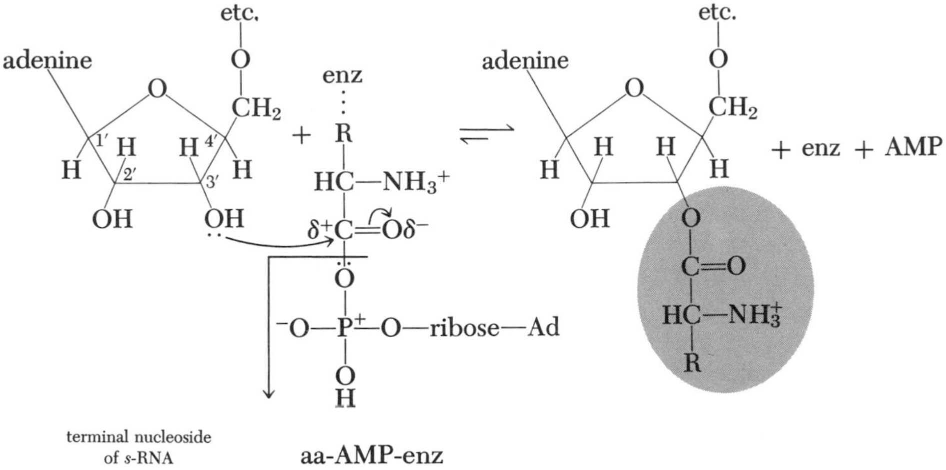

terminal nucleoside
of *s*-RNA   aa-AMP-enz

$$s\text{-RNA} + \text{aa-AMP-enz} \rightleftharpoons \text{aa-}s\text{-RNA} + \text{AMP} + \text{enz}$$

CONTROLLED SYNTHESIS OF MESSENGER RNA

The third step involves the transfer of genetic information from the specific gene to the site of protein synthesis; the latter is the surface of the ribosomal particles which are associated with the endoplasmic reticulum in the cytoplasm.   There is now excellent evidence that the DNA associated with a specific gene—a structural gene in Monod's terminology—can transfer its information, which in turn governs the precise sequence of amino acids in a specific protein, through the agency of a very labile, short-lived ribonucleic acid called messenger RNA (*m*-RNA).   The evidence supporting this conclusion is based in part on the following observations:

(1) In 1957, Volkin and Astrachan of the Oak Ridge National Laboratories discovered that a small fraction of the total RNA of *E. coli* infected with phage T-2 had a high rate of synthesis and had a base ratio complementing that of phage T-2 RNA.   In 1960, J. Hurwitz of New York University and S. Weiss of the University of Chicago discovered an enzyme, RNA-polymerase, in extracts of *E. coli*, that rapidly incorporated ribonucleoside triphosphates into a polyribonucleotide, provided DNA was present.   Of great interest was the observation that the newly synthesized RNA had a base composition precisely complementing that of

the DNA primer. Thus when polythymidylic acid was used as a primer, only a polyadenylic acid was formed. The DNA primer was obviously functioning as a template with its specific code imprinted onto the template on which the RNA was being assembled. This RNA, controlled in its synthesis by DNA, had all the properties necessary for the transfer of information from a suitable gene (See Chapter 14 for additional discussion).

(2) A molecular complex of DNA and RNA has been isolated from *Neurospora crassa* and is considered to be an intermediate in the expression of genetic information. This complex apparently consists of a hydrogen-bonded helix consisting of two strands of DNA and one strand of RNA. It thus consists of a triple-stranded hybrid molecule. It is assumed that this complex is the intermediate involved in the formation of messenger RNA; the DNA programs its information to the *m*-RNA as it is being assembled. This complex presumably breaks up with a separation of the single-stranded *m*-RNA and the double-stranded, helical DNA.

THE FINAL STEPS IN PROTEIN SYNTHESIS

In the final stages of protein synthesis, *m*-RNA with a mol wt of approximately 300,000 moves away from its DNA template and associates for a very brief period of time with the surface of the ribosomal nucleoprotein. At this point the amino acid-*s*-RNA complexes line up as dictated by the code carried by the *m*-RNA for the synthesis of a specific type of protein. In the presence of ATP, GTP, Mg^{2+}, GSH, and a soluble transfer enzyme, peptide bonds are formed at a very rapid rate. The newly formed polypeptide or protein separates as does the discharged *s*-RNA; the latter is then ready to be recharged with specific amino acids. In the meantime the *m*-RNA depolymerizes and loses all its information capability. New *m*-RNA molecules are formed, however, with new coding information. There is good evidence that the ribosomal nucleoprotein functions in establishing and stabilizing the conditions for the critical polymerization sequence to take place. But no informational coding is found in the RNA of the ribosomes. Thus ribosomes of *E. coli* can be used to make hemoglobin from amino acids, provided *m*-RNA from *reticulocytes* is added to the reaction mixture. RNA from tobacco mosaic virus can be added to *E. coli* ribosomes and control thereby the synthesis of tobacco mosaic virus protein in the presence of amino acids.

The coding problem for each amino acid has been attacked with great vigor by many workers in the field. The breakthrough was made in 1961 by M. W. Nirenberg of the National Institutes of Health. In a classical experiment, he employed a system from *E. coli* which consisted of a centrifuged supernatant solution and ribosomes supplemented with *s*-RNA.   To this system he added a mixture of radioactive amino acids and polyuridylic acid (poly-U) which had been prepared by the action of polynucleotide phosphorylase on UDP.   From this complex mixture of amino acids, the only amino acid incorporated into an acid-insoluble fraction consisting of newly synthesized protein was phenylalanine. The product proved to be polyphenylalanine.   Nirenberg correctly concluded that the synthetic poly-U was in effect serving as *m*-RNA and was providing the information which specified that only phenylalanyl-*s*-RNA units should become associated with ribosomal nucleoprotein for peptide formation.   By this method, randomly mixed polynucleotides were prepared by the addition of varying amounts of CDP, ADP, or GDP together with UDP to polynucleotide phosphorylase.   When the synthetic RNA polymers of different base composition were added to the test system we have described, different amino acids were incorporated into the proteins.   A minimum coding ratio of three nucleotide bases for each amino acid was determined, although the precise order of the base in each triplet code is not known as yet.   Table 15-1 lists those determined by both Nirenberg's group and Ochoa's group at New York University.

The entire process of protein synthesis can now be summarized.   The

Table 15-1.   Nucleotide Composition of Coding Unit

Amino Acid	Base Composition° of Synthetic *m*-RNA
Phenylalanine	UUU
Valine	UG (U > G)
Leucine	UG, UC (U > G, U > C)
Cysteine	UG
Tryptophan	UGG
Glutamic	UGC
Methionine	UG
Glycine	UGG
Arginine	UGC
Alanine	UGC
Serine	UC, UGC, (U > C or G)
Proline	UC (U > C)
Tyrosine	UA (U > A)
Isoleucine	UA
Lysine	UA (U > A)

° Except for the phenylalanine code, the order of bases is not specified in *m*-RNA.

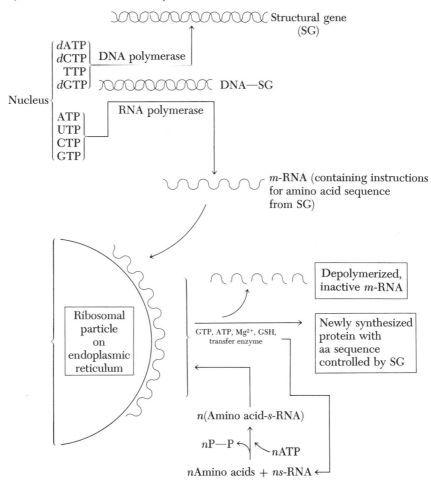

Fig. 15-3. The current scheme for the biosynthesis of proteins (as of fall, 1962).

molecular structure of a protein is of course related to the structure of a specific gene with its specific sequence of bases, the structural gene. The structural gene transfers its information to its m-RNA through the agency of the RNA polymerase. In turn, the amino acid activating enzyme, s-RNA, and the transfer system associated with ribosomal particles provide additional critical information so that identical molecules can be synthesized. Once the primary structure of the protein is formed with its ionic, hydrophilic, hydrophobic, and sulfhydryl groups distributed along the peptide chain as dictated by the DNA code, the secondary and tertiary structures develop spontaneously as the only ones that satisfy the restrictive stereochemical requirements. Thus only one *stable* tertiary structure is possible for any given amino acid sequence, and the amino acid sequence is determined precisely by one particular gene.

REFERENCES

1. *Metabolic Pathways,* edited by David M. Greenberg, Academic Press, New York, 1961, Vol. 2.

   An excellent collection of chapters on amino acid metabolism and protein synthesis.

2. M. B. Hoagland in *The Nucleic Acids,* edited by E. Chargaff and J. N. Davidson, Academic Press, New York, 1960, Chapter 37.

   A good summary of the problems of protein synthesis by an expert in the field.

3. Anfinsen, C. B., *The Molecular Basis of Evolution,* New York, John Wiley and Sons, 1959.

   This short book integrates the fields of genetics, nucleic acids, and proteins in a very stimulating manner. Recommended for the inquisitive, more advanced student.

4. B. J. Bell and J. K. Grant, editors, in Biochemical Society Symposia 21, *The Structure and Biosynthesis of Macromolecules,* Cambridge, Cambridge University Press, 1962.

   Three excellent chapters in this book should be read by the student. They are: "Biochemical Aspects of Polynucleotide Biosynthesis," by J. N. Davidson (pp. 29–44); "Structure of Proteins," by M. F. Perutz (pp. 80–87); and "Biosynthesis of Adaptive Enzymes," by J. Monod, F. Jacob, and F. Gros (pp. 104–132).

Part III

Integration of Metabolism

Sixteen

Integration of Carbohydrate, Lipid, and Protein Metabolism

Three Main Phases of Energy Production

At this point it is advisable to review what is known about the general aspects of the intermediary metabolism of fats, carbohydrates, and proteins. Since these three types of foodstuffs are the chief energy sources for most living organisms, it is encouraging to note that considerable integration of information is possible. Krebs and Kornberg have emphasized that, although many different compounds can serve as foodstuffs, the number of reactions involved in obtaining energy from these compounds is astonishingly small, whether the organism involved is animal, higher plant, or micro-organism. Thus nature has practiced great economy in the processes developed for handling these compounds. These authors divide substrate degradation into three phases, as indicated in Table 16-1.

In phase 1, polysaccharides, which serve as an energy source for many organisms, are hydrolyzed to monosaccharides, usually hexoses. Similarly proteins can be hydrolyzed to their component amino acids, and triglycerides, which make up the major fraction of the lipid food sources, are hydrolyzed to glycerol and fatty acids. These processes are, for the most part, hydrolytic, and the energy released as the reactions occur is made available to the organism as heat.

In phase 2 the monosaccharides, glycerol, fatty acids, and amino acids are further degraded to three compounds by processes which may result in the formation of some energy-rich phosphate compounds. Thus in glycolysis the hexoses are converted to pyruvate and then to acetyl-CoA by reactions involving the formation of a limited number of high-energy phosphate bonds, as described in Chapter 9. Similarly, in phase 2, the long-chain fatty acids are oxidized to acetyl-CoA (Chap-

Table 16-1. The Main Phases of Energy Production from Foodstuffs.

Outline of Chemical Change

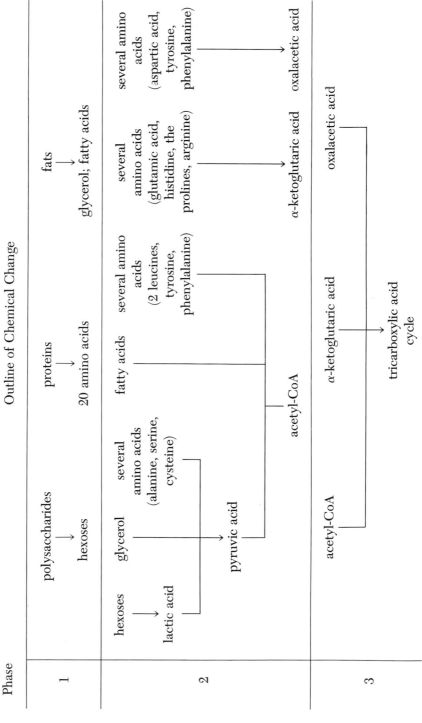

ter 13). Glycerol obtained from hydrolysis of triglycerides is converted to pyruvate and acetyl-CoA by means of the glycolytic sequence.

For the amino acids the situation is somewhat different. In phase 2 some amino acids (alanine, serine, cysteine) are converted to pyruvate on degradation, and thus acetyl-CoA formation is predicted if these amino acids are utilized by an organism for energy production. Other amino acids (the prolines, histidine, arginine) are converted to glutamic acid on degradation; this amino acid in turn undergoes transamination to yield α-ketoglutarate, a member of the tricarboxylic acid cycle. Aspartic acid is readily transaminated to form oxalacetate, another intermediate of the cycle. Some amino acids (the leucines) yield acetyl-CoA on degradation, and phenylalanine and tyrosine, on oxidative degradation, produce both acetyl-CoA and oxalacetic acid through fumaric acid.

Thus the carbon skeletons of essentially all the amino acids yield either an intermediate of the tricarboxylic acid cycle (oxalacetate, or α-ketoglutarate) or acetyl-CoA, which is in turn oxidized by means of the cycle. During the oxidation of these compounds energy-rich ATP is produced by oxidative phosphorylation. Specifically, twelve energy-rich bonds are produced for each mole of acetyl-CoA oxidized. Hence hundreds of organic compounds that can conceivably serve as food for biological organisms are utilized by their conversion to acetyl-CoA or an intermediate of the tricarboxylic acid cycle and their subsequent oxidation by the cycle.

In considering the actual steps involved in making energy available to the organisms, the reactions of oxidative phosphorylation that occur during electron transport through the cytochrome system are quantitatively the most significant. Even here an economy in the number of reactions is involved. As discussed in Chapter 12, the oxidation of substrates in the tricarboxylic acid cycle is accompanied by the reduction of either a pyridine or a flavin nucleotide. It is the oxidation of the reduced nucleotide by molecular oxygen in the presence of mitochondria that results in the formation of the energy-rich ATP. As pointed out, three phosphorylations occur during the transfer of a pair of electrons from NADH to O_2. We have discussed only three other reactions leading to the production of energy-rich compounds where none previously existed before. These are (a) the formation of acyl-phosphate in the oxidation of triose phosphate (Chapter 9), (b) the formation of phosphoenol pyruvate (Chapter 9), and (c) the formation of thioesters (Chapter 11). It is indeed a beautiful design which permits the energy in the myriad foodstuffs to be trapped in only six different processes. Even here a single compound, ATP, is the energy-rich substance formed.

Interconversion of Carbohydrate, Lipid, and Protein

The interconversions among the three major foodstuffs may be summarized with the help of Figure 16-1 as follows. In this figure two reactions that are effectively irreversible are indicated by heavy unidirectional arrows.

(a) Carbohydrates are convertible to fats through the formation of acetyl-CoA.

(b) Carbohydrates may also be converted to certain amino acids (alanine, aspartic and glutamic acids), provided a supply of dicarboxylic acid is available for formation of the keto acid analogs of the amino acids. One source of dicarboxylic acids is the formation of malic acid from pyruvate, the reaction catalyzed by the malic enzyme, as shown in Figure 16-1. Another important source is the formation of oxalacetic acid from phosphoenol pyruvic acid, catalyzed by PEP carboxykinase (Chapter 11).

(c) Fat may be similarly converted to certain amino acids provided a source of dicarboxylic acid is available.

(d) Fat *cannot* be converted to carbohydrate by the reactions shown in Figure 16-1. This inability is due to the fact that the equivalent of the two carbon atoms acquired in acetyl-CoA have been lost as CO_2

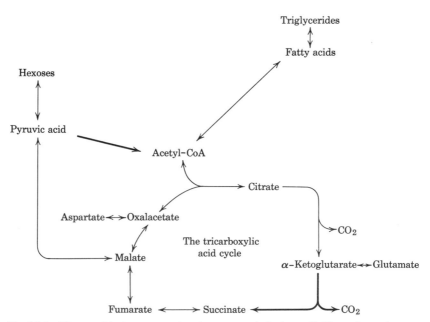

Fig. 16-1. The possible interconversions between carbohydrates, lipids, and certain amino acids.

prior to the production of the dicarboxylic acids.   Note, however, that the glyoxylate cycle (discussed in Chapter 13) can enable an organism to form carbohydrate from fat, as it does, for instance, in plants, some bacteria, and some molds.

(e) The naturally occurring amino acids are convertible to carbohydrates and lipids.   Each of the twenty amino acids may be classified as *glucogenic, ketogenic,* or both *glucogenic and ketogenic,* depending on the specific metabolism of the amino acid.   As an example, aspartic acid is glucogenic through formation of oxalacetic acid and its subsequent conversion to phosphoenol pyruvic acid.

REFERENCES

1. H. A. Krebs and H. L. Kornberg, *Ergebnisse der Physiologie, biologischen Chemie und experimentellen Pharmakologie, 49,* 212(1957).
    An excellent summary of the interrelation among carbohydrates, lipids, and proteins with emphasis on the energy transformation involved.

Seventeen

Photosynthesis

Introduction

The preceding chapters have dealt with the process of *respiration,* whereby carbon compounds are oxidized to CO_2 and H_2O and the energy in these compounds is made available to the cell. As has been done previously, the respiration of glucose by a cell may be represented as:

$$C_6H_{12}O_6 + 6O_2 \longrightarrow 6CO_2 + 6H_2O \qquad (17\text{-}1)$$

$$\Delta F' = -686,000 \text{ cal}$$

Although respiration is a fundamental process in nature, it would not be possible without another fundamental process known as *photosynthesis.* This is the process by which CO_2 and H_2O are converted back to the organic compounds associated with living cells. The conversion of CO_2 to glucose, for example, may be represented as the reverse of reaction 17-1 and will require the expenditure of a large amount of energy. As the term *photosynthesis* implies, the energy for this process is provided by light. Respiration and photosynthesis constitute the two parts of a fundamental cycle of nature—the carbon cycle. We shall deal with yet another fundamental cycle—the nitrogen cycle—in the following chapter.

Properties of Light

The study of radiant energy has disclosed that light may be treated as a wave of particles known as *photons.* The energy of these photons is inversely proportional to the wavelength λ of the wave of particles; in particular, the energy is equal to a constant (Planck's constant) h divided by λ, the wavelength. Thus the energy of blue light of short wavelength is greater than that of a corresponding amount of red light of longer wavelength. The actual unit of light commonly dealt with

Table 17-1.   Energy Content of Light of Different Wavelengths

Color of light	Wavelength, Å	Einstein, cal/mole
Far red	7500	37,800
Red	6500	43,480
Yellow	5900	48,060
Blue	4900	57,880
Ultraviolet	3950	71,800

is the *Einstein* or one mole, 6.06×10^{23}, of photons.   Table 17-1 lists the energy contents of Einsteins of different types of light.

One of the important properties of light is its ability to be absorbed. Briefly, the ability of a substance to absorb light is dependent upon its atomic structure.   In a stable atom the number of electrons surrounding the nucleus is equal to the positive charges (the atomic number) in the nucleus.   These electrons are arranged in different orbitals around the nucleus and those in the outer orbitals are less strongly attracted to the nucleus.   Still other orbitals further out from the nucleus can be occupied by these electrons, but energy is required to place an electron into these outer, unoccupied orbitals because the placement involves moving a negative charge further away from the positively charged nucleus.

One way in which the electron can acquire this energy and be moved into an outer or higher orbital is to absorb a photon of light.   When this occurs the atom is said to be in an excited state.   The amount of energy required to excite the atom depends on the energy difference between the two orbitals.   Thus only certain wavelengths of light—those having sufficient energy—will be effective in exciting the atom.

An atom in an excited state is not stable; the tendency is for the electron to return from the outer orbital to the lower energy level.   Its return is done in stages and is accompanied by the release of some of the energy acquired in excitation.   The initial act is to return to a slightly lower energy level from the excited state, a process accompanied by the production of heat.   When the electron returns to its original or ground state, the remainder of the excitation energy is released in a form of light known as fluorescence.   Since some of the energy of the excited state is released as heat, the amount represented by fluorescence is less than the energy acquired initially on excitation.   Therefore the fluorescing light will be of longer wavelength (and hence lower energy) than the absorbed light.

The Photosynthetic Apparatus

The compounds responsible for the absorption of light energy and its ultimate transformation into chemical energy are the *chlorophyll* pigments *a* and *b* and carotenoids. These pigments occur as protein or lipoprotein complexes within the chloroplast, an ellipsoidal structure with a long axis of 3–5 microns. The number of chloroplasts in a leaf cell of the higher green plants may be several hundred; in algae, there may be only one.

The structure of the chloroplast, as revealed by electron microscopy, is highly organized (see Figure 17-1). Small, disk-like bodies known as grana are distributed in layers, or lamellae, throughout the chloroplast. The detailed structure of an individual lamella is believed to consist of alternate layers of protein, which contain the necessary enzymes, and lipoidal layers, which contain the pigments and phospholipids. A sketch of these is indicated in Figure 17-2.

Little is known of the details of the quantum conversion process, whereby light energy is converted into chemical energy; consequently this is an active area of research today. It is apparent, however, that knowledge of the physical structure of the chloroplast is essential. Such knowledge will allow us to learn more of the manner in which the electrons of the chlorophyll molecule reach an excited state after absorbing light and utilize this excitation energy for the chemical reactions of

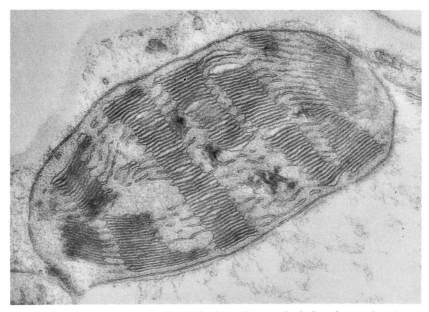

Fig. 17-1. Electron micrograph of a single chloroplast in a leaf of a tobacco plant (reproduced from T. E. Weier, *Am. J. Bot.*, 48, 615 (1961)).

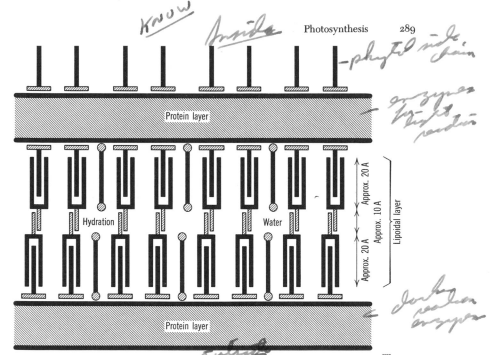

Fig. 17-2. Sketch of an individual lamella. The lipoidal layer is shown to contain ⊤ chlorophyll, ⫫ phospholipids, and ⌊ carotenoids. Model of Hubert, as modified by Frey-Wyssling and by Brown in *Plant Physiology*, Vol. 1A, 3 (1960), ed. by F. C. Steward, Academic Press, New York.

photosynthesis. Chlorophyll *a* is the one pigment common to all plants; it is tempting to postulate an essential role for it in all photosynthetic organisms.

chlorophyll *a*

$$C_{20}H_{39}O- = CH_3-CH(CH_3)-CH_2(CH_2CH_2-CHCH_2)_2-CH_2-CH_2-C(CH_3)=CHCH_2OH$$

phytol

As shown in our diagram, chlorophyll a is a magnesium porphyrin which contains an aliphatic alcohol, phytol, as an ester of the propionic acid side chain; chlorophyll b contains a formyl (—CHO) group instead of a methyl group at position 3.

Utilization of H_2O in Photosynthesis

As indicated in reaction 17-2 the formation of carbohydrate in photosynthesis may be represented as an endergonic oxidation reduction reaction. The reducing agent is H_2O, which is oxidized to O_2; the oxi-

$$CO_2 + H_2O \xrightarrow{\ h\nu\ } C(H_2O) + O_2 \qquad (17\text{-}2)$$

oxidized

reduced

$$\Delta F' = +118{,}000 \text{ cal}$$

dizing agent, CO_2, is reduced to the level of carbohydrate represented as $C(H_2O)$. The necessary energy, 118,000 cal/mole of CO_2 reduced, is supplied by light ($h\nu$).

In 1905, Blackman obtained evidence that there was a nonphotochemical reaction involving CO_2 in photosynthesis. It was postulated that the CO_2 could be incorporated into some product independently of light action and that this product in turn was reduced by cofactors produced in light-dependent reactions. As a result, it is possible to consider reaction 17-2 from the standpoint of (a) how H_2O is utilized as a reducing agent in photosynthesis, and (b) how CO_2 is eventually converted to a reduced carbon compound.

A study of photosynthetic organisms other than green plants has provided information on the manner of utilization of H_2O. The purple sulfur bacteria utilize H_2S instead of H_2O as a reducing agent in photosynthesis; elemental sulfur is produced and no oxygen is formed.

$$CO_2 + 2H_2S \xrightarrow{\ h\nu\ } C(H_2O) + 2S + H_2O \qquad (17\text{-}3)$$

C. B. Van Niel at Stanford University pointed out the similarity of this reaction to the one which occurs in green plants and suggested that a general reaction for photosynthesis may be represented as

$$CO_2 + 2H_2A \xrightarrow{\ h\nu\ } C(H_2O) + 2A + H_2O \qquad (17\text{-}4)$$

where H_2A is a general expression for a reducing agent which, in the two examples cited, may be H_2O or H_2S. Some of the purple sulfur bacteria can also utilize compounds such as thiosulfate or selenium as reducing agents. The reaction with thiosulfate may be written as:

$$2CO_2 + Na_2S_2O_3 + 5H_2O \xrightarrow{h\nu} 2C(H_2O) + 2H_2O + 2NaHSO_4$$

Thus it is apparent that the reducing agent need not contain hydrogen itself, but simply must be capable of furnishing electrons for the eventual reduction of CO_2. Since H_2S is a much stronger reducing agent than $Na_2S_2O_3$ or H_2O, we might expect that less light energy would be required for photosynthesis with H_2S as the reducing agent than with NaS_2O_3 or H_2O. Experimentally the same amount of light energy is required, however, regardless of the nature of the external reducing agent. This caused van Niel to postulate that the primary reaction is the same in all organisms and that it consists of the splitting of a molecule of H_2O to yield a reducing agent [H] and an oxidizing agent [OH].

$$H_2O \xrightarrow{h\nu} [H] + [OH] \tag{17-5}$$

The use of [H] does not imply that the reducing agent is a hydrogen atom or radical, but simply the existence of some form of potential reducing power. The [OH] similarly represents potential oxidizing power which, in green plants, reacts with H_2O to form O_2, and in purple sulfur bacteria reacts with H_2S to form sulfur. Similarly, it reacts with $Na_2S_2O_3$ to oxidize this compound to $NaHSO_4$.

$$\textit{green plants:} \quad 2H_2O + 4[OH] \longrightarrow O_2 + 4H_2O \tag{17-6}$$

$$\textit{purple bacteria:} \quad 2H_2S + 4[OH] \longrightarrow 2S + 4H_2O \tag{17-7}$$

An interesting consequence of reactions 17-2 and 17-3 (or 17-6 and 17-7) is that the O_2 evolved in green-plant photosynthesis must be derived from H_2O and not from the CO_2. This was confirmed experimentally by Ruben and Kamen in a classical experiment, in which H_2O labeled with the isotope O^{18} was utilized in photosynthesis by algae. The oxygen produced under these conditions contained the same concentration of O^{18} as the H_2O. These relationships are indicated as follows:

$$CO_2 + 2H_2O^{18} \xrightarrow{h\nu} C(H_2O) + H_2O + O_2^{18}$$

Note that the reaction is written as both requiring and producing H_2O; this is necessary in order to indicate the proper stoichiometry in the formation of O_2.

The Hill Reaction

In 1937, Robin Hill of Cambridge University attempted to study the reactions of photosynthesis by working with isolated chloroplasts rather than intact plants. He reasoned that more information might be obtained if grana or chloroplasts, which contain the chlorophylls, were studied separately from the cell. It would have been ideal if the chloroplasts could have carried out both the oxidation of H_2O and the reduction of CO_2 to organic carbon compounds. This was not accomplished at that time. Nevertheless, chloroplasts were able to produce O_2 photochemically in the presence of a suitable oxidizing agent, potassium ferric oxalate. In this reaction the ferric ion substitutes for CO_2 as an oxidizing agent during the photolysis of H_2O:

$$4Fe^{3+} + 2H_2O \xrightarrow[\text{chloroplasts}]{h\nu} 4Fe^{2+} + 4H^+ + O_2$$

This observation was of fundamental importance for it permitted the study of the nature of [H] and [OH] in isolated chloroplasts; O_2 was evolved in an amount stoichiometrically equivalent to the reducing agent added. The reaction is known as the *Hill reaction*, and potassium ferric oxalate is known as a *Hill reagent*. Other compounds were subsequently shown to serve as Hill reagents in studies on isolated chloroplasts; Warburg showed that benzoquinone could function as such:

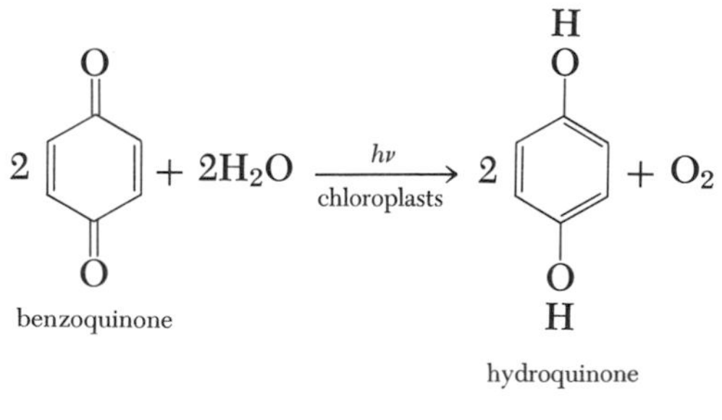

benzoquinone

hydroquinone

Oxidized dyes were later shown to function as Hill reagents by being reduced. Although this approach was criticized because the substances that could serve as Hill reagents were not physiologically important compounds, the properties of these reactions were extensively studied.

In 1952, three American laboratories reported that $NADP^+$ (and NAD^+) could serve as Hill reagents in the presence of spinach grana and light. With intact chloroplasts $NADP^+$ was preferentially reduced. Thus for the first time a physiologically important compound could function as a Hill reagent. This observation was of prime importance; it constituted a mechanism whereby reduced pyridine nucleotides were produced as the result of a light-dependent reaction.

$$\text{2NADP}^+ + 2\text{H}_2\text{O} \xrightarrow[\text{chloroplasts}]{h\nu} 2\text{NADPH} + 2\text{H}^+ + \text{O}_2 \qquad (17\text{-}8)$$

Numerous examples have been given earlier in this text of the ability of NADPH and NADH to reduce various substrates in the presence of the proper enzyme. As will be described, NADPH and NADH are needed in the reduction of intermediates in the conversion of CO_2 to carbohydrates in photosynthesis. There was hence no reason to doubt the physiological significance of the ability of the pyridine nucleotides to serve as Hill reagents.

In 1954, Arnon of the University of California reported that whole chloroplasts isolated under suitable conditions could carry out the reduction of CO_2 to carbohydrates in the light unaided by other cellular components. This Hill reaction involving CO_2 as a Hill reagent was accompanied by the oxidation of H_2O to O_2 (equation 17-2). Thus an extremely important compound, CO_2, was added to the list of physiologically significant Hill reagents.

Path of Carbon

The series of reactions whereby CO_2 is eventually converted to carbohydrates and other organic compounds has been largely worked out in the laboratories of Calvin, Horecker, and Racker. The problem was not extensively pursued, however, until the first product into which CO_2 is incorporated in photosynthesis was identified by Calvin and his associates. This research is an outstanding example of the application of new techniques by excellent scientific investigators to the solution of an extremely complicated problem.

The basic experimental approach was as follows: In a plant which is carrying out photosynthesis at a steady rate, CO_2 is being converted to glucose through a series of intermediates.

$$CO_2 \longrightarrow \begin{array}{c}\text{compound}\\A\end{array} \longrightarrow \begin{array}{c}\text{compound}\\B\end{array} \longrightarrow \begin{array}{c}\text{compound}\\C\end{array} \longrightarrow \text{glucose}$$

$$\longrightarrow \begin{array}{c}\text{compound}\\X\end{array} \longrightarrow \text{glucose}$$

If, at time zero, radioactive CO_2 ($C^{14}O_2$) is introduced into the system, some of the labeled carbon atoms will be converted to glucose, and during the time for this to occur all the intermediates will be labeled. If, after a relatively short period of time, the photosynthesizing plant is plunged into hot alcohol to inactivate its enzymes and stop all reactions, the labeled carbon atom will have had time to make its way through only the first few intermediates. If the time interval is short enough, the labeled carbon atoms will have made their way only into the first stable intermediate, compound A, and only the first product of CO_2 fixation will be labeled.

In 1946, carbon-14 was made available in appreciable amounts from the Atomic Energy Commission. Moreover, the technique of paper chromatography (see Appendix 3 for description) was in full development and provided a means for separating the large number of cell constituents which occur in a plant. With these tools Calvin's group was able to identify the early stable intermediates in the path of carbon from CO_2 to glucose. They used suspensions of algae, *Scenedesmus* or *Chlorella*, which were grown at a constant rate in the presence of light and CO_2. $C^{14}O_2$ was introduced into the reaction mixture at zero time and a period of time was allowed to elapse. The cells were then extracted with boiling alcohol and the soluble constituents of the alcohol solution were analyzed by paper chromatography. When the algae were exposed to $C^{14}O_2$ for 30 seconds, hexose phosphates, triosephosphates, and phosphoglyceric acid were labeled. With longer periods, these compounds as well as amino acids and organic acids were labeled. With 5-second exposure most of the radioactive carbon was located in 3-phosphoglyceric acid and, within this compound, the carboxyl group contained the majority of the radioactivity.

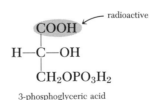

3-phosphoglyceric acid

This result suggested that 3-phosphoglyceric acid was formed by the carboxylation of some unknown compound containing two carbon atoms. Attempts to demonstrate any such acceptor molecule failed, however. More careful examination of the early products of photosynthesis disclosed that sedoheptulose-7-phosphate and ribulose diphosphate were also present as labeled compounds, and this in turn suggested that the sugars might be involved in forming the acceptor molecule for CO_2.

During this period, the reactions of the pentose phosphate pathway (Chapter 10) were being elucidated in other laboratories and the possible relationships between tetroses, pentoses, and heptoses established. More careful examination of the labeling of carbon-14 in these sugars permitted Calvin's laboratory to postulate that a carbon reduction cycle (Figure 17-3) was operating in photosynthesis. As can be seen this cycle is based largely on reactions catalyzed by enzymes previously encountered in glycolysis (glyceraldehyde-3-phosphate dehydrogenase, aldolase, and triose phosphate isomerase) and pentose phosphate metabolism (transketolase, phosphopentoisomerase, and phosphoketopento-epimerase). These enzymes are known to occur in photosynthetic tissues.

A key reaction in the carbon reduction cycle is the carboxylation *not of a 2-carbon compound, but of a 5-carbon compound,* ribulose-1-5-diphosphate, to yield 2 moles of 3-phosphoglyceric acid.

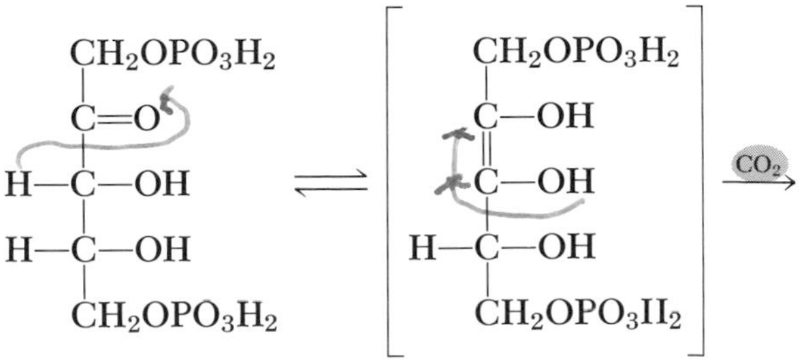

D-ribulose-1-5-diphosphate   enediol

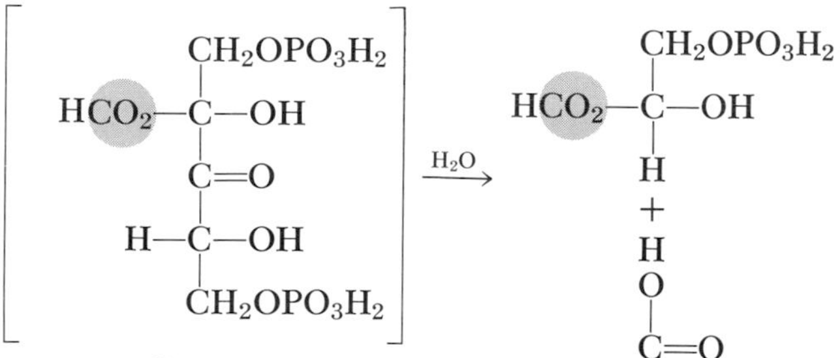

β-keto acid intermediate   two molecules of 3-phosphoglyceric acid

In the presence of the enzyme *carboxydismutase*, CO_2 adds to the enediol of ribulose diphosphate to form an unstable β-keto acid, which undergoes hydrolysis to form *two* molecules of phosphoglyceric acid. Carboxydismutase has been purified as a homogeneous protein by

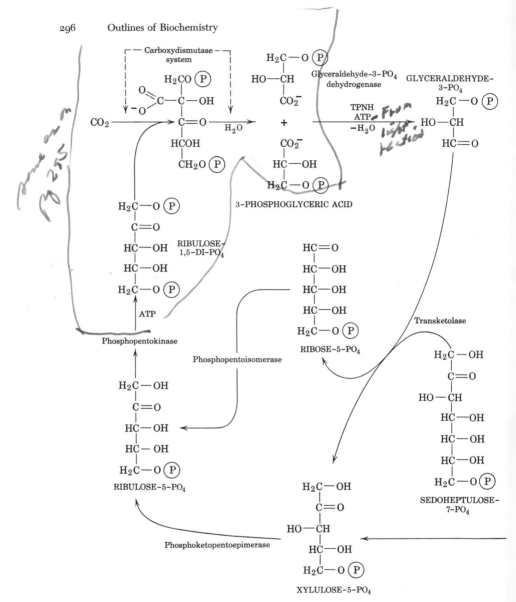

Fig. 17-3. The photosynthetic carbon reduction cycle. From J. A. Bassham and M. Calvin, *The Path of Carbon in Photosynthesis*, Prentice-Hall, Englewood Cliffs, N. J. (1957). Reprinted by permission.

Horecker from spinach leaves, where it apparently constitutes 5 to 10 per cent of the soluble protein. The ribulose-1-5-diphosphate required as a substrate is produced by the action of ATP on ribulose-5-phosphate in the presence of an appropriate *kinase*.

When the reactions of the carbon reduction cycle are tabulated as

Dark reaction

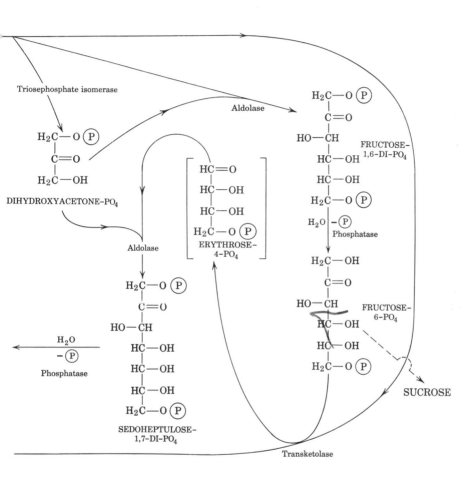

shown in Table 17-2, it is possible to account for the conversion of 3 moles of CO_2 to glyceraldehyde-3-phosphate. As can be seen, this requires a source of both ATP and reduced pyridine nucleotide. The photochemical reduction of pyridine nucleotides in the Hill reaction can furnish the necessary reducing agent. If part of the reduced pyridine nucleotide were oxidized by molecular O_2 through the cytochrome electron transport system, oxidative phosphorylation could result in the formation of ATP (Chapter 12). In fact, it has been possible to demonstrate the reductive carboxylation of CO_2 to hexose phosphate in the presence of spinach chloroplasts, a soluble cytoplasmic fraction (which presumably contains the necessary enzymes of the pentose phosphate pathway), spinach mitochondria, and catalytic quantities of ATP and $NADP^+$. In further support of the overall reaction found in Table 17-2, the labeling pattern predicted from the reactions indicated is for the most part, the one found experimentally.

know

Table 17-2.   Stoichiometry of the Carbon Reduction Cycle

41 3 Pentosephosphate + 3ATP $\longrightarrow$ 3 ribulose diphosphate + 3ADP

1 3 Ribulose diphosphate + $3CO_2$ + $3H_2O$ $\longrightarrow$ 6 phosphoglycerate

2 6 Phosphoglycerate + 6ATP $\longrightarrow$ 6 diphosphoglycerate + 6ADP

3 6 Diphosphoglycerate + 6NADPH + $6H^+$ $\longrightarrow$ 6 glyceraldehyde-3-phosphate + $6NADP^+$ + $6H_3PO_4$

4 2 Glyceraldehyde-3-phosphate $\longrightarrow$ 2 dihydoxyacetone phosphate

5 1 Dihydroxyacetone phosphate + 1 glyceraldehyde-3-phosphate $\longrightarrow$ 1 fructose diphosphate

6 1 Fructose diphosphate + H_2O $\longrightarrow$ 1 fructose phosphate + H_3PO_4

7 1 Fructose phosphate + 1 glyceraldehyde-3-phosphate $\longrightarrow$ 1 tetrose phosphate + 1 pentose phosphate

8 1 Tetrose phosphate + 1 dihydroxyacetone phosphate $\longrightarrow$ heptulose diphosphate

9 1 Heptulose diphosphate + H_2O $\longrightarrow$ 1 Heptulose phosphate + H_3PO_4

10 1 Heptulose phosphate + 1 glyceraldehyde-3-phosphate $\longrightarrow$ 2 pentose-phosphate

Sum: $3CO_2$ + 9ATP + $5H_2O$ + 6NADPH + $6H^+$ $\longrightarrow$ 1 glyceraldehyde-3-phosphate + 9ADP + $6NADP^+$ + $8H_3PO_4$

Photosynthetic Phosphorylation

As mentioned previously, the photolysis of H_2O leads to the production of reduced pyridine nucleotides. The reoxidation of the reduced pyridine nucleotide through the cytochrome electron transport system of mitochondria in turn could result in the production of ATP. It was possible in this manner to account for the production of the two coenzymes NADPH and ATP, required to drive the photosynthetic carbon reduction cycle of Figure 17-3. Recently Arnon and his associates have questioned whether ATP is so produced. When, in 1954, these workers discovered that chloroplasts isolated by special techniques could convert CO_2 to carbohydrates in the light, it was necessary to postulate that, in the absence of mitochondria, chloroplasts could synthesize ATP in a light-dependent reaction.

More recently chloroplasts have been shown to carry out two types of light-dependent phosphorylation reactions that result in ATP formation. The first type, *noncyclic photophosphorylation*, is associated with the production of an equivalent amount of NADPH formation and oxygen evolution. The overall reaction may be described as a phosphorylation of ADP that occurs simultaneously during a Hill reaction with $NADP^+$.

$$2NADP^+ + 2H_2O + 2ADP + 2H_3PO_4 \xrightarrow{h\nu}$$
$$2NADPH + 2H^+ + 2ATP + 2H_2O + O_2$$

In further studies of the reaction, Arnon discovered that chloroplasts could also catalyze the phosphorylation of ADP even if $NADP^+$ were omitted. This process does not involve the evolution of O_2; oxidizing agents such as $NADP^+$ need not be added. In the presence of FMN, which has been shown to be a cofactor for this *cyclic* photophosphorylation, the reaction proceeds anaerobically. The reaction may be written simply as

$$ADP + H_3PO_4 \xrightarrow{h\nu} ATP + H_2O$$

The two types of phosphorylation reaction are referred to as *photophosphorylations*. The details of the reactions are no more established than are those of oxidative phosphorylation. It is postulated, however, that photophosphorylations occur when an electron produced in the primary photochemical act traverses a chain of carriers similar to those of the electron transport chain in mitochondria. As shown in Figure 17-4, cyclic photophosphorylation involves the release of an electron from a chlorophyll *a* molecule in the excited state and its subsequent transfer to ferredoxin and then to a cytochrome by a cofactor such as FMN. The return of the electron to the excited chlorophyll molecule results in a phosphorylation reaction.

The process of cyclic photophosphorylation may be represented as a portion of the sequence of reactions involved in noncyclic photophosphorylation. In this latter process (Figure 17-4) the water dissociates to a proton and a OH^- ion. The OH^- ion reduces an excited chlorophyll *b* molecule to its ground state and simultaneously releases oxygen. The chlorophyll *b* molecule is excited by light and an electron, raised to an oxidation-reduction potential of about 0.0 v, reduces plastoquinone, a quinone occurring naturally in chloroplasts. The electron is now transferred along a cytochrome chain to which is associated a phosphorylation mechanism capable of coupling the phosphorylation of ADP with inorganic phosphate to ATP. The electron reduces an excited chlorophyll *a* to return it to the ground state. Another photon of light now strikes chlorophyll *a* with the ejection of electron being raised to an oxidation reduction potential of at least -0.423 v. Ferredoxin serves as the electron acceptor and in its reduced state will readily reduce $NADP^+$ to NADPH.

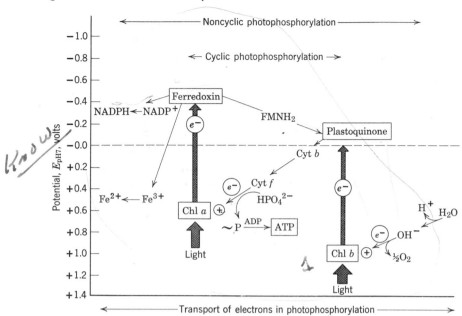

Fig. 17-4. Cyclic and noncyclic photophosphorylation as related to the scale of oxidation-reduction potentials.

The following important points should be noted:

(1) By absorption of photons of light, both chlorophyll a and chlorophyll b are excited and electrons are raised to a higher energy level or to a higher oxidation reduction potential where they become capable of reducing suitable acceptors.

(2) There appear to be two sites where light absorption can occur. (a) Excitation of chlorophyll b results in an electron which is raised to an oxidation potential sufficiently negative (about -0.0 v) to reduce the cytochrome sequence; (b) excitation of chlorophyll a gives rise to an electron having a potential of -0.432 v and in turn able to reduce NADP$^+$ to NADPH.°

(3) Noncyclic photophosphorylation takes in the entire range of reactions, from the ionization of water to the final transfer of an electron, derived originally from the hydroxyl ion of H_2O, to NADP$^+$. Cyclic

° Very recently Tagawa and Arnon have isolated a compound from spinach chloroplasts, ferredoxin, a remarkable iron-containing protein which is readily photoreduced. Its oxidation reduction potential is -0.432 v., the most electronegative electron carrier found in nature. In the presence of a chloroplast-bound flavoprotein, reduced ferredoxin readily reduces NADP$^+$ to NADPH.

photophosphorylation is of a more limited scope.   It involves only chlorophyll *a*, the cytochrome system and a pigment such as FMN.   No oxygen is formed nor is $NADP^+$ reduced.

Summary

In contrasting respiration with photosynthesis it is apparent that the uniqueness of the latter process lies chiefly in the photochemical reaction—the process by which the energy of light is utilized to produce reduced pyridine nucleotides and ATP.   Once these compounds are available the reactions employed in synthesizing the organic constituents of the cell are for the most part those which are also responsible for the degradation of these compounds.   Thus the living organism has at its disposal enzyme-catalyzed reactions which are mainly reversible, and the factor that determines whether synthesis or degradation occurs is the concentration of the individual reactants.

R E F E R E N C E S

1. J. A. Bassham and M. Calvin, *The Path of Carbon in Photosynthesis*, Prentice-Hall, Englewood Cliffs, N. J., 1957.
   This modest-sized book is an excellent summary of the investigations on the path of carbon in photosynthesis.
2. D. I. Arnon in *Light and Life*, edited by W. D. McElroy and B. Glass, The Johns Hopkins Press, Baltimore, 1961, p. 489.
   The discoverer of the process of photosynthetic phosphorylation describes the recent work and reviews the past efforts of his laboratory in a well-written article.
3. M. Calvin, *J. Theoret. Biol.* 2, 258(1961).
   This article describes some of the current ideas on the conversion of light energy into chemical energy in photosynthesis.

Eighteen

The Nitrogen Cycle

Introduction

A third fundamental process in addition to photosynthesis and respiration is that of *nitrogen fixation*. This process in turn is part of the cycle of reactions known as the *nitrogen cycle*. Many constituents of the living cell contain nitrogen; they include proteins, amino acids, nucleic acids, purines, pyrimidines, porphyrins, alkaloids, and vitamins. The nitrogen atoms of these compounds eventually travel the nitrogen cycle, in which the nitrogen of the atmosphere serves as a reservoir. Nitrogen is removed from the reservoir by the process of fixation; it is returned by the process of denitrification.

To give some measure of the magnitude of the chemical processes that occur, it has recently been estimated that 25×10^6 tons of nitrogen are removed yearly from the soils of the United States, chiefly by the harvesting of crops and to a small extent by the leaching of soils. To restore the fertility of the soil it is estimated that 3×10^6 tons of nitrogen are returned in the form of fertilizers (manure, urine, and commercial fertilizers). The restoration of an equal amount is accomplished by rainfall with the hydration of nitrogen oxides produced in the atmosphere by lightning storms. The most significant amount (10×10^6 tons of nitrogen) is returned through nitrogen fixation by biological organisms. Even so, it is apparent that a nitrogen deficit is developing and must be remedied if the fertility of the soil is to be maintained.

Several inorganic nitrogen compounds, as well as a myriad number of organic nitrogen compounds, can be considered as components of the nitrogen cycle. The former include N_2 gas, NH_3, nitrate ion (NO_3^-), nitrite ion (NO_2^-), and hydroxylamine (NH_2OH). At a glance it is apparent that the nitrogen atom can possess a variety of oxidation numbers. Some of these are:

	nitrate ion	nitrite ion	hyponitrite ion	nitrogen gas	hydroxyl- amine	ammonia
	NO_3^-	NO_2^-	$N_2O_2^{2-}$	N_2	NH_2OH	NH_3
oxidation number	$+5$	$+3$	$+1$	0	-1	-3

Thus, in nature, nitrogen may exist in either a highly oxidized form (NO_3^-) or a highly reduced state (NH_3).

Nonbiological Nitrogen Fixation

The term *fixation* is defined as the conversion of molecular N_2 into one of the inorganic forms just listed. The distinguishing feature of this process is the separation of the two atoms of N_2 which are triply bonded ($N{\equiv}N$). N_2 is an extremely stable molecule; it may be estimated that the energy required to sever the triple bond in this molecule is about 225 kcal, or three times the energy required to break the $C-C$ bond. An indication of the difficult nature of this reaction is seen in the conditions for the fixation of nitrogen in the Haber process, developed in Germany during World War I. The English naval blockade of Germany prevented German access to the Chilean nitrate fields, and it was necessary to develop another source of nitrate for their explosives. The Haber process involves the reaction of N_2 and H_2 at extreme temperatures and pressures to form NH_3. The latter then can be oxidized to HNO_3. The Haber process is used today for the fixation of N_2 by the chemical industry in the production of commercial fertilizer.

$$N_2 + H_3 \xrightarrow[\text{200 atm}]{500°C} 2NH_3$$

A second manner in which nitrogen may be fixed is through the electrical discharges that occur during lightning storms. During the discharge oxides of nitrogen are formed which are subsequently hydrated by water vapor and carried to earth as nitrites and nitrates.

$$N_2 + O_2 \longrightarrow 2NO \xrightarrow{O_2} 2NO_2$$

Although these processes are significant in the nitrogen economy, the major amount of N_2 fixed is fixed by living organisms.

Biological Nitrogen Fixation

The biological fixation of nitrogen is accomplished either by nonsymbiotic micro-organisms which can live independently of any other living thing or by certain bacteria living in *symbiosis* with higher plants. The former group includes aerobic organisms of the soil (*Azotobacter*), soil anaerobes (*Clostridium sp.*), photosynthetic bacteria (*Rhodospirillum rubrum*), and algae (*Myxophyceae*). The symbiotic system consists of *Rhizobia* living in symbiosis with legumes such as clover, alfalfa, and soy beans.   Legumes are not the only higher plants that can fix nitrogen symbiotically; 190 species of shrubs and trees, including the Sierra Sweet Bay, ceanothus, and alder, are nitrogen fixers.   Indeed, the fertility of high-altitude mountain lakes may be determined by groups of alder trees growing near their inlets.

An essential feature of symbiotic fixation is the nodules, which form on the roots of the plant.   The nodules, formed by the joint action of specific plants and specific bacteria, are thoroughly infected by the bacteria.   Neither the plant nor the bacteria can fix nitrogen when grown separately.   When the plants are grown in soil inoculated with the bacteria, root nodulation occurs and nitrogen fixation is possible. These nodules contain a pigment (leghemoglobin) similar to hemoglobin. It has been implicated in the nitrogen fixation reaction.

Despite the economic significance of the process, little is known of the reactions of biological fixation. NH_3 appears to be an early if not the initial product of nitrogen fixation by free-living bacteria and by the symbionts.   If N_2 labeled with nitrogen-15 isotope is made available for a short period of time to *Azotobacter* or excised root nodules from legumes, the first inorganic compound to acquire the isotope is NH_3. Similarly, the first organic compound to acquire a high concentration of labeled nitrogen is glutamic acid; the concentration of N^{15} in the amino acid is always less than that of any NH_3 which may be isolated, however.

Although the data indicate that N_2 is early converted to NH_3, it is difficult to believe that the overall reaction, which involves the addition of six electrons to the two nitrogen atoms, does not involve intermediates:

$$N_2 \xrightarrow{2e^-} ? \xrightarrow{2e^-} ? \xrightarrow{2e^-} 2NH_3$$

Very recently it has been possible to prepare cell-free extracts from the anaerobic bacterium *Clostridium pasteurianum* that will carry out the conversion of N_2 to NH_3.   In order for fixation to occur, pyruvic acid must be added to the extracts where it is oxidized to acetate, CO_2, and H_2.   The extracts can be separated into two different components; one, the HD component or hydrogen-donating system, catalyzes the breakdown of pyruvic acid.   The other component, the NA or nitrogen activation system, contains the enzymes for the conversion of N_2 to NH_3.   Each component is inactive alone and must be combined with the other for activity.   Of considerable interest is the observation that when the *Clostridia* are grown in the presence of NH_3 as the sole source of nitrogen, the HD system still occurs in the organism but the NA component is no longer found.

Although NH_3 is an early if not the first product of biological nitrogen fixation, it is not accumulated by organisms performing this process. In the case of bacteria such as *Azotobacter* it is probably utilized as the chief nitrogen source for growth of the bacterial cells. Specifically, the NH_3 will be incorporated into glutamic acid by the enzyme glutamic dehydrogenase, and the amino group will then be passed on by transamination to make the other amino acids of the bacterial protein.

$$NH_3 + \begin{array}{c} COOH \\ | \\ C=O \\ | \\ CH_2 \\ | \\ CH_2 \\ | \\ COOH \end{array} + NADH + H^+ \rightleftharpoons \begin{array}{c} COOH \\ | \\ NH_2-C-H \\ | \\ CH_2 \\ | \\ CH_2 \\ | \\ COOH \end{array} + NAD^+ + H_2O$$

When the bacterial cell perishes, the proteins will be hydrolyzed to amino acids and these subsequently deaminated by decay bacteria through the action of amino acid oxidases, or transaminases and glutamic dehydrogenase. The reactions of interest, which result in the formation of NH_3, have been described in Chapter 15.

Legumes and other higher plants also can utilize NH_3 which has been fixed by the symbiotic process for growth. These plants hence contain protein which, on death and decay of the plant, will release NH_3 to the soil. There is evidence, however, that legumes and alders growing in sand culture excrete NH_3 and some amino acids into the sand surrounding their roots. The blue-green algae also excrete NH_3 as well as amino acids and peptides. Thus the fertility of the soil is built up by the acquisition of NH_3 directly from nitrogen-fixing systems and indirectly after the nitrogen atom has made a cycle into the amino acids and proteins of the nitrogen fixers.

Nitrification

Despite the fact that NH_3 is the form in which nitrogen is normally added to the soil, little NH_3 is found there. Studies have shown that it is rapidly oxidized to nitrate ion; the latter represents the chief source of nitrogen for nonfixing organisms. The oxidation of NH_3 is carried out by two groups of bacteria called the nitrifying bacteria. One group, *Nitrosomonas*, converts NH_3 to nitrite ion with O_2 as the oxidizing agent:

$$NH_3 + \tfrac{3}{2}O_2 \longrightarrow NO_2^- + H_2O + H^+$$
$$\Delta F' = -66{,}500 \text{ cal}$$

The other group, *Nitrobacter*, oxidizes nitrite to nitrate.

$$NO_2^- + \tfrac{1}{2}O_2 \longrightarrow NO_3^-$$
$$\Delta F' = -17{,}500 \text{ cal}$$

Both reactions are exergonic; the first involves the oxidation of nitrogen from -3 to $+3$; the second is a two electron oxidation from $+3$ to $+5$. Both groups of organisms are *autotrophs*, that is, they make all their cellular carbon compounds (protein, lipids, carbohydrates) from CO_2. As was indicated in the preceding chapter, the conversion of CO_2 to carbohydrate requires energy. In photosynthesis, that energy is supplied by light; in the cases of *Nitrosomonas* and *Nitrobacter* the energy for the reduction of CO_2 to carbohydrate and other carbon compounds is furnished by the oxidation of NH_3 and NO_2^- ion, respectively. Since the organisms obtain their energy for growth by the oxidation of simple inorganic compounds, they are termed *chemoautotrophs*.

Little is known about the intermediates in the oxidation of NH_3 to NO_2^- by *Nitrosomonas*, nor is there much information on the intermediary metabolism of the carbon compounds found in these bacteria. The lack of knowledge is due chiefly to the difficulty encountered in growing adequate amounts of the bacteria for experimentation. From the standpoint of comparative biochemistry, it may be predicted that the carbon compounds will undergo reactions resembling those described for animals, plants, and other micro-organisms. The unique reactions, if any, may be expected to involve NH_3 and NO_2^-, the compounds that supply the energy for the growth of these bacteria.

Utilization of Nitrate Ion

With NO_3^- as the most abundant form of nitrogen in the soil, plants and soil organisms have developed an ability to utilize the anion as the nitrogen source required for their growth and development. In Chapter 15, however, it was pointed out that the major route for the incorporation of inorganic nitrogen into organic nitrogen is the reaction catalyzed by glutamic dehydrogenase. It is hence not surprising to find that higher plants and micro-organisms which use NO_3^- must first reduce it to the valence level of NH_3. There is considerable information on the intermediates in this process: for example, the first step is the reduction of NO_3^- to NO_2^-, which is catalyzed by the enzyme *nitrate reductase*. The balanced reaction is:

$$NO_3^- + NADH + H^+ \longrightarrow NO_2^- + NAD^+ + H_2O$$

Nitrate reductases have been purified from bacteria, higher plants (soya beans), and the bread mold, *Neurospora*. In each case one of the reduced pyridine nucleotides (NADH or NADPH) serves as a source of electrons for the reduction. The enzymes are flavoproteins which require FAD and the metal molybdenum as cofactors which undergo oxidation reduction during the reaction.

The process is apparently repeated in the further reduction of nitrite through the intermediates, hyponitrite and hydroxylamine, to NH_3. The enzymes involved are indicated in the complete sequence

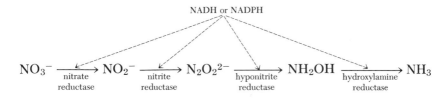

Each reaction involves the addition to the nitrogen atom of two electrons, which are furnished by reduced pyridine nucleotide. Thus the reactions proceed as do most biological reductions. There is evidence that each enzyme requires flavin nucleotides and a metal as cofactors.

This utilization of nitrogen, in which aerobic micro-organisms and higher plants reduce nitrate ion to NH_3 in order to incorporate it into cell protein, is referred to as *nitrate assimilation*. It is perhaps difficult to understand why in nature NH_3 is readily oxidized to NO_3^- which, in turn, must be again reduced to NH_3 before incorporation into amino acids. One advantage, of course, is that NO_3^- represents a more stable storage form than the somewhat volatile NH_3, although the existence of the latter as NH_4^+ is more likely in neutral and acid soils. A second advantage is that the ammonia molecule is rather toxic and therefore cannot be stored as such in tissue, whereas nitrate is relatively non-toxic and can accumulate in large amounts in plant sap.

Some micro-organisms, including *E. Coli* and *B. subtilis,* reduce NO_3^- to NH_3 for another purpose; they utilize NO_3^- as a terminal electron acceptor instead of O_2. NO_3^-, with its high oxidation reduction potential of 0.96 v at pH 7.0, can accept electrons released during the oxidation of organic substrates. The intermediates are NO_2^-, $N_2O_2^{2-}$, and NH_2OH as in nitrate assimilation. In the case of *Achromobacter fischeri*, the reduction of NO_3^- has been associated with the oxidation of reduced cytochrome *c;* the presence of a cytochrome electron transport chain which can react with NO_3^- rather than O_2 is therefore indicated. Many bacteria (*Pseudomonas denitrificans, Denitrobacillus*) that carry out nitrate respiration produce N_2 instead of NH_3. In this case the return of the nitrogen atom to the nitrogen of the atmosphere is accomplished. This sequence is referred to as *denitrification*. There is little detailed information on the enzyme systems involved.

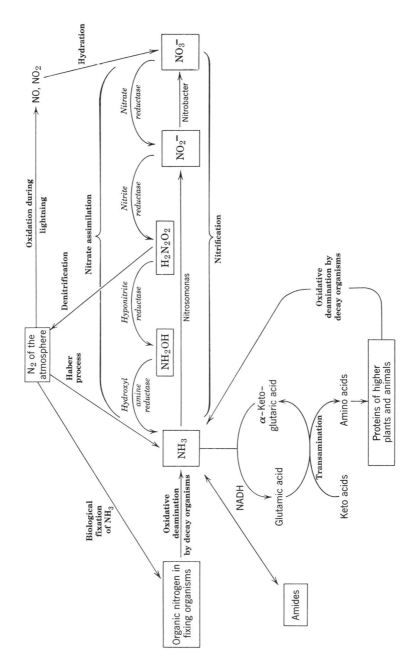

Fig. 18-1. The nitrogen cycle.

The different processes that constitute the nitrogen cycle are diagrammed in Figure 18-1.

REFERENCES

1. *A Symposium on Inorganic Nitrogen Metabolism,* edited by W. D. McElroy and B. Glass, The Johns Hopkins Press, Baltimore, 1956.

   This symposium contains both the recent findings (up to 1956) and the literature on the various reactions of the nitrogen cycle. The student will have to select the chapters or topics of interest from the many covered.

Nineteen

Digestion, Absorption,

and Excretion: The Urea Cycle

Introduction

It is possible to trace out food chains in any plant or animal community. Invariably the chain begins with green plants, which, being autotrophic, can synthesize all their cell constituents from CO_2 and simple inorganic substances in the presence of light. The plants then can serve as direct foodstuffs for herbivorous animals or, on death and decay, can furnish amino acids, carbohydrates, and lipids for micro-organisms. Carnivorous animals in turn can prey on the herbivorous ones as well as eat the autotrophic plants; carnivores are therefore dependent either directly, or indirectly through the herbivorous forms of life, on the numerous foodstuffs and essential nutrients such as vitamins which the plants supply.

In contrast to lower animals, which can feed by phagocytosis, the higher animals, men in particular, must digest their food before it can be absorbed. Man may also resort to cooking his food, which results in denaturation of the protein molecules and the physical bursting of starch grains. Digestion in turn results in the degradation of the molecules of carbohydrates, proteins, and lipids to smaller units which may be absorbed and rapidly utilized by tissues. The degradation is catalyzed in man by enzymes secreted in the mouth, stomach, and small intestine.

Digestion in the Mouth

The salivary glands of man secrete about 1 l/day of saliva, which contains a single enzyme, *ptyalin* or *salivary amylase*. A viscous glycoprotein, *mucin*, together with water, makes up the other important component of the saliva. The mucin lubricates the food particles and permits them to be formed into a bolus which then passes into the stomach. Ptyalin is an α-amylase that catalyzes the hydrolysis of the α-glucosidic bonds in the interior of the starch molecule. Since the pH optimum for ptyalin is 6.6 and the pH of saliva is about 6.8, conditions are about perfect for the hydrolysis of starch in the mouth.

The food particle spends little time in the mouth, however, and soon moves into the acid medium of the stomach. Here the action of ptyalin ceases, except for that portion of the enzyme which is in the interior of the food bolus. Even this amount is soon exposed to the acidity of the stomach by the churning and mixing movements of the stomach, so that enzymatic hydrolysis of the carbohydrates soon ceases.

Digestion in the Stomach

Although enzymic hydrolysis of carbohydrates does not continue in the stomach, the high acidity and warmth of the stomach contents probably result in some hydrolysis of sucrose, which is very acid labile. The acidity of the stomach contents is due to secretion of HCl in gastric juice by the mucosa, the lining of the stomach; the pH ranges between 1 and 2. A gastric *lipase* is also found in the gastric juice, but, with an optimum pH near 7.0, it does not hydrolyze lipids. The *zymogen pepsinogen* is secreted in the gastric juice and, in the presence of HCl, is converted to its active enzyme form, *pepsin*. Pepsin is an *endopeptidase*, a proteolytic enzyme which hydrolyzes peptide bonds in the interior of the peptide chain. It has an optimum pH near 2 and hence catalyzes the hydrolysis of dietary proteins to form smaller molecules known as peptones or proteoses.

The flow of gastric juice into the stomach cavity is under hormonal control. The hormone *histamine* is released into the blood stream when the smell and taste of food provide the necessary stimulus, and gastric flow increases. Other hormones inhibit its flow thereby exercising a delicate control mechanism.

Digestion in the Small Intestine

Digestion is completed in the small intestine, where the action of three different digestive juices from the pancreas, the small intestine, and the liver may be considered. These juices are sufficiently alkaline to raise the pH of the acid contents from the stomach to a value near neutrality. The pancreatic juice contains two zymogens, *trypsinogen* and *chymotrypsinogen*. The former is converted to trypsin by *entero-*

kinase, an enzyme secreted by the intestinal wall. Trypsin in turn can convert chymotrypsinogen to chymotrypsin. Both trypsin and chymotrypsin are endopeptidases, which hydrolyze peptide bonds in the interior of a protein molecule to form smaller polypeptides.

The pancreatic juice also contains *carboxypeptidase,* an enzyme which catalyzes the hydrolysis of smaller polypeptides by attacking the end of the chain which has the free carboxyl group. As a result of the action of this enzyme, which is known as an *exopeptidase,* free amino acids are formed. The pancreas also produces a lipase and an amylase; the latter is similar in its action to ptyalin. The pancreatic lipase together with intestinal lipase catalyzes the hydrolysis of triglycerides through the stage of di- and monoglycerides to form free fatty acids and eventually glycerol.

The intestinal juice, which amounts to about 3 l/day, contains another exopeptidase, *aminopeptidase,* which catalyzes the hydrolysis of smaller peptides by starting at the end of the peptide chain having the free amino group. Intestinal juice also contains a *dipeptidase* as well as three enzymes that catalyze the hydrolysis of disaccharides—*sucrase, maltase,* and *lactase.* The substrates for these enzymes are evident from their names.

The bile contains no enzymes but does contain bile salts, the sodium salts of glycocholic and taurocholic acid, which aid in the digestion of fats. The bile salts are surfactive agents which, by lowering surface tension, tend to emulsify the lipids. The di- and monoglycerides formed during the action of lipases on neutral fats also aid in the emulsification of undigested fats.

Absorption

Little absorption occurs in the stomach except in the case of ethanol, which is absorbed almost completely in that organ. Small amounts of glucose can also be absorbed in the stomach. The major amount of absorption, however, occurs in the small intestine where the monosaccharides and amino acids formed by the digestive process are absorbed. These substances pass into the capillaries of the intestine and are transported through the portal circulation to the liver. There they may be metabolized, resynthesized into glycogen and blood proteins, or transported further throughout the body to the peripheral tissues.

In the case of lipids it appears that some of the triglycerides are hydrolyzed to glycerol and fatty acids. The fatty acids, together with di- and monoglycerides and the bile salts, may emulsify other lipids to the extent that they will pass through the intestinal wall without hydrolysis. The lipids and hydrolyzed lipids for the most part pass into the lacteals and then into the lymphatic system, where they empty eventually into the blood stream through the thoracic duct. Again the liver is a site of metabolism including resynthesis into triglycerides and phospholipids.

Water is the chief product absorbed in the large intestine, an absorption that results in the solidification of the feces.

Excretion

Three major products of metabolism are excreted by members of the animal kingdom: CO_2, H_2O, and some form of nitrogen. The carbon substrates have been oxidized to CO_2; H_2O is produced in the reduction of O_2. Also important, H_2O is used as a solvent for soluble waste products (including urea) which must be excreted. In addition, about 500 ml of H_2O are lost each day from the surface of man's skin as insensible (unnoticed) perspiration, and about 500 ml are excreted as water vapor in the air exhaled from his lungs.

The third major product excreted by animals is a nitrogen compound, usually NH_3, urea, or uric acid. The nitrogen atoms in these compounds have their origin in the α-amino acids of the dietary protein. To the extent that the amino acids are oxidized, the nitrogen atoms removed as NH_3 in oxidative deamination will be excreted as such or will be converted to urea or uric acid and excreted.

In addition to these three excretory products, which are the result of metabolism, undigested and unabsorbed food material (cellulose, for example) constitutes a fourth excretory product.

Comparative Biochemistry of Nitrogen Excretion

If we survey the animal kingdom, we find that three nitrogen excretory products are common: NH_3, urea, and uric acid. An organism's choice of one of these forms depends in part on certain properties of the compounds: NH_3 is very toxic but it is also extremely soluble in H_2O; urea is far less toxic and is appreciably soluble in H_2O; uric acid is quite insoluble and, as such, is fairly nontoxic. There is abundant evidence to suggest that the form in which nitrogen is excreted by an organism is determined largely by the accessibility of H_2O to that organism.

Marine animals, living in H_2O, have large amounts of H_2O into which their waste products can be excreted. Although NH_3 is fairly toxic, it can be excreted and will be diluted out instantly in the H_2O of the environment. As a result, many marine forms excrete NH_3 as the major nitrogenous end product, although there are important exceptions to this among the bony fishes.

Land-dwelling animals no longer have an unlimited supply of H_2O in intimate contact with their tissues. Since NH_3 is toxic it cannot be conveniently accumulated. As a result, most terrestrial animals have developed procedures for converting NH_3 into either urea or uric acid.

According to Needham, the English biochemist, the choice between urea and uric acid is determined by the conditions under which the embryo develops. The mammalian embryo develops in close contact with the circulatory system of the mother. Thus urea, which is quite soluble, can be removed from the embryo and excreted. On the other hand, the embryos of birds and reptiles develop in a hard-shelled egg in an external environment. The eggs are laid with enough water to see them through the hatching period. Production of NH_3 or even urea in such a closed system would be fatal because they are so toxic. Instead, uric acid is produced by these embryos and precipitates out as a solid in a small sac on the interior surface of the shell. These characteristics, which are so necessary for development of the embryo, are then carried over to the adult organism.

There are interesting examples in support of the principles we have cited. The tadpole, which is aquatic, excretes chiefly NH_3. When it undergoes metamorphosis into the frog, however, it becomes a true amphibian and spends much of its time away from water. During the metamorphosis the animal begins excreting urea instead of NH_3, and by the time the change is complete, urea is the predominant nitrogen excretory product.

Lungfish are another interesting example. While in water they excrete chiefly NH_3, but as the river or lake runs dry, the lungfish settles down in the mud, begins to estivate, and accumulates urea as the nitrogen end product. When the rains return, the lungfish excretes a massive amount of urea and sets about excreting NH_3 again.

Within one group of animals, the chelonia (tortoises and turtles), there are totally aquatic species; semiterrestrial species, and a third group (the tortoises) which is wholly terrestrial. The aquatic forms secrete a mixture of urea and ammonia, the semiterrestrial species on the other hand excrete urea, and the tortoises excrete almost all their nitrogen as uric acid.

The topic of nitrogen excretion is one of the best examples of comparative biochemistry that has been developed.

The Urea Cycle

Urea is the chief nitrogen end product excreted by mammals. Sir Hans Krebs, then of Germany, and K. Henseleit were among the first to study the formation of urea in animal tissues. They observed that rat liver slices could convert CO_2 and NH_3 (2 moles/mole of CO_2) to urea provided some energy source was available. The requirement for some oxidizable substance such as lactic acid or glucose was understandable, since the formation of urea from NH_3 and CO_2 required energy.

The amino acid arginine was also implicated in this process, since the enzyme arginase, which catalyzes reaction 19-6 (p. 318), was known to form urea and ornithine on the hydrolysis of arginine. The extract relationship was indicated, however, when Krebs showed that catalytic quantities of arginine, and ornithine or citrulline as well, stimulated the formation of appreciable amounts of urea from ammonia. In 1932, Krebs proposed a cycle of reactions which accounted for the production of urea from NH_3 and CO_2 and explained the catalytic action of arginine, ornithine, and citrulline. That cycle, known as the urea or ornithine cycle, is:

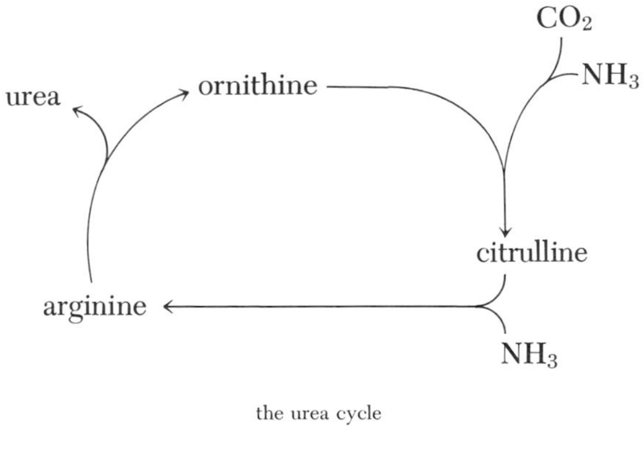

the urea cycle

Although the essential features of this cycle remain unchanged, it is possible to write out some of the reactions in greater detail.

Carbamyl phosphate is implicated in the reaction of NH_3 and CO_2 with ornithine to form citrulline. In bacteria an enzyme *carbamyl kinase* has been shown to catalyze the phosphorylation of the ammonium salt of carbamic acid (reaction 19-2). The chemistry of carbamic acid is complex, but carbamyl phosphate has been identified as the product of the action of carbamyl kinase. The reaction is relatively endergonic; its $\Delta F'$ is $+2000$ cal/mole.

$$2NH_3 + CO_2 \longrightarrow \left[NH_4 \right]^{+} \left[\begin{array}{c} O \\ \parallel \\ O-C-NH_2 \end{array} \right]^{-} \quad \text{(19-1)}$$

ammonium carbamate

$$NH_4^+O-\overset{\overset{\textstyle O}{\parallel}}{C}-NH_2^- + ATP \xrightarrow[\substack{\text{carbamyl} \\ \text{kinase}}]{Mg^{2+}}$$

$$H_2PO_3-O-\overset{\overset{\textstyle O}{\parallel}}{C}-NH_2 + ADP + NH_3 \quad \text{(19-2)}$$

carbamyl phosphate

In frog and mammalian livers, another enzyme *carbamyl phosphate synthetase* catalyzes the formation of carbamyl phosphate from NH_3 and CO_2; in this reaction 2 moles of ATP and a cofactor, N-acetyl-glutamic acid, are required. The details of the reaction are not clear but the stoichiometry has been established.

$$NH_3 + CO_2 + 2ATP \xrightarrow{\text{cofactor}} H_2PO_3-O-\overset{\overset{\textstyle O}{\parallel}}{C}-NH_2 + 2ADP + H_3PO_4$$

This reaction is not readily reversible.

Carbamyl phosphate, which has been synthesized chemically, will react with ornithine to form citrulline in the presence of the enzyme *ornithine transcarbamylase*. The enzyme has been purified a hundred-

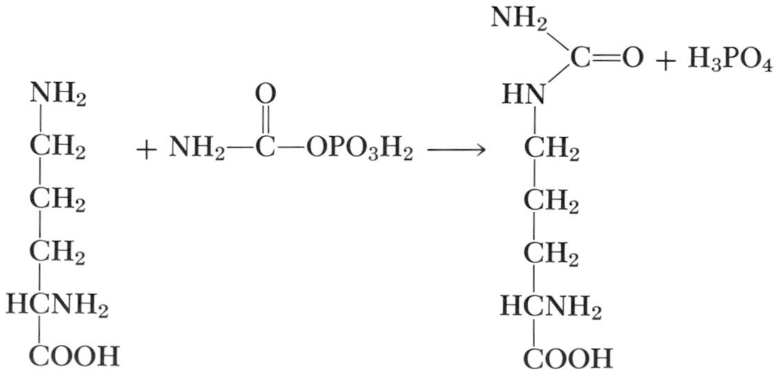

$$
\begin{array}{c}
NH_2 \\
| \\
CH_2 \\
| \\
CH_2 \\
| \\
CH_2 \\
| \\
HCNH_2 \\
| \\
COOH
\end{array}
+ NH_2-\overset{\overset{\textstyle O}{\parallel}}{C}-OPO_3H_2 \longrightarrow
\begin{array}{c}
\overset{\textstyle NH_2}{\underset{\textstyle HN}{\diagdown C=O}} + H_3PO_4 \\
| \\
CH_2 \\
| \\
CH_2 \\
| \\
CH_2 \\
| \\
HCNH_2 \\
| \\
COOH
\end{array}
\quad \text{(19-3)}
$$

L-ornithine   carbamyl   L-citrulline
phosphate

fold from beef liver; it has no cofactors and exhibits extreme substrate specificity. The equilibrium is in the direction of citrulline synthesis.

The next step in the cycle, the formation of arginine from citrulline, was largely worked out by Sarah Ratner at New York University who first showed that two enzymes were involved. The first of these, *argininosuccinic synthetase,* catalyzes the formation of argininosuccinic acid from citrulline and aspartic acid. This may be conveniently represented by picturing the enolic form of citrulline as reacting with the aspartic acid to form a new compound, argininosuccinic acid. This

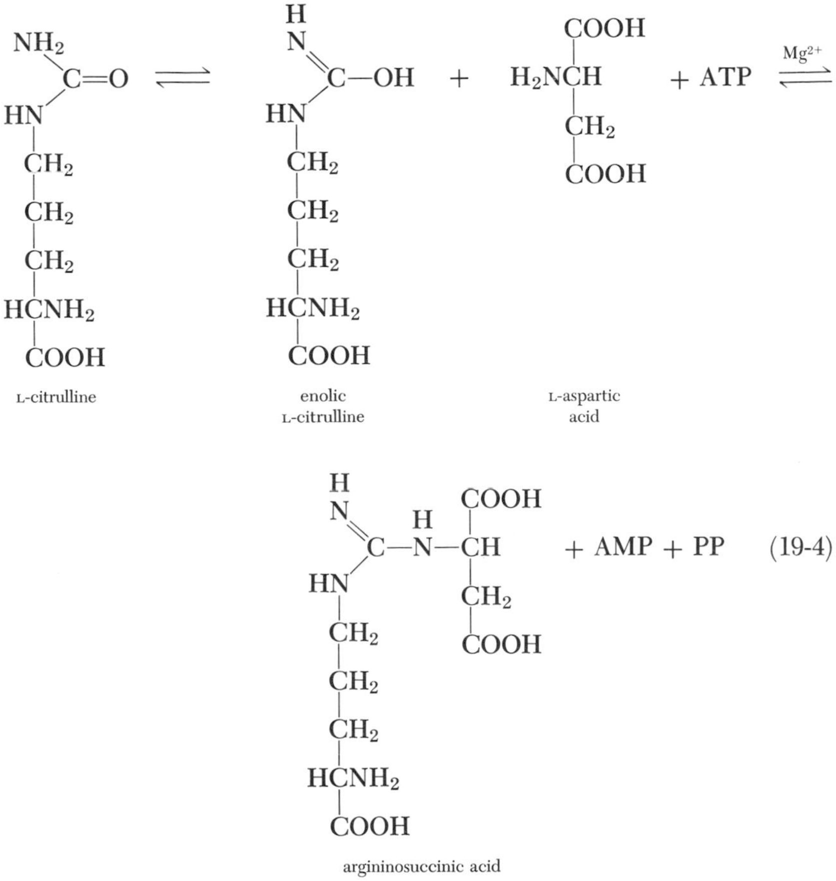

L-citrulline	enolic L-citrulline	L-aspartic acid

$$+ \text{AMP} + \text{PP} \qquad (19\text{-}4)$$

argininosuccinic acid

complex reaction requires ATP and Mg^{2+}. The K_{eq} for this reaction is approximately 9 at pH 7.5; therefore the reaction is readily reversible. Note that the nitrogen atom which eventually becomes one of the two such atoms in urea is contributed by aspartic acid in this reaction and not by NH_3.

The subsequent cleavage of argininosuccinic acid is catalyzed by the *argininosuccinic cleavage enzyme,* which has been purified 150-fold from ox liver; it has also been observed in plant tissues and micro-

$$
\begin{array}{c}
\text{H} \\
\text{N} \\
\diagdown \\
\quad\text{C—N—CH} \quad\overset{\text{COOH}}{|} \\
\text{IIN} \quad \text{H} \\
|\qquad \text{HCH} \\
\text{CH}_2 \qquad \text{COOH} \\
| \\
\text{CH}_2 \\
| \\
\text{CH}_2 \\
| \\
\text{HCNH}_2 \\
| \\
\text{COOH}
\end{array}
\;\rightleftharpoons\;
\begin{array}{c}
\text{H} \\
\text{N} \\
\diagdown \\
\quad\text{C—NH}_2 \\
\text{HN} \\
| \\
\text{CH}_2 \\
| \\
\text{CH}_2 \\
| \\
\text{CH}_2 \\
| \\
\text{HCNH}_2 \\
| \\
\text{COOH}
\end{array}
\;+\;
\begin{array}{c}
\text{H} \quad \text{COOII} \\
\diagdown\;/ \\
\text{C} \\
\| \\
\text{C} \\
/\;\diagdown \\
\text{HOOC} \quad \text{H}
\end{array}
\qquad (19\text{-}5)
$$

argininosuccinic   L-arginine   fumaric
acid   acid

organisms. Reaction 19-5 is an elimination process in which a substituted amine is eliminated to form fumaric acid. The K_{eq} for the reaction is 11.4×10^{-3} at pH 7.5. Since the reaction as written from left to right results in the formation of two products from a single reactant, this value of K_{eq} determines that argininosuccinic acid will predominate in concentrated solutions whereas arginine and fumaric acid will predominate in dilute solution.

$$
\begin{array}{c}
\text{H} \\
\text{N} \\
\diagdown \\
\quad\text{C—NH}_2 \\
\text{HN} \\
| \\
\text{CH}_2 \\
| \\
\text{CH}_2 \\
| \\
\text{CH}_2 \\
| \\
\text{HCNH}_2 \\
| \\
\text{COOH}
\end{array}
\;+\;\text{H}_2\text{O}\;\longrightarrow\;
\begin{array}{c}
\text{NH}_2 \\
\diagdown \\
\quad\text{C—NH}_2 \\
\| \\
\text{O}
\end{array}
\qquad
\begin{array}{c}
\text{NH}_2 \\
| \\
\text{CH}_2 \\
| \\
\text{CH}_2 \\
| \\
\text{CH}_2 \\
| \\
\text{HCNH}_2 \\
| \\
\text{COOH}
\end{array}
\qquad (19\text{-}6)
$$

L-arginine   urea   L-ornithine

Arginase catalyzes the final reaction of the urea cycle. This enzyme has been known almost from the beginning of the century. It is found in the liver of all animals known to excrete urea and has been crystallized from beef liver. The enzyme is quite specific for L-arginine, and the catalyzed reaction is not reversible.

The sequence of reactions just discussed is shown in Figure 19-1. The cycle accounts for the formation of urea from NH_3, CO_2, and the

amino group of aspartic acid.   The requirement for the oxidizable substrates reported by Krebs is explained by the participation of ATP in
the formation of carbamyl phosphate and argininosuccinic acid.   By the

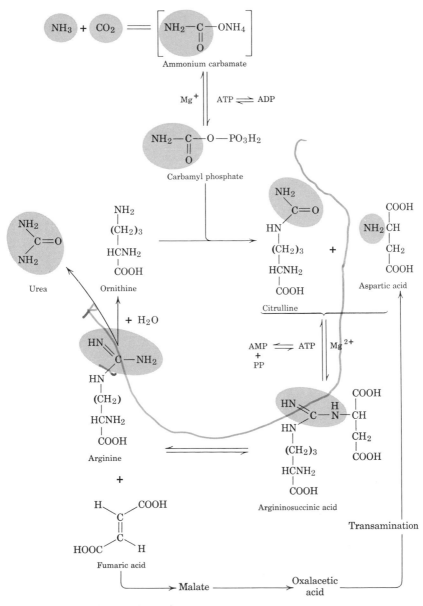

Fig. 19-1. The urea cycle.

eventual conversion of fumaric acid back to aspartic acid, another mole of amino nitrogen can be brought to the point of reaction in the cycle.

REFERENCES

1. C. H. Best and N. B. Taylor, *The Physiological Basis of Medical Practice*, Williams and Wilkins, Baltimore, 6th edition, 1955).

    Chapters 37 through 41 deal thoroughly with the subject of digestion.

2. P. P. Cohen and G. W. Brown, Jr. in *Comparative Biochemistry*, edited by M. Florkin and H. S. Mason, Academic Press, New York, 1960, Vol. 2, Chapter 4.

    An excellent review of ammonia metabolism and the urea cycle by two active workers in the field.

3. E. Baldwin, *An Introduction to Comparative Biochemistry*, Cambridge University Press, Cambridge, 3rd edition, 1949.

    The title of this small monograph accurately describes the subject matter it contains. All students in biochemistry should be familiar with this work.

Twenty

Biochemical Genetics

Introduction

In recent years great progress in genetics has been made by applying biochemical knowledge to many facets of the field. In this chapter we intend only to review briefly the basic principles of genetics and to show how this knowledge can be used to elucidate complex metabolic processes. The role of genetics in the biological sciences is described in several monographs referred to at the end of this chapter.

Review of Genetics

TERMINOLOGY

Although Mendel laid the foundations for the science of genetics in 1866, the concept of the *gene* was introduced as recently as 1911 by Johannsess, who described the gene as an expression of the "unit factor" demonstrated by Mendel. Soon Morgan and others demonstrated the physical existence of the unit factor or gene and its linear arrangement on *chromosomes*, the physical structures which carry genes. The term *genotype* describes the total complement of genes in the fertilized egg with its capacity to develop certain characteristics; the term *phenotype* describes the end result or expression of gene action in terms of the morphological and physiological properties of the organism.

Two fundamental processes in genetics are those of *meiosis* and *mitosis*. In *mitosis* a cell gives rise to daughter cells with the same number and kind of chromosomes. Thus the genetic information in the mother cell is carried accurately to the daughter cells. Higher organisms are mostly *diploid* with 2N chromosomes, a term which signifies that each cell carries two similar sets of chromosomes. Mitosis preserves the diploid character of the cell. In special cells involved in sexual reproduction, however, where male and female gametes are formed, there must be a reduction in the number of chromosomes from 2N to

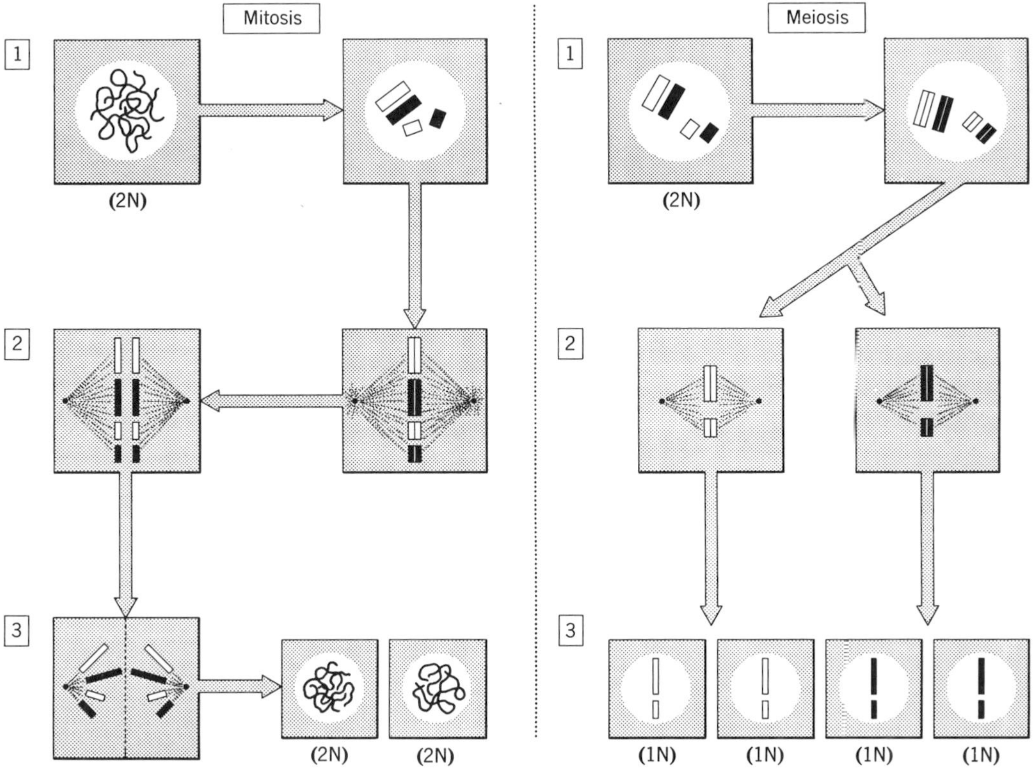

Fig. 20-1. During mitosis, nuclear material is organized into chromosomal strands (stage 2) which split longitudinally to form two identical sets of chromosomes. These move apart (stage 3) and reorganize into two daughter nuclei and finally into two cells. The process is continuous.

During meiosis, homologous chromosomes pair off or synapse (stage 1) and shortly thereafter each chromosome duplicates itself. The each pair becomes a *tetrad*. The homologous chromosomes now separate by the first division (stage 2). In the second division there is a further separation of the chromosome pair to form four cells (stage 3) each with a haploid set of chromosomes (1N). Two important points to note are (*a*) each haploid (1N) gamete represents each homologous pair, and (*b*) segregation of the homologues is random. Thus at stage 2 the pair of long whites could just as well have paired with the short blacks and conversely.

322

1N or to the *haploid* stage. If it did not occur, the fusion of the male and female gametic nuclei would result in an indefinite increase in the chromosome complement of the fused nuclei or *zygote*. The mechanism of reduction is called *meiosis*. The two processes are outlined schematically in Figure 20-1.

THE LAW OF SEGREGATION

One hundred years ago Mendel made the basic discoveries that established genetics as a science. When he crossed strains of garden peas which differed in one contrasting visual character, that of having purple or white petals, he observed that the progeny (F_1 generation) was all purple. When two members of the F_1 generation were crossed, however, three-fourths of the progeny or F_2 generation were purple, but the remainder were white. He concluded that the purple color was the *dominant* trait which masked the white trait or the *recessive* other character. In the F_1 generation the recessive character was only masked by the dominant character and had not been destroyed; instead it appeared again in the F_2 generation. The frequency of occurrences of purple and white flowers in the F_2 generation is $3:1$.

Mendel also reasoned that any particular character-determining unit exists in two forms or *alleles* which do not blend but retain their full characteristics. If two alleles are identical (two purple and two whites) they are *homozygous*, but if they differ from each other (purple and white alleles) they are *heterozygous*. These character-determining units are of course the genes.

The behavior is precisely that expected if the dominant allele (purple or P) and the recessive allele (white or p) segregate to equal numbers of P and p units in the germ cells and then combine randomly form to an F_2 generation. This is indicated in Figure 20-2.

MUTATION

A final process of great importance, *mutation*, is defined as an abrupt, stable change of a gene which is expressed in some unusual phenotypic character, frequently as a biochemical modification. In a mutation there may be a loss of the capacity to carry out some specific biochemical function. Mutations are induced by exposure to radiation and to certain chemicals.

The molecular basis of mutation is alteration of the nucleotide sequence in DNA. Modification or deletion of a base in the nucleotide sequence will result in a mutation. On a molecular level, X-rays and gamma radiation may break individual phosphoester linkages by the

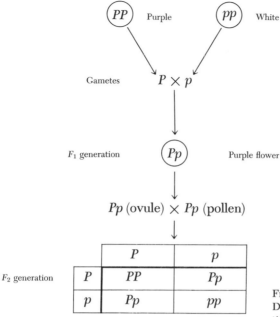

Fig. 20-2. Law of segregation. Demonstration of the segregation of genes and their maintenance of identification and random recombination.

action of free radicals such as H and OH, which are produced when the radiation is absorbed by water. A DNA molecule will only separate if the breaks occur at opposite positions in the two chains; if not opposite, the hydrogen bond system of the double helix will probably retain the molecular shape of the DNA. Alkylating agents, for example the sulfur mustards [S(CH$_2$CH$_2$Cl)$_2$] and the nitrogen mustards [RN(CH$_2$CH$_2$Cl)$_2$], cause chromosome breakage and mutation by attacking the nitrogen atoms of the bases, interalkylating closely aligned bases, and thereby greatly impeding the separation of the double-helical structure of DNA during replication. Other sites of action could also include the rupture by ionizing radiation of the cross-linking of the hydrogen bonds. Disappearance of hydrogen bonds from a section of the DNA molecule would destroy the helical structure and thereby impair the replication process.

Chemistry of the Gene

Much evidence supports the concept that deoxyribonucleic acid (DNA) is associated with the storage and transfer of hereditary information. The evidence in support of this statement may be outlined:

(a) The site of the chromosomes in nuclei is always associated with DNA.

(b) The DNA content of somatic cells (2N) of a particular species is exactly twice that of the sperm cells (1N).

(c) The rate of mutation increases when cells are exposed to agents like X-rays or mutagenic chemicals. These agents affect the DNA molecule directly or indirectly.

(d) DNA once formed is metabolically inert. Some workers believe that this suggests genetic stability.

(e) The phenomenon of *transformation*, a process discovered by F. Griffith in 1928, is one of the more dramatic demonstrations of the role of DNA in a cell. Griffith studied *Pneumococcus* strains which consist of a smooth (S) type with a polysaccharide capsule, and a noncapsulated, rough form (R). The R form is genetically stable but, if placed in a medium containing cell-free extracts of S cells, will transform to the S cell. This transformation is permanent, and the S cells will reproduce themselves through successive generations. The active principle in the cell-free extract of S cells has been identified as DNA. As little as one part of DNA in 600,000,000 will transform R cells to the S cell type.

$$\text{rough cells} \quad \xrightarrow[\text{DNA}]{\left(\begin{array}{c}\text{from} \\ \text{smooth} \\ \text{cells}\end{array}\right)} \quad \text{smooth cells}$$

This transformation is not peculiar to *Pneumococcus* but has been obtained with several different bacteria. What probably happens in the process of transformation is that DNA from the S strain enters the R cell and becomes part of the genotypic structure of the R strain. We have here an addition to the genotype rather than a change in the existent genotype.

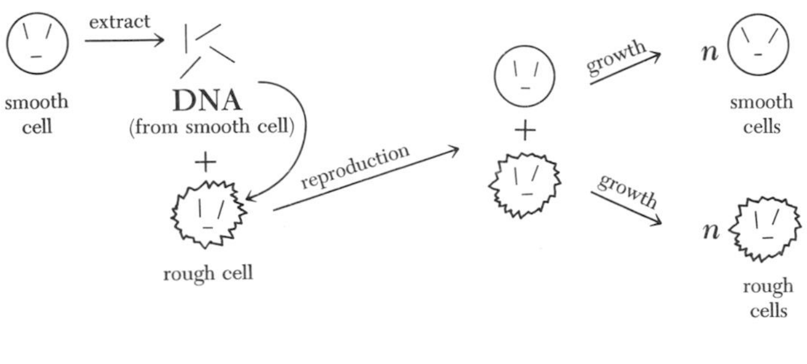

Biochemical Genetics

Having reviewed the working definitions of genetics we may now discuss the value of this science in the study of metabolism.

LOWER ORGANISMS

The bread mold *Neurospora crassa* has provided excellent material for the biochemical geneticist. Wild strains of *N. crassa* will usually grow well in a simple culture medium composed of sugar, salts, and biotin. When these cultures are exposed to a mutagenic agent such as X-rays, we can obtain mutants which only grow when suitable nutritional additions are made to the initial medium. A systematic analysis of the needs of the mutant will frequently indicate a single new nutritional requirement. We do not discuss here the details of the genetic analysis that relates the new nutritional requirement to a position or locus on the chromosomes, but instead we indicate by several examples the great value of this general method in metabolic studies.

Biosynthesis of Arginine: Three genetically distinct mutants of *N. crassa* have been observed and thoroughly documented in the metabolism of arginine; these mutants will grow when one or more of three amino acids, namely arginine, citrulline, and ornithine, are added to the minimal medium. Mutant 1 grows only when supplied with arginine but not when given ornithine or citrulline. Mutant 2 can use both citrulline and arginine, but not ornithine, and mutant 3 will grow on any of the three amino acids. These results can be summarized as in our diagram, where the vertical bars indicate a metabolic block in a mutant.

	mutant 3		mutant 2		mutant 1	
Chain of Synthesis	―‖→	ornithine	―‖→	citrulline	―‖→	arginine

The nutritional mutant will in general grow on substrates that come after the metabolic block but not on those coming before the block. There may, on some occasions, be an actual accumulation of an intermediate because it is not further metabolized. Thus in mutant 1 citrulline may accumulate since its further metabolism is blocked by the absence of the enzyme required for its conversion to arginine. By this analysis the biochemist can state that the sequence of synthesis of arginine must follow the order → ornithine → citrulline → arginine.

Biosynthesis of Lysine: This method can be applied to organisms other than *N. crassa* to reveal a different or alternate pathway of biosynthesis. Mutants requiring lysine for growth have been found in *N. crassa* and *E. Coli*, both of which normally synthesize lysine from sugar and inorganic nitrogen compounds such as nitrate and ammonia. In *N. crassa*, α-amino adipic acid is converted to lysine by some mutants, but these will not use diaminopimelic acid. Some *E. Coli* mutants will grow on this acid with ease, however. Diaminopimelic acid and its precursors will also accumulate in different *E. Coli* mutants. The mutants that accumulate precursors are deficient in a normally present enzyme which permits utilization of a given precusor. These results are pictured in the accompanying diagram.

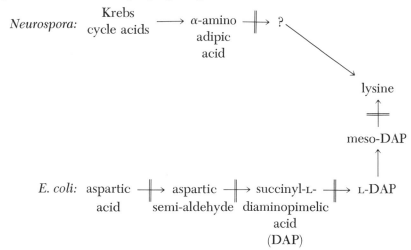

The value of this type of study is apparent; it reveals new pathways as well as confirms established routes in a variety of organisms. Similar studies have been carried out with mutants from a large number of organisms in the metabolism of amino acids, nucleic acids, vitamins, porphyrins, pigments, and fatty acids. Besides contributing greatly to our knowledge of metabolism, these studies also indicate a direct relation between the enzymatic potential of an organism and its heredity. These studies have led G. W. Beadle and E. L. Tatum to develop the *one gene-one enzyme hypothesis*, which states that a single gene controls the synthesis of one enzyme. Thus mutant 2 in the arginine pathway no longer has the capacity to synthesize the critical enzyme protein needed to produce arginine because of the destruction of a specific genetic locus.

Although the Beadle-Tatum postulate is at first glance a simple one, there are at least three ways by which a genetic modification could affect enzyme activity. It could (1) cause a change in the molecular structure of the enzyme; (2) decrease the concentration of the enzyme and thereby modify the rate of the reaction; or (3) exert an indirect effect that involves no change in the enzyme itself. Some aspects of these problems are discussed in Chapter 21.

INBORN ERRORS OF METABOLISM IN MAMMALS

The three best-known diseases related to a genetic block in man are *alkaptonuria*, in which there is a genetic block in the utilization of homogentisic acid, an intermediate in the oxidation of tyrosine;

phenylketonuria, in which phenylalanine cannot be converted to tyrosine; and *galactosemia,* in which galactose cannot be directly utilized. Let us examine this last condition more closely. In this disease the sugar as well as its phosphorylated derivative, galactose-1-phosphate, is not used. Clinically, patients show a loss in weight, an enlargement of the liver, and a development of cataracts. Control of the disease is simply the exclusion of all galactose from the diet.

The biochemical basis of galactosemia has been clarified by the research work of Kalckar now at Massachusetts General Hospital. Galactose is metabolized chiefly into galactolipids—important components in nerve tissue and membranes. Reactions 20-1 and 20-2 prepare galactose for the synthesis of galactolipids (see also Chapter 9).

$$\text{galactose} + \text{ATP} \longrightarrow \text{galactose-1-PO}_4 + \text{ADP} \qquad (20\text{-}1)$$

$$\text{galactose-1-PO}_4 + \text{UDPG} \longrightarrow \text{glucose-1-PO}_4 + \text{UDP-galactose} \qquad (20\text{-}2)$$

genetic
block

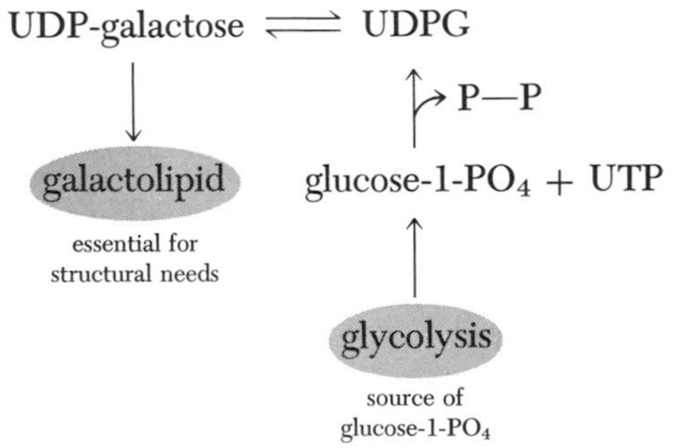

$$\text{UDP-galactose} \rightleftharpoons \text{UDPG} \qquad (20\text{-}3)$$

$$\downarrow \qquad\qquad \uparrow\!\!\nearrow \text{P}\!-\!\text{P}$$

galactolipid   glucose-1-PO$_4$ + UTP

essential for
structural needs

$$\uparrow$$

glycolysis

source of
glucose-1-PO$_4$

The enzyme that catalyzes reaction 20-2 is missing in patients with galactosemia. Although galactose may be lacking in the diet, the patient can still make galactolipid by converting glucose through reaction 20-3 to a galactose derivative (UDP-galactose) used for galactolipid biosynthesis. The disease itself is therefore a reflection of toxic effects of the accumulated galactose phosphates rather than of a lack of an enzyme for the formation of UDP-galactose. Genetically, galactosemia is the result of a single recessive Mendelian gene which in some manner controls the synthesis of the enzyme for reaction 20-2.

Another interesting inheritable disease is called sickle cell anaemia.

In this disease an abnormal hemoglobin of lower solubility than usual is synthesized and is responsible for an abnormal or sickle shape of the erythrocytes. The difference between the normal and abnormal hemoglobin is the substitution of a valine residue in the abnormal hemoglobin for a glutamic acid residue. This occurs at a particular point in one of the two pairs of protein chains of which the complete molecule is constituted:

normal: hist-val-leu-leu-thr-pro-glu-glu-lys-
abnormal: hist-val-leu-leu-thr-pro-val-glu-lys-

This change in the synthesis of a part of the peptide chain of these hemoglobins represents a difference of only one amino acid out of nearly three hundred. The appearance of the abnormal protein is strictly inherited by Mendelian laws and is indeed controlled by a single gene, the normal and sickle cell genes being allelic. Thus the genetic difference of a small part of the DNA of a chromosome reveals itself in the difference of one amino acid in the complicated peptide sequence!

Replication

We have already noted that DNA directs the sequence of bases when RNA as well as DNA polymerases catalyze the condensation of nucleotides to form RNA or DNA (see Chapter 14). Because the bonding rules require the base adenine to associate with thymine, and cytosine with guanine, the composition and sequence of bases in strand I (see the next page) automatically determines the composition and sequence in strand II in a DNA molecule.

If strands I and II can be separated in some manner and then acquire new deoxyribonucleotides (with the bonding rules operative) in two new double helices, they will have the structures I–II' and I'–II, where I' and II'' represent newly synthesized chains that obey the base bonding rules, are complementary to their opposite strands, and are therefore precise copies of their original strands I and II. The problem of the separation of the intertwined strains of the parent DNA and the simultaneous maintenance of the helical configuration and duplication is still not solved, but there is evidence that DNA unwinds very rapidly. These ideas are illustrated in the accompanying diagram.

This process is called the complementary type of replication. Here we have a molecular model of the process of mitosis by which daughter cells (or genes) have the same information found in the parent cell (or gene).

The amalgamation of the concepts of genetics and biochemistry has

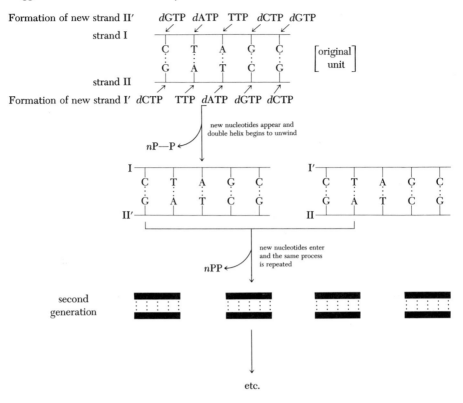

resulted in an explosion of new information. In the near future, this new information will be used to explore the very frontiers of growth and reproduction and the factors that influence these life processes.

REFERENCES

1. C. B. Anfinsen, *The Molecular Basis of Evolution*, John Wiley and Sons, New York, 1959.
   A fine summary of the basic aspects of genetics and the application of modern biochemistry to the problems of genetics.

2. B. S. Strauss, *An Outline of Chemical Genetics*, W. B. Saunders Company, Philadelphia, 1960.
   A short but excellent treatment of modern genetics, well designed for the student who desires a modern review of the highlights of the subject.

3. R. P. Wagner and H. K. Mitchell, *Genetics and Metabolism*, John Wiley and Sons, New York, 1955.
   A complete and thorough discussion of the subject although out of date because of the dramatic advances since its printing.

4. R. B. Drysdale and A. R. Peacocke in *Biological Reviews*, 36, 537(1961).
   A good review of the chemistry of heredity up to 1961.

Twenty-One

Metabolic Regulation

Introduction

The growth and maintenance of a cell require a highly integrated interplay of anabolism and catabolism. Since the functioning unit of the metabolic machinery is the enzyme-catalyzed reaction, the regulation of this unit becomes of primary importance in the economy of the cell.

Metabolic regulation must include (a) kinetic factors, which affect reaction rates; (b) structural factors bearing on the relation of the organization of the cell to enzymic action; and (c) special inhibitory factors in which low-molecular weight compounds act on an enzyme reaction or on enzyme formation directly or indirectly.

Kinetic Factors

The kinetics of a single reaction is governed by the concentration of the enzyme, substrates, coenzymes, cations, and anions; by the temperature and pH; and, where applicable, by the $-SS-/-SH$ ratio, the $NADPH/NADP^+$ and $NADH/NAD^+$ ratios, and the occurrence of activators or inhibitors. Indirect factors include the rate of conversion of enzymes or proenzymes to the fully active enzymes, the rate of synthesis, and the breakdown of enzyme protein and coenzymes. The action of hormones is superimposed on the more direct kinetic factors. A small change of any of these factors by the physical environment, disease, or hormonal effects may have a rather profound effect on the overall performance of the metabolic machinery.

Structural Factors

An important number of enzymes are for the most part firmly associated with cytoplasmic particles. Thus the cytochrome system, the major electron transport system of the cell, is subtly interlocked with the enzymes of oxidative phosphorylation in a specific geometric organization on the mitochondrial membranes or cristae. This organization strongly suggests a high order of efficiency and biochemical stability. Physical factors such as changes in the osmotic conditions of the surrounding medium or in the permeability of the mitochondrial membrane, and biochemical factors, such as the uncoupling of phosphorylation from oxidation by dinitrophenol, may affect the structural organization of enzymes in particles, however, and result in striking changes in the normal sequence of metabolic events.

Another consideration is the spatial separation of multi-enzyme systems from each other. Thus in the degradation of glucose to carbon dioxide and water, at least three pathways are involved: Glycolysis, the pentose cycle, and the tricarboxylic acid cycle. The glycolytic enzymes and the enzymes of the pentose cycle are found outside the particles, whereas enzymes of the tricarboxylic acid cycle are associated with mitochondria as are the tightly bound particulate enzymes of electron transport and oxidative phosphorylation. A close partnership must exist between the three metabolic sequences, and any interference in that partnership will result in a breakdown or modification of glucose metabolism. Furthermore, any change in the concentration of phosphate and magnesium ions, the ratio of ADP to ATP, $NADP^+$ to NADPH, NAD^+ to NADH, or the tension of oxygen and carbon dioxide would also affect this partnership.

Still another factor in metabolic control and regulation is the ability of mitochondria, for example, to concentrate coenzymes, substrates, and enzymes far above the concentration found outside the particles. By this mechanism the kinetic responses of enzyme-catalyzed reactions in mitochondria are greatly changed.

A final but difficult factor to evaluate is the possible physical compartmentation of enzymic sequences, which would introduce new variables such as permeability barriers toward substrates, enzymes, and cofactors. By compartmentation we mean the actual physical separation of enzymes or substrates into areas in the cell.

Control of Enzyme Concentration and Activity

Substances that decrease the rate of an enzyme-catalyzed reaction are known as *inhibitors* (see Chapter 7 for a discussion of inhibitors). The influences of competitive and noncompetitive inhibitors on enzymic rates are simple and well known. A more complex effect is the action of dinitrophenol on the uncoupling of oxidative phosphorylation with a resultant loss of utilizable energy for the cell.

An even more subtle type of control of enzyme action is designated as *feedback inhibition*. This is demonstrated most easily by considering the following sequence:

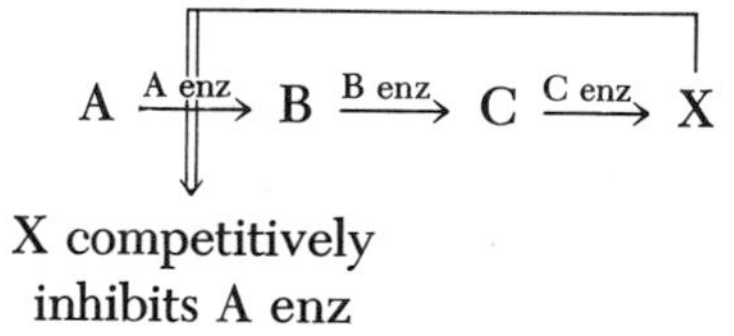

$$A \xrightarrow{A\ enz} B \xrightarrow{B\ enz} C \xrightarrow{C\ enz} X$$

X competitively
inhibits A enz

The inhibition of the conversion of A to B by X would be such an inhibition. Here X, the ultimate product of the sequence, serves to prevent the formation of one of its own precursors by inhibiting the action of enzyme A. Enzyme A can be called the pacemaker since the entire sequence is effectively regulated by inhibiting it. An actual example is the formation in *E. coli* of cytidylic acid from aspartic acid and carbamyl phosphate. As a critical concentration of cytidylic acid is built up, the acid slows down its own formation by inhibiting the first or pacemaker step of its own synthesis. When the concentration of cytidylic acid is sufficiently lowered by metabolic utilization, inhibition is released, and its synthesis renewed (see the accompanying diagram).

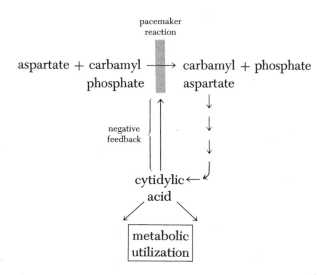

pacemaker
reaction

aspartate + carbamyl ⟶ carbamyl + phosphate
phosphate   aspartate

negative
feedback

cytidylic ←
acid

metabolic
utilization

metabolic utilization low: cytidylic acid concentration high;
negative feedback operates

metabolic utilization high: cytidylic acid concentration low;
negative feedback inoperative

Thus the feedback mechanism is responsible for continually adjusting the rate of synthesis of metabolic intermediates according to the demands of synthesis. Usually an end product inhibits an early reaction in its synthesis, thereby avoiding the buildup of several intermediates, which would be wasteful to the cell.

Another important mechanism of the cell is that of *repression*. This mechanism controls the concentration of certain cellular enzymes. A small molecule—frequently an end product (also called a metabolic repressor)—inhibits the formation of an enzyme which acts on an early stage of the synthesis of the repressor. Thus X would inhibit the *formation* of enz A. The act of repression appears to inhibit the actual synthesis of an enzyme protein from amino acids rather than the inhibition of a specific enzyme. Hence repression is too slow for the continuous adjustment of metabolic sequences we have seen, whereas the mechanism of feedback inhibition is rapid. Repression of the formation of an enzyme by a product of the enzyme's action enables the cell to dispense with making more enzymes than it actually needs for optimal growth, however. The cell thus releases amino acids for the synthesis of other enzymes that catalyze the formation of compounds in short and needed supply.

Just as *repression* cuts back on the formation of a critical enzyme by a product of that sequence, so *induction* is an important means by which the rate of synthesis of an enzyme can be stimulated several thousandfold. This is accomplished by the addition of the enzyme's substrate to the medium in which the cell is growing. With *sequential induction*, the addition of compound A to the medium induces the formation of A enz, which catalyzes the conversion of A to B.

A corollary of sequential induction is that when compound C is introduced to the system, C enz is induced but not A enz and only slightly B enz. Stanier of the University of California introduced the technique of *sequential induction* as a means of elucidating the metabolism of a compound. Thus a cell may not normally be too concerned in the metabolism of compound A but if it is forced to use compound A as its sole source of carbon for growth, it will synthesize large quantities of A enz, B enz, C enz, etc., in order to utilize A. Furthermore, if compound C is added to a cell which has been exposed to A, there will be no lag period in the utilization of C for further conversions, since C enz has already been induced by A. If compound M, which is not on the pathway of A to C, is added, the cell cannot cope with M for a finite period of time, dependent on the induction of enzyme M for the utilization of M. This valuable tool was used to explore the metabolism of compounds such as tyrosine and many other compounds in bacteria.

By feedback control, repression, and induction, enzymes in metabolic pathways can be maintained at precise levels so that substrates or intermediates can in turn be kept at physiologically proper concentrations. While inducibility is the rule for *catabolic* enzyme sequences—degradation of exogenous substrates—repressibility is the rule for *anabolic* sequences involved in the synthesis of amino acid and nucleotides. Both repression and induction are highly specific, but inducers are *substrates* of the sequences, whereas metabolic repressors are *products* of the sequences.

The role of hormones in metabolic regulation remains as yet unexplained. These substances have not been recognized to function either as enzymes or as coenzymes. Because of the latent period of hormone action, the extremely low concentrations required to produce physiological effects, and their high degree of specificity in action *in vivo*, hormones probably function in controlling either the synthesis or activation of enzymes. In support of this view, Sutherland has shown that the drug *epinephrine* remarkably increases the concentration of the active form of phosphorylase (phosphorylase *a*) in rabbit liver. This effect is related to the conversion of the inactive form, phosphorylase *b*, to the active enzyme *in vivo*.

Still another view of hormone action is emerging. Tompkins of the National Institutes of Health has made the interesting observation that a number of steroid hormones can cause reversible disaggregation of some crystalline enzymes, notably glutamic dehydrogenase, into inactive subunits. ADP remarkably reverses the dissociation reaction and hence maintains activity. Further investigation has shown that the subunits of glutamic dehydrogenase, while inactive as catalysts for L-glutamic acid as substrate, attain a new dehydrogenase activity for another amino acid, namely L-alanine. Since there is a definite correlation between the ability of a steroid hormone to inhibit the reaction catalyzed by glutamic dehydrogenase and its capacity to promote disaggregation of the enzyme and a shift in substrate specificity, a new mechanism of hormone action is suggested. The role of hormones on the control of metabolic activity by this type of mechanism is obvious. We can summarize these results with the diagram on the next page.

A Postulated Mechanism for Induction and Repression

J. Monod of the Pasteur Institute in Paris and his colleagues F. Jacob and F. Gros have recently proposed a mechanism for induction and repression. In part based on experimental evidence and in part speculative, it provides the student with a framework on which to consolidate the information in this chapter with that in Chapters 15 and 20.

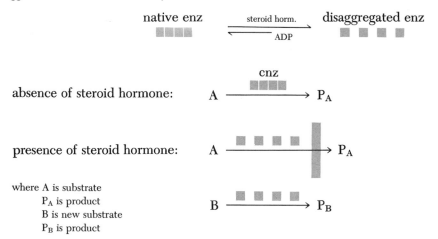

where A is substrate
    P_A is product
    B is new substrate
    P_B is product

Monod assumes that there are, in general, two types of genes, the *structural genes* (SG) which act to assemble ribonucleotides to form *m*-RNA, and the *regulator genes* (RG) whose nucleotide sequence is assumed to be identical with the specific sequence of the *operator* (O). The operator is considered to be the initiation point at certain parts of the DNA strands of genes and is adjacent to its specific structural gene. The operator and structural-gene complex is called an *operon*. The regulator gene is assumed to function by forming a polyribonucleotide called a *repressor* (R) which tends to associate reversibly with its homologous operator. This association blocks completely the formation of *m*-RNA by the adjacent structural gene and in turn prevents synthesis of the protein whose synthesis is controlled by its *m*-RNA. One set of repressors reacts with an inducer and is converted to an inactive form (R′), thereby permitting SG to form its *m*-RNA. The newly assembled *m*-RNA now migrates to ribosomal RNA to permit the synthesis of the specific protein controlled by the *m*-RNA. The mechanism of repression differs somewhat. In this case the repressor is thought to be normally inactive and is thus unable to block synthesis of the specific *m*-RNA. It may react, however, with its specific metabolic repressor (MR) to become activated (Ra) and now can combine with its homologous operator to prevent *m*-RNA synthesis.

Inactivation of a regulator gene or of its repressor by mutation results in uncontrolled or "constitutive" synthesis of enzymes.

These ideas are formulated in Figures 21-1 and 21-2.

The regulation of enzyme synthesis appears to hinge on the inactivation or activation of the repressor by cytoplasmic factors, namely metabolic repressors and inducers. The concentration or availability of these compounds and the rate of their effects on repressor activation or inactivation provide a sensitive control of enzyme or protein synthesis.   The actual isolation and chemical characterization of Monod's postulated repressors hence become of paramount importance; they would provide the necessary proof of this exciting postulate.

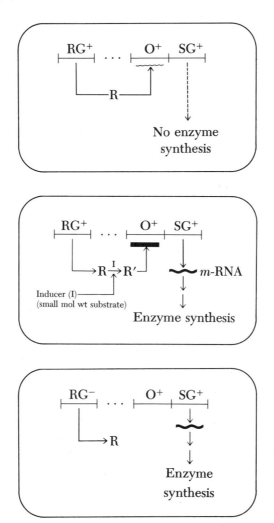

Fig. 21-1.   Postulated mechanism for induction and constitutive enzyme synthesis.   The top sketch shows a wild-type cell.   R synthesized by RG^+ attaches to O^+ and prevents formation of m-RNA by SG^+.   The middle sketch shows that, in presence of inducer(I), $R \rightarrow R,'$ which is inactive and cannot combine with O^+ to block SG^+ synthesis of m-RNA.   Therefore m-RNA is formed and in turn controls synthesis of specific protein.   In the third sketch, inactivation of $RG^I \rightarrow RG$ by mutation prevents formation of R, and thus uncontrolled or constitutive synthesis of enzyme protein occurs.

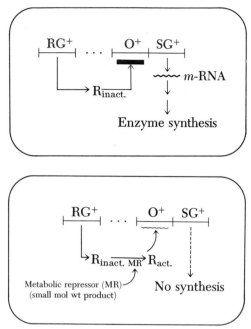

Fig. 21-2. Postulated mechanism of repression. In the top drawing, RG^+ forms a repressor which is inactive and which cannot block m-RNA synthesis. In the lower sketch, introduction of the metabolic repressor (MR) activates R_{inact} R_{act} which can now combine with O^+ to block m-RNA synthesis and thereby repress protein synthesis.

In summary, the precise nature of the regulation of metabolism is still obscure. The concepts of negative feedback, repression, and induction have been developed from experimentation with bacteria. There is, however, increasing evidence that these concepts also apply to similar problems in plant and animal tissues. The new developments in the field of biochemistry we have outlined must be implicated as major factors in the control mechanisms of metabolism. The nature of the master mechanism that determines the overall control or that triggers the many mechanisms at its disposal remains as yet a fertile but unexplored field. Monod's postulate, which brings together the role of genes with protein synthesis and metabolic regulation, is a challenging concept to the explorers of this field.

REFERENCES

1. *Ciba Foundation Symposium on the Regulation of Cell Metabolism,* J. and A. Churchill, London, 1959.
    A most stimulating compilation of original papers presented at a Ciba Foundation Sym-

posium in 1959 in London.   Authorities in the field present many views which are promptly challenged by members of the symposium in the printed discussion period after each major paper.   Excellent for the advanced student.

2. Arthur B. Pardee in *The Enzymes,* edited by Paul D. Boyer, Henry Lardy, and Karl Myr-back, Academic Press, New York, 2nd edition, 1959, Vol. 1, p. 681.

    A good review article in a rapidly expanding field.

3. F. Jacob and J. Monod, *Journal of Molecular Biology,* 3, 318–356(1961).

    A very important contribution by leaders in the field to the genetic regulatory mechanism in the synthesis of proteins—highly recommended for the advanced student.

4. Cold Spring Harbor Symposia in Quantitative Biology, Vol. 26, *Cellular Regulatory Mechanisms,* The Biological Lab., Cold Spring Harbor, Long Island, New York, 1962.

    Exceedingly well timed and useful compilation by leaders in the field.   A must for the advanced student.

Appendix 1

Buffer and pH Problems

Solution of Quadratic Equations

In Chapter 1 the solution of the quadratic equation 1-11 is referred to the appendix. The equation is

$$\frac{x^2}{1-x} = 1.8 \times 10^{-5}$$

This may be rearranged to:

$$x^2 = (1.8 \times 10^{-5})(1 - x)$$
$$x^2 = 1.8 \times 10^{-5} - (1.8 \times 10^{-5})x$$
$$x^2 + (1.8 \times 10^{-5})x - 1.8 \times 10^{-5} = 0$$

This equation is then in the form: $ax^2 + bx + c = 0$, in which

$$a = 1$$
$$b = 1.8 \times 10^{-5}$$
$$c = -1.8 \times 10^{-5}$$

The solution of a quadratic equation is found as:

$$x = \frac{-b \pm \sqrt{b^2 - 4ac}}{2a}$$

Substituting the values for a, b, and c in the quadratic solution,

$$x = \frac{-(1.8 \times 10^{-5}) \pm \sqrt{(1.8 \times 10^{-5})^2 - 4(-1.8 \times 10^{-5})}}{2}$$

$$= \frac{-(1.8 \times 10^{-5}) \pm \sqrt{3.22 \times 10^{-10} + 7.2 \times 10^{-5}}}{2}$$

$$= \frac{-(1.8 \times 10^{-5}) \pm \sqrt{72 \times 10^{-6}}}{2}$$

$$= \frac{-1.8 \times 10^{-5} \pm 8.48 \times 10^{-3}}{2}$$

$$= +4.231 \times 10^{-3} \quad \text{or}$$
$$\quad -4.249 \times 10^{-3}$$

Since in this problem x is the concentration of hydrogen ions $[H^+]$ and can have only positive values, the positive value for x is appropriate. Therefore

$$[H^+] = 4.23 \times 10^{-3} \text{ moles/l}$$

Review of Logarithms

There are two systems of logarithms; one is the natural or Naperian system, which employs the base e, and the other is the common system, which has 10 as its base. The logarithm (x or y respectively) of any number a to the base number e or 10 is the power to which the base e or 10 must be raised to equal a. These may be written

$$x = \log_e a \qquad y = \log_{10} a$$
$$= \ln a$$

The two systems are related by:

$$x = \log_e a = 2.303 \log_{10} a = 2.303 y$$

In this book logarithms to the base 10 are used almost exclusively. Examples of logarithms to the base 10 are

$$\log 10 = 1$$
$$\log 100 = \log 10^2 = 2$$
$$\log 1000 = \log 10^3 = 3$$
$$\log 0.001 = \log 10^{-3} = -3$$
$$\log 1 = 0$$

For numbers between 1 and 10, tables of logarithms are available or may be read directly from a slide rule. Examples:

$$\log 2 = 0.301$$
$$\log 3 = 0.477$$
$$\log 6 = 0.778$$
$$\log 7 = 0.845$$

The student should be familiar with the operations employed in logarithms. For example, the logarithms are added in multiplication; in division, the logarithms are subtracted. Examples:

$$4 \times 6 = 24$$
$$\log 24 = \log 4 + \log 6$$
$$= 0.602 + 0.778$$
$$= 1.380$$

As a check,

$$\begin{aligned}
\log 24 &= \log (10 \times 2.4) \\
&= \log 10 + \log 2.4 \\
&= 1.0 + 0.380 \\
&= 1.380
\end{aligned}$$

In pH problems two operations are frequently encountered. As an example, when the $[H^+]$ is given

$$[H^+] = 3 \times 10^{-4} \text{ moles/l}$$

calculate the pH:

$$\begin{aligned}
pH &= \log \frac{1}{[H^+]} = -\log [H^+] \\
&= -\log (3 \times 10^{-4}) \\
&= -\log 3 - \log 10^{-4} \\
&= -0.477 - (-4) \\
&= 3.523
\end{aligned}$$

The other common operation is to calculate the $[H^+]$ from a given pH. Calculate the $[H^+]$ of a solution whose pH is 9.26:

$$\begin{aligned}
pH &= 9.26 \\
[H^+] &= \text{antilog} -9.26 \\
&= \text{antilog} (-10 + 0.74) \\
&= 10^{-10} \times 5.5 \\
&= 5.5 \times 10^{-10} \text{ moles/l}
\end{aligned}$$

PROBLEMS

1. Calculate the pH of

	Answer:	
$10^{-4}M$ $[H^+]$		4.00
$7 \times 10^{-5}M$ $[H^+]$		4.16
$5 \times 10^{-8}M$ $[H^+]$		7.30
$3 \times 10^{-11}M$ $[H^+]$		10.52

2. Calculate the $[H^+]$ of a solution whose pH is given:

pH		
2.73	Answer:	$1.86 \times 10^{-3}M$ $[H^+]$
5.29		$5.13 \times 10^{-6}M$ $[H^+]$
8.65		$2.24 \times 10^{-9}M$ $[H^+]$
11.12		$7.59 \times 10^{-12}M$ $[H^+]$

3. *Problems on Chemical Stoichiometry*

(a) Concentrated H_2SO_4 is 96% H_2SO_4 by weight and has a density of 1.84. Calculate the amount of concentrated acid required to make 750 ml of $1N$ H_2SO_4.

Answer: One l of concentrated acid weighs 1840 g and contains 1840×0.96 or 1760 g of H_2SO_4. One l of concentrated H_2SO_4 is therefore 1760/98 or 18 molar (18M). Since H_2SO_4 is a diprotic acid producing 2 protons for 1 mole of H_2SO_4, concentrated H_2SO_4 is 36 normal (36N). 750 ml of 1N H_2SO_4 contains 750 meq. Therefore 750/36 or 20.8 ml of concentrated H_2SO_4 will contain 750 meq. If 20.8 ml of concentrated H_2SO_4 are diluted to 750 ml with H_2O, the solution will be 1N.

(b) Concentrated HCl is 37.5% HCl by weight and has a density of 1.19. Describe the preparation of 500 ml of 0.2N HCl.

Answer: Dilute 8.18 ml of concentrated HCl to 500 ml with H_2O.

(c) Glacial CH_3COOH is 100% CH_3COOH by weight and has a density of 1.05. Describe the preparation of 300 ml of 0.5N CH_3COOH.

Answer: Dilute 8.6 ml of glacial CH_3COOH to 300 ml with H_2O.

(d) Calculate the $[H^+]$ of the final solution when 100 ml of 0.1N NaOH is added to 150 ml of 0.2M HCl.

Answer: 0.08M.

(e) Calculate the $[H^+]$ of the final solution when 100 ml of 0.1N NaOH is added to 150 ml of 0.2M H_2SO_4.

Answer: 0.2N.

4. *Buffer Problems*

(a) Calculate the pH of the final solution when 100 ml of 0.1M NaOH is added to 150 ml of 0.2M CH_3COOH ($K_a = 1.8 \times 10^{-5}$). 150 ml of 0.2M CH_3COOH contains 0.03 moles of CH_3COOH; similarly, 100 ml of 0.1M NaOH contains 0.01 mole of NaOH. When these are mixed, 0.01 mole of NaOH will neutralize an equal amount of CH_3COOH to form 0.01 mole of sodium acetate; 0.02 mole of CH_3COOH will remain. Both of these are contained in a volume of 250 ml. The pH may be solved for by use of the Henderson-Hasselbalch equation:

$$pH = pK_a + \log \frac{[\text{conjugate Brönsted base}]}{[\text{Brönsted acid}]}$$

Calculate the pK_a first:

$$\begin{aligned} pK_a &= -\log 1.8 \times 10^{-5} \\ &= -\log 1.8 - \log 10^{-5} \\ &= -0.26 + 5 \\ &= 4.74 \end{aligned}$$

Therefore

$$pH = 4.74 + \log \frac{[CH_3COO^-]}{[CH_3COOH]}$$

$$= 4.74 + \log \frac{(0.01/250)}{(0.02/250)}$$

Note, however, that the volume (250 ml) which contains the acetate anion and acetic acid is found in both the numerator and denominator. The last equation simplifies to:

$$\begin{aligned} pH &= 4.74 + \log \tfrac{1}{2} \\ &= 4.74 - \log 2 \\ &= 4.74 - 0.30 \\ &= 4.44 \end{aligned}$$

(b) The pK_a's for H_3PO_4 are: $pK_{a_1} = 2.1$; $pK_{a_2} = 7.2$; $pK_{a_3} = 12.7$. Describe the preparation of a phosphate buffer, pH 6.7, starting with a $0.1M$ solution of H_3PO_4 and $0.1M$ NaOH.

Answer: The second dissociation of phosphoric acid will be the buffer system.

$$H_2PO_4^- \rightleftharpoons HPO_4^{2-} + H^+ \qquad pK_{a_2} = 7.2$$

The ratio of conjugate base (HPO_4^{2-}) to the Brönsted acid ($H_2PO_4^-$) may be calculated from the Henderson-Hasselbalch equation:

$$pH = pK_{a_2} + \log \frac{[HPO_4^{2-}]}{[H_2PO_4^-]}$$

$$6.7 = 7.2 + \log \frac{[HPO_4^{2-}]}{[H_2PO_4^-]}$$

$$-0.5 = \log \frac{[HPO_4^{2-}]}{[H_2PO_4^-]}$$

$$0.5 = \log \frac{[H_2PO_4^-]}{[HPO_4^{2-}]}$$

$$\text{ratio} \frac{[H_2PO_4^-]}{[HPO_4^{2-}]} = \text{antilog } 0.5$$

$$\frac{[H_2PO_4^-]}{[HPO_4^{2-}]} = \frac{3.16}{1}$$

In this buffer there will be 316 parts of $H_2PO_4^-$ and 100 parts of HPO_4^{2-} for a total of 416. Since all the phosphate buffer components must come from $0.1M$ H_3PO_4, start by taking 41.6 ml of $0.1M$ H_3PO_4 and add 41.6 ml of $0.1N$ NaOH to neutralize the first proton, which dissociates at $pK_{a_1} = 2.1$. Then add 10.0 ml more of alkali to produce 1.0 meq of HPO_4^{2-} and leave 3.16 meq of $H_2PO_4^-$. This would give the desired ratio of $H_2PO_4^-/HPO_4^{2-}$ and consequently a pH of 6.7. The buffer concentration would be equal to the milliequivalents of H_3PO_4 (4.16) divided by the milliliters of the final solution (93.2), or $0.045M$.

(c) Describe the preparation of 100 ml of $0.1M$ phosphate buffer, pH 6.7, starting with $1M$ H_3PO_4 and $1M$ NaOH.

Solution: The same ratio of $H_2PO_4^-/HPO_4^{2-}$ of 3.16 must be obtained. To prepare 100 ml of $0.1M$ phosphate buffer, take 10 ml of $1M$ H_3PO_4. Then add 10 ml of $1M$ NaOH to neutralize the first proton that dissociates. Then, to obtain the correct ratio, add $10 \times 1/4.16$ or 2.4 ml more of $1M$ NaOH and dilute to final volume of 100 ml.

PROBLEMS

1. What would be the pH and concentration of the resulting buffer solution when 3.48 g of K_2HPO_4 and 2.72 g of KH_2PO_4 are dissolved in 250 ml of deionized water?

Answer: pH = 7.2; the concentration is $0.16M$.

2. A buffer solution contains $0.1M$ CH_3COOH and $0.1M$ sodium acetate (that is, it is a $0.2M$ acetate buffer). Calculate the pH after addition of 4 ml of $0.025N$ HCl to 10 ml of the buffer. The pK_a for acetic acid is 4.74.

Answer: pH = 4.65.

3. Describe the preparation of a glutaric acid buffer at pH 4.2 starting with 0.1M NaOH and 0.1M glutaric acid ($pK_{a_1} = 4.32$; $pK_{a_2} = 5.54$).

Answer: Add 100 ml NaOH to 232 ml of glutaric acid or any similar ratio of base to acid.

4. Pyridine is a conjugate base which reacts with H^+ to form pyridine hydrochloride. The hydrochloride dissociates to yield H^+ with a pK_a of 5.36. Describe the preparation of a pyridine buffer at pH 5.2 starting with 0.1M pyridine and 0.1M HCl.

Answer: Add 14.5 ml of 0.1M HCl to 24.5 ml of 0.1M pyridine.

5. Describe the preparation of 1 l of a 0.1M ammonium chloride buffer, pH 9.0, starting with solid ammonium chloride ($pK_a = 9.26$) and 1M NaOH.

Answer: Dissolve 5.35 g NH_4Cl in approximately 500 ml of H_2O, add 35.5 ml of 1M NaOH, and dilute to 1.0 l.

6. Describe the preparation of 1 l of 0.1M ammonium chloride buffer, pH 9.0, starting with 1M NH_4OH and 1M HCl.

Answer: Add 64.5 ml of 1M HCl to 100 ml of 1.0M NH_4OH and dilute to 1 l.

7. What volume of glacial acetic acid and what weight of sodium acetate trihydrate ($CH_3COONa \cdot 3H_2O$) are required to make 100 ml of 0.2M buffer at pH 4.5 (pK_a of acetic acid is 4.74)?

Answer: 0.725 ml glacial acetic acid and 0.993 g of sodium acetate trihydrate.

8. What weight of sodium carbonate (Na_2CO_3) and sodium bicarbonate ($NaHCO_3$) are required to make 500 ml of 0.2M buffer, pH 10.7 (pK_{a_1} of H_2CO_3 is 6.1; $pK_{a_2} = 10.3$)?

Answer: 7.58 g of Na_2CO_3 and 2.40 g of $NaHCO_3$.

9. What volume of concentrated HCl and what weight of tris-(hydroxymethyl)-amino methane (as the base) are required to make 100 ml of 0.25M buffer, pH 8.0 (pK_a of Tris hydrochloride is 8.0)?

Answer: 3.025 g of Tris (as the base) and 1.025 ml of concentrated HCl.

10. Describe the preparation of 250 ml of 0.6M triethanolamine buffer, pH 7.2, from the free amine and concentrated HCl (pK_a for the amine hydrochloride is 7.8).

Answer: Dissolve 22.4 g of amine in approximately 100 ml of H_2O, add 9.85 ml of HCl, and dilute to 250 ml.

Appendix 2

Review of Some Modern Concepts in Organic Chemistry

A review of the effect of functional groups on their neighboring atoms will greatly assist the student in understanding the mode of action of coenzymes in biochemical reactions. The student should consult Cram and Hammond's *Organic Chemistry* (McGraw-Hill, New York, 1960), Cason's *Introduction to Organic Chemistry* (Prentice-Hall, New York, 1956), and Ingraham's *Biochemical Mechanisms* (Wiley, New York, 1962) for further information.

Introduction

Atoms are held together by means of a chemical bond which restrains the motions of atoms in a molecule. This restraint fixes the distance between atoms. The chemical bond is usually represented by a dash (—), and a single dash represents a pair of electrons attracted by the positive charge of the nuclei of the two similar atoms. The attraction is equal if the atoms are alike (C:C) but differs if the atoms are unlike (C:O). If the attraction is unequal, the atoms will assume a fractional positive or negative charge (δ^+ or δ^-) depending on the direction of attraction of the electrons by the unlike atoms. An important determinant is the electronegativity of an atom. This is a term introduced by Linus Pauling to describe empirically the relative attraction of electrons by an atom.

As a general rule the affinity of an atom for electrons in a given period of the periodic table increases from left to right, because the increasing nuclear charge of the atom exerts a greater pull for the valence electrons rotating around the nucleus. Thus fluorine exerts the greatest pull whereas oxygen, nitrogen, and carbon exert decreasing pulls in that order. In addition, electron affinity decreases from the top to the bottom of a given group of the periodic table. Although the nuclear charge increases in this case, the greater number of electron shells effectively shields the nuclear charge from the valence electron shell. Thus the electronegativity of fluorine is the greatest whereas chlorine, bromine, and iodine decrease in that order.

The electronegative effect in hydrogen fluoride gas can be represented as:

$$H \overset{\delta+}{\underline{\quad\quad}} : \overset{..}{\underset{..}{F}} : {}^{\delta-}$$

indicating that in the bonding electron cloud, the electrons are more concentrated around F than around H, for the reasons already cited. This electrically asymmetric bond is a *polar bond*. An intensely polar molecule tends to ionize in polar solvents, revealing an ionic character. There is complete removal of an electron from the cation by the anion. Both ions then assume the stable valence shell of a noble gas:

$$Li\cdot \; + \; .\overset{..}{F}: \; \longrightarrow \; Li^+ \; + \; :\overset{..}{\underset{..}{F}}:^-$$

atom	atom	cation	anion
		(like helium	(like neon
		structure)	structure)

Nonpolar bonds are *covalent*, a term indicating an equal sharing of an electron pair by two atoms. When two atoms are unlike, the shift or polarization of electrons toward or away from an atom, depending on the electronegative character of the atom, yields a molecule partially polarized. A shift or drift of a lone electron pair toward an electron attracting atom is indicated by a curved arrow ($\frown$):

$$A \overset{\frown}{\quad} B \; \longleftrightarrow \; \overset{\delta+}{A} \overset{\delta-}{-B}$$

$$>C \overset{\frown}{=} O \; \longleftrightarrow \; >\overset{\delta+}{C} - \overset{\delta-}{O}:$$

Functional groups, found so frequently in biochemical compounds, *have a pronounced effect* on the reactivity of a given biochemical through their inductive effect on the electron pair constituting a covalent bond. Many examples of induced charge effects will be found throughout this book.

Resonance

Many molecules are not completely described by simple, fixed, electronic structures. Thus acetic acid can be written as two forms, both completely equivalent to a third form. Each form is a *resonance structure* but the actual structure of acetic acid is *a resonance hybrid* of the three forms I, II, and III. The double-headed arrow ($\longleftrightarrow$) indicates

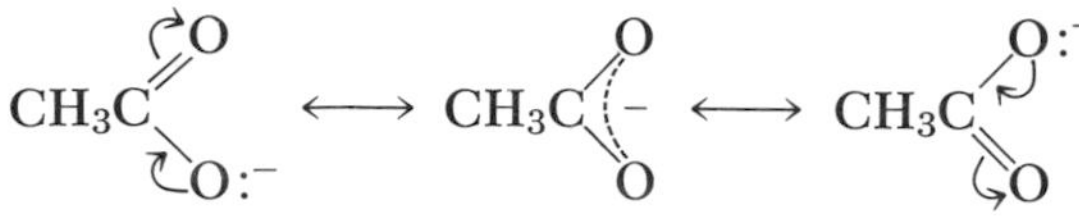

I   II   III
resonance

that all three forms are superimposable on each other and fully equivalent.   Molecules for which a number of resonance structures can be
written are unusually stable.   This stability may be related to the delo-
calization of electrons indicated in structures I, II, and III.

The term *resonance energy* may be defined as the difference in the
actual heat of formation (ΔH) of a compound and that calculated from
tabulated bond energies for its *most stable bond structure*.   The difference in calories represents the amount by which the molecule is actually
more stable than it would be if it were present in a rigid structure such as
only I or III, not as I $\longleftrightarrow$ II $\longleftrightarrow$ III.

Resonance involves only a movement of electrons over the same
atomic skeleton, and these forms can never be isolated.   Resonance
structures therefore differ from *tautomers*, structures which show a real
difference in structure and can be isolated chemically.   Most frequently,
a proton migrates from one site to another.

ketol form   enol form

Inductive Effects

Acids are ideal molecules on which to study the effect of structure on
reactivity.

Table A-2-1 lists a series of derivatives of propionic acid.   It will be
noted that if an α-hydrogen atom is replaced by the electronegative
chlorine atom (—Cl) or the strongly positive center —NH_3^+, a large

Table A-2-1

Acid	pK_a
CH_3CH_2COOH	4.85
$CH_3CHClCOOH$	2.83
$ClCH_2CH_2COOH$	3.98
$CH_3CH(NH_3^+)COOH$	2.3
$(NH_3^+)CH_2CH_2COOH$	3.6

acid-strengthening effect is observed. In the case of chlorine the electronegative character of the chlorine atom attracts electrons from the carboxylate group, thereby permitting a greater ease of dissociation of a proton. In the case of the $-NH_3^+$ center, the large repulsion force pushes the positively charged proton away from the carboxylate group. A separation of these groups by one methylene group ($-CH_2-$) greatly weakens these effects and demonstrates the short-range forces involved.

Strong electron withdrawing, inductive effects are found in $-NR_3$, $-ONO_2$, $-C\equiv N$, $-CO_2H$, $C=O$, F, Cl, and Br.

Another important factor is the presence of a charged group in a molecule, which induces an effect on a similar group. The effect is greater or smaller depending on the geometric relation in space of the second group. Thus

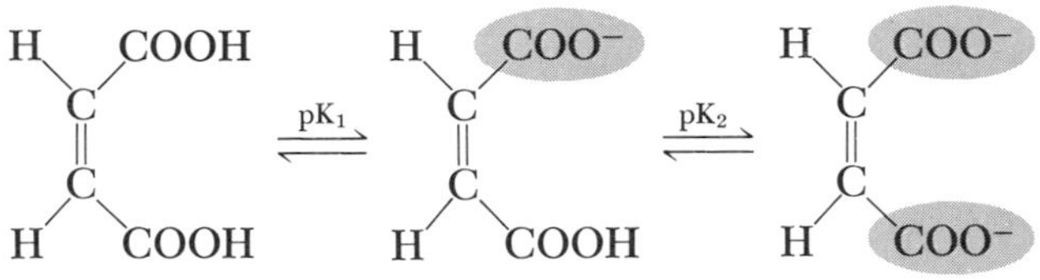

maleic acid (*cis*)
$pK_1 = 1.93; \quad pK_2 = 6.58$

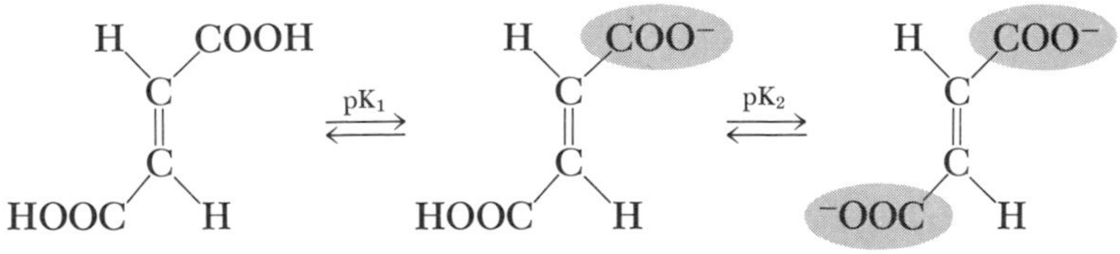

fumaric acid (*trans*)
$pK_1 = 3.03; \quad pK_2 = 4.54$

Note that the ionized carboxyl group of the *cis* acid, maleic acid, is considerably closer to the second carboxyl group than are the carboxyl groups in the *trans* isomer; the pK_a of the second carboxyl of the *cis* acid will therefore be much weaker than that found in the *trans* acid, fumaric acid.

Hydrogen Bonds

Compounds that contain O—H or N—H bonds show considerable evidence of association. Thus water (H_2O) melts at $0°C$, methanol (CH_3OH) at $-98°C$, and dimethyl ether (CH_3OCH_3) at $-140°C$.

The HOH structure in water pronouncedly increases the interaction of the molecules of water with each other, whereas in methanol the interaction is less, and in dimethyl ether the CH_3 groups have replaced the H atoms of the HOH structure with a marked decrease in interaction.

This association tendency on the part of molecules with —O—H and $>$N—H bonds is explained in terms of *hydrogen bonding*. Thus the oxygen and nitrogen atoms will tend to attract the electron pair which they share with hydrogen. As a result the hydrogen atom assumes the character of a proton and will tend to share electrons of neighboring oxygen or nitrogen atoms. This is illustrated by the examples given in our diagram.

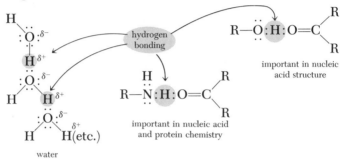

The hydrogen bond is weak with a bond energy of approximately 4.5 kcal/mole in contrast to the average covalent bond energy of 80 kcal/mole for a C—C bond. Many of these bonds, oriented in a specific manner, reinforce each other to form very stable structures, however. The secondary structure of proteins is determined by hydrogen bonding of the peptide bond groups; base pairing in RNA and DNA structures is intimately related to the capacity of the bases adenine and uracil or thymine, and guanine and cytosine, to associate by hydrogen bondings. It is believed that avidin forms its very tight affinity to biotin by hydrogen bonding of part of its protein structure to the ureido group in the biotin molecule.

Characterization of Reactions

The most important bond-making and bond-breaking reaction in biochemistry is a heterolytic (ionic) cleavage of a covalent bond. The bond is broken unsymmetrically in such a manner that the pair of electrons making up the covalent bond are now shared wholly by one atom.

$$C|:\overset{\curvearrowright}{C} \longrightarrow C^+ + :C^-$$

or

$$\overset{\curvearrowleft}{C}:|C \longrightarrow C:^- + C^+$$

The negatively charged carbon atom is called a *carbanion* ($:C^-$) and the positively charged carbon atom is called a *carbonium ion* (C^+). A carbanion, because it has a pair of unshared electrons, is also called a *nucleophile* (N). Nucleophiles also include negatively charged anions such as

$$R-O-\overset{+}{P}\overset{O:^-}{\underset{O:^-}{-}}O:^-$$

molecules with unshared electrons such as $:NH_3$, $H_2O:$ and CoAS̈H or a highly polarized molecule such as $^-:CH_2COSCoA$.

A carbonium ion is deficient in electrons, very transient, and not isolatable. It can also be classified as an *electrophile* (E; electron-loving). Electrophiles include positively charged sites in a molecule

$$\underset{\overset{|}{H}\ \overset{|}{H}}{\overset{\overset{|}{H}\ \overset{O}{\nwarrow}}{CH_3C=CC}}-S-CoA \longleftrightarrow CH_3\overset{\delta+}{C}HCH=\overset{O^{\delta-}}{C}-S-CoA$$

and positively charged atoms such as the phosphorus atoms in ATP

$$adenosyl\text{-}ribotide-O-\underset{OH}{\overset{O^-}{\overset{|}{P^{\pm}}}}-O-\underset{OH}{\overset{O^-}{\overset{|}{P^{\pm}}}}-O-\underset{OH}{\overset{O^-}{\overset{|}{P^{\pm}}}}-OH$$

Types of Reaction

SUBSTITUTION

In substitution reactions, which are found frequently in biochemistry, single bonds are made and broken as a new (incoming or I) group substitutes or displaces the old (leaving or L) group. The I and L groups are usually nucleophiles or nucleophilic reagents of different reactivity, implying that they possess an unshared pair of electrons. An arrow ($\lceil:x \longrightarrow$) indicates the group that is leaving with its pair of electrons.

A typical example is the hydrolysis of an acyl-CoA ester by water catalyzed by a thioesterase. Here I is the nucleophilic reagent which displaces the leaving group L. The reactivity of the leaving group is determined in part by its ability to accommodate a negative charge and/or the polarizability of the compound being attacked. Phosphate ion is a good leaving group in biochemical systems because it is the anion of a strong acid and therefore can accommodate a negative charge. Coenzyme A is equally good as a leaving group because of the polarizable

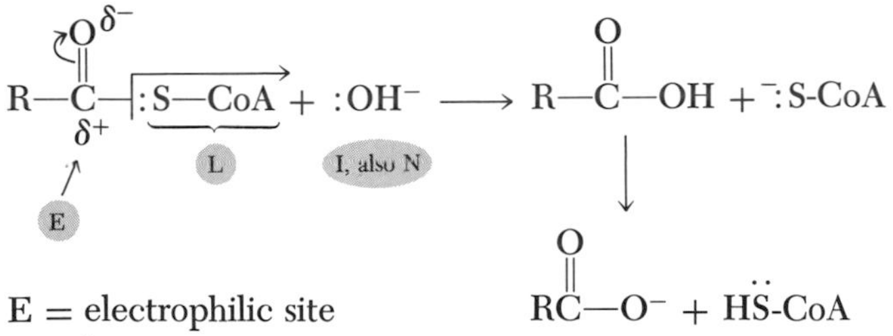

$$R—\overset{\overset{\displaystyle O^{\delta-}}{\|}}{\underset{\delta+}{C}}\underbrace{—[:S—CoA}_{L} + :OH^- \longrightarrow R—\overset{\overset{\displaystyle O}{\|}}{C}—OH + {}^-:S\text{-}CoA$$

E (electrophilic site pointing to C)   I, also N

$$\downarrow$$

$$R\overset{\overset{\displaystyle O}{\|}}{C}—O^- + H\overset{..}{S}\text{-}CoA$$

E = electrophilic site
L = leaving group
I = incoming group
N = nucleophile attack

sulfur atom, as well as equally effective as an incoming group, since the sulfhydryl group is a good nucleophile.

ADDITION AND ELIMINATION

Whereas addition reactions imply the addition of two substituent groups across a double-bond system, elimination reactions are essentially the reverse, producing a double bond. A good example is the hydration of fumaric acid by fumarase to form malate by a *trans* addition:

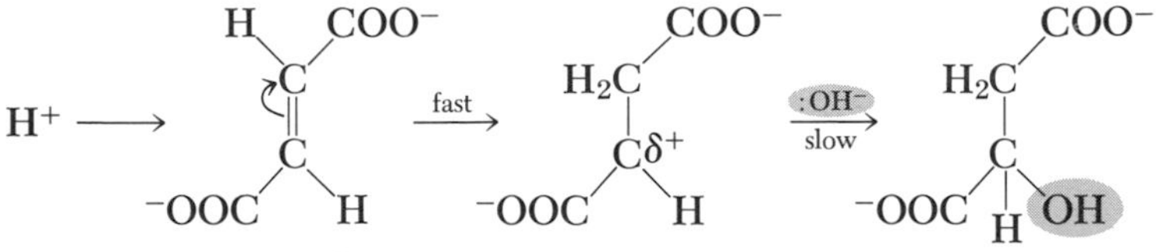

$$H^+ \longrightarrow$$

fumaric acid   L-malic acid

Other enzymes which catalyze addition and elimination reactions include aconitase, crotonase, and aspartase.

CONDENSATIONS

This reaction is represented by an *aldol condensation* in which the following sequence can take place:

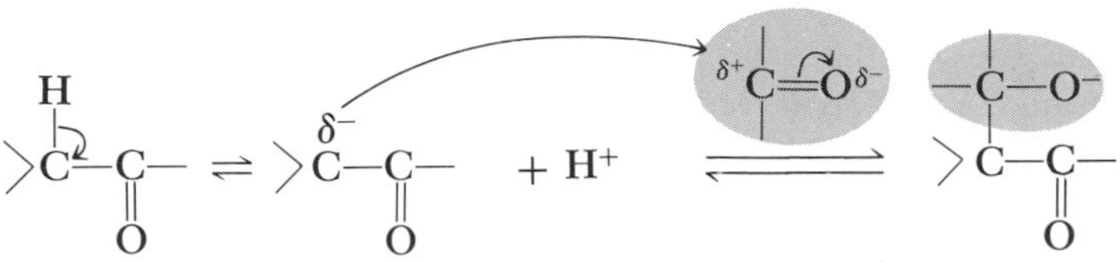

An excellent example in biochemistry is the reaction catalyzed by aldolase.

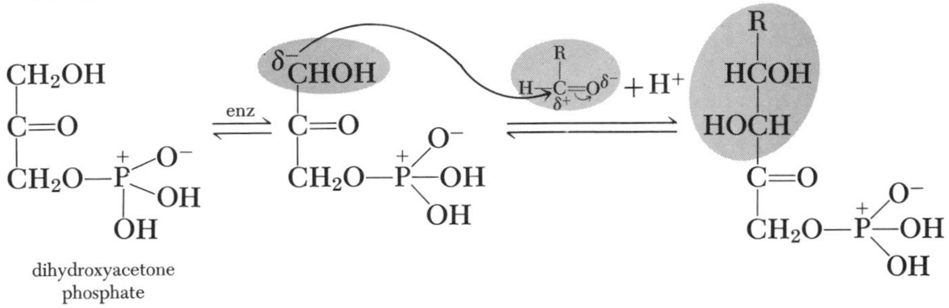

$$\text{CH}_2\text{OH}$$
$$\text{C}=\text{O}$$
$$\text{CH}_2\text{O}-\overset{+}{\text{P}}\overset{\text{O}^-}{\underset{\text{OH}}{\diagup}}$$

dihydroxyacetone
phosphate

DECARBOXYLATION

When an acid is decarboxylated the carbon dioxide leaves without a pair of electrons. The electron pair is left with the R group, which is stabilized as a carbanion by some group X.

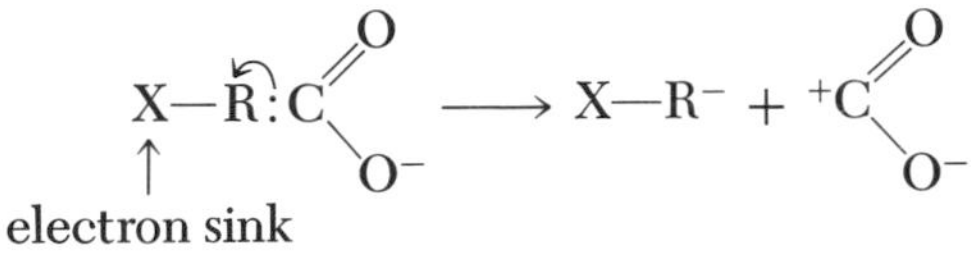

$$\text{X}-\overset{\frown}{\text{R}}\!:\!\text{C}\overset{\text{O}}{\underset{\text{O}^-}{\diagup}} \longrightarrow \text{X}-\text{R}^- + {}^+\text{C}\overset{\text{O}}{\underset{\text{O}^-}{\diagup}}$$

electron sink

Pyridoxal phosphate, metal cations, and thiamin pyrophosphate serve as electron sinks to make it easier to separate the electron pair from carbon dioxide. The polyvalent metal cation catalysis of the decarboxylation of β-keto acids illustrates the role of the metal as an electron sink.

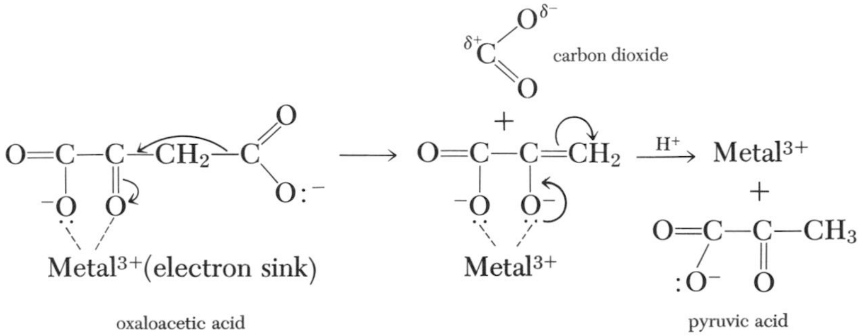

oxaloacetic acid   pyruvic acid

Rearrangements, hydrolysis, transfer reactions, carboxylations, oxidation reduction systems, and isomerization reactions are illustrated in the text. By now the student has reviewed the basic concepts; by applying them to examples given in the text he should be able to unify and classify the many seemingly unrelated metabolic reactions in the living cell in terms of modern organic chemical reactions.

Appendix 3

Methods in Biochemistry

Introduction

Some of the techniques employed in biochemical research have been collected in this appendix, not to serve as a laboratory guide, but rather to acquaint the student with the terms and methods that are the language of the practicing biochemist.

Glass Electrode

The most effective way of accurately measuring the pH value of a biochemical system is to employ a pH meter with a glass electrode. The potential of the glass electrode (E_g) relative to the external reference electrode (E_{ref}) is related to the pH as follows:

$$pH = \frac{E_g - E_{ref}}{0.0591} \qquad \text{at } 25°C$$

The typical glass electrode assembly consists of:

Ag, AgCl(s), HCl(0.1M)‖glass membrane‖solution X | KCl(Sat), Hg$_2$Cl$_2$(s), Hg

silver-silver chloride   calomel half-cell
electrode

When two solutions of different H$^+$ ion concentrations are separated by a thin glass membrane, a potential difference related to differences in pH of the two solutions is obtained. A typical glass electrode is illustrated in Figure A-3-1.

The potential difference ($E_g - E_{ref}$) is carefully measured either with a potentiometer-type pH meter or with a direct-reading pH meter (line operated) consisting normally of a simple triode amplifier using the negative feedback principle. Regardless of how the potential difference is measured, the student should note that the results obtained are in terms of *activity* (a_H) rather than concentration of hydrogen ion [H$^+$]. Unless

354

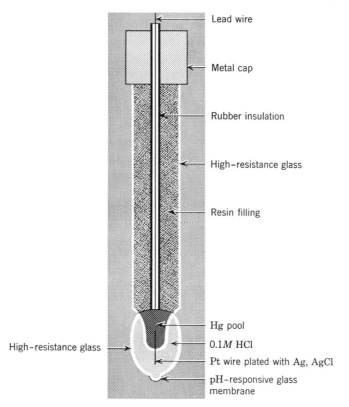

- Lead wire
- Metal cap
- Rubber insulation
- High-resistance glass
- Resin filling
- Hg pool
- 0.1M HCl
- Pt wire plated with Ag, AgCl
- pH-responsive glass membrane

High-resistance glass

Fig. A-3-1. Construction of a typical glass electrode.

special glass membranes are used, pH responses are usually adequate between 1 and 11, but above and below these values errors do become evident, and corrections must be introduced. The glass electrode should be carefully washed after each pH determination, particularly after dealing with protein solutions, since proteins may adsorb on the glass membrane surface with serious errors resulting. In nonaqueous solutions a partial dehydration of the glass membrane may occur with changes in the potential difference, also leading to errors. Poorly buffered solutions should be thoroughly stirred during measurements since a thin layer of solution at the glass solution interface may not reflect the true activity of the rest of the solution. It must also be noted that in organic solvents dissociation of acids is decreased and thereby the pH is raised. The student should be aware of these factors. Despite these difficulties the glass electrode pH meter is the preferred tool since it is an extremely sensitive and stable instrument.

Isotopic Methods

The single most important technique in biochemistry is the critical, careful use of radio- as well as stable isotopes.

RADIOISOTOPES

From a biochemical standpoint the most useful radioisotopes C^{14}, S^{35}, P^{32}, and H^3 are β-ray emitters; that is, when the nuclei of these atoms disintegrate one of the products is an electron which moves with energies characteristic of the disintegrating nucleus. The so-called β-rays interact with the molecules through which they traverse, causing dissociation, excitation, or ionization of the molecules. It is the resultant ionization property which is used to measure quantitatively the amount of radioisotope present. See Table A-3-1 for some properties of useful radioisotopes.

Table A-3-1.   Some Properties of Useful Radioisotopes

Element	Radiation	Half-Life	Energy of Radiation
H^3	β^-	12.1 years	0.0185 mev°
C^{14}	β^-	5100 years	0.156
P^{32}	β^-	14.3 days	1.71
S^{35}	β^-	87.1 days	0.169

° million electron-volts.

Units: A *curie* is the amount of emitter which exhibits 3.7×10^{10} disintegrations/sec (dps). More common units are a millicurie, mc (10^{-3} curie), and a microcurie, μc (10^{-6} curie).

Specific Activity: This is defined as disintegrations/minute per unit of substance (mg, μ mole, etc.)

Dilution Factor: The factor is defined as

$$\frac{\text{specific activity of precursor fed}}{\text{specific activity of compound isolated}}$$

This factor is used frequently to express the precursor relation of a compound in the biosynthesis of a second compound. Thus in the sequence $A \rightarrow B \rightarrow C \rightarrow D$, the dilution factor for $C \rightarrow D$ would be small whereas for A it would be large. Therefore a small dilution factor would indicate that compound C fed to a tissue has a better precursor relationship to the final product than compound A with a large dilution factor.

Per Cent Incorporation: This is also used to compare the proximity of a precursor in the biosynthesis of a second compound. If labeled compound A is administered to an experimental system and some of the radioactivity is incorporated into compound D, the per cent incorporation is expressed as counts/min in D divided by counts/min in A × 100 [(cpmD/cpmA) × 100].

Measurements.   The Geiger-Müller counter (or a G-M tube) is probably the most popular device for measuring radioisotopes. It consists of a large, round, outer electrode with a fine wire stretched in the center as the second electrode; the fine wire is maintained at a high potential (1000–2500 v) with respect to the outer electrode. The tube is filled with helium and an organic quenching compound such as ethanol. The open end of the tube is covered with an extremely thin window of mica or synthetic plastic. Beneath this window (or a windowless tube with a positive pressure of helium and ethanol) is placed the radioactive material. The radioactive particle enters the counter tube and ionizes the gas molecules with a subsequent release of a shower of electrons. These free electrons are then accelerated to the positive wire. As they progress through the gas, additional molecules are ionized, with the final result that a brief current surge is measured by suitable electronic circuits (scalers) and registered as one count. Figure A-3-2 is a representation of a typical arrangement.

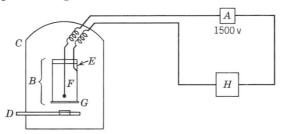

Fig. A-3-2.   Schematic diagram of a Geiger-Müller tube and scaler. A = source of potential, B = Geiger-Müller tube, C = lead shield, D = sample pan holder, E = cathode sheath, F = anode wire, G = mica window (1.5–2.0 mg/cm²), H = scaler. From R. Cowgill and A. Pardee, *Experiments in Biochemical Research Techniques*, John Wiley and Sons, New York, 1957.

Several factors must be listed for consideration in order to avoid inaccurate counting.

(a) Self absorption. When weak radiation (from H^3 or C^{14}) is absorbed by the mass of its own source, inefficient counting will occur. This phenomenon is called self absorption, and the amount of absorption is proportional to the thickness of the sample being measured. Correction curves can be constructed so that adjustment to infinite thinness can be made. Infinite thickness techniques have also been developed, since the counts of an infinitely thick sample will be directly related to the radioactivity of a constant surface area of the sample.

(b) Geometry. Poor spreading of samples on the sample holders or planchets (metal holders for samples) can lead to serious errors. Care should be taken to distribute the material in a completely consistent, uniform manner.

(c) Coincidence Correction. When the disintegrations/minute are so high the counter cannot register all the electrical surges, counts lower than the actual events will be recorded. Correction factors may be introduced, but the recovery time of modern counters are usually such that up to 3000–4000 dpm can be made without serious errors.

(d) Background. The count recorded in absence of any radioactive samples is called background count and is always subtracted from the counts registered for samples. Background count represents ionization caused either by cosmic rays or by radioactive contamination of the counting chamber striking the G-M tube.

Scintillation counters are extremely effective counting systems since problems of geometry, coincidence, and self absorption are completely avoided. In liquid scintillation devices, the radioisotopic substance is dissolved directly in a suitable organic solvent containing a phosphor such as diphenyloxazole. Phosphors have the property of emitting a scintillation or a light flash when they absorb radiation from a radioactive compound and the number of light flashes is proportional to the amount of radioisotope present.

The scintillations are counted by very sensitive photomultiplier tubes which record these as counts/minute by suitable electronic devices. Weak emitters such as H^3 and C^{14} are counted with the amazing efficiencies of 15 per cent and 85 per cent respectively. Some problems related to these counting systems are (1) quenching of the scintillations by highly colored, pigmented samples, and (2) the limited solubility of highly polar compounds in nonpolar solvents; methods have been developed to overcome these difficulties.

STABLE ISOTOPES

Stable isotopes of several of the biologically important elements are available in enriched concentrations and therefore may be used to "tag" or label compounds. As an example, deuterium, the hydrogen atom with mass of 2, is present in most H_2O to the extent of only 0.02 per cent. The remainder of the hydrogen atoms has, of course, a mass of 1. This concentration of 0.02 per cent is known as the normal abundance of deuterium. It is possible to obtain *heavy* water in which 99.9 per cent of the hydrogen atoms are deuterium. The concentration of a heavy isotope is usually measured as *atom per cent excess;* this is the amount, in per cent, by which the isotope exceeds its normal abundance. Thus, the two stable isotopes of nitrogen are $_7N^{14}$ and $_7N^{15}$, which have a normal abundance of 99.62 and 0.38 per cent respectively. If a sample of nitrogen gas contains 4.00 per cent $_7N^{15}$ (and 96.00 per cent $_7N^{14}$), the concentration of $_7N^{15}$ in this sample is said to be 3.62 atom per cent excess. Other stable isotopes that are available in enriched concentrations and therefore may be used as tracers in biochemistry are $_8O^{17}$, $_8O^{18}$, $_6C^{13}$, $_{16}S^{33}$, and $_{16}S^{34}$; the normal abundance of these isotopes can be found in any chemical handbook.

The principles underlying the use of stable isotopes are similar to those employed with radioisotopes. The stable isotopes are measured quantitatively in a mass spectrometer, however. A discussion of the different types of spectrometer available may be found in reference 2. Prior to the development of the spectrometer, methods based on the refractive index, density, and thermal conductivity were available for measuring the concentration of stable isotopes.

USES OF ISOTOPES

Countless techniques have been developed to study biochemical reaction sequences. Hundreds of commercially available biochemicals labeled with different isotopes at known positions are used in modern research, and this book cites many examples. Some precautions should be pointed out, most important being the isotope effect affecting *rates* of reaction. Because of differences in atomic weight, slight changes in reaction rates will be noted. With tritium ($_1H^3$) the rate effect is large and may represent a twentieth of the rate of cleavage of a $C-_1H^1$ bond. With deuterium ($_1H^2$) the rate effect is about one sixth. With $C^{12}-C^{14}$ cleavage the rate effects are small providing these are the rate-limiting steps.

It is also of note that with both tritium and deuterium such bonds as $N-_1H^3$ and $O-_1H^3$ rapidly exchange with water ($_1H_2{}^1O$) in the medium and are washed out. The $_1H^3$ label in acetic acid, CH_3COOH^3, will be immediately washed out because of the great exchange by ionization with normal protons in water. In addition, all compounds that are counted must be carefully purified; another technique is to remove any occluded contaminating radioisotopic substance by "washing out" with the corresponding nonradioactive compound. Thus $CH_3C^\circ OOH$ (carboxyl labeled acetic acid) is readily removed from a desired compound by adding large amounts of normal ($_6C^{12}$) acetic acid which could mix with and greatly dilute out the contaminating C°-acetic acid. Another useful criterion is purification to constant specific activity.

Spectrophotometry

This technique is of prime importance in biochemical research. Three different usages are commonly found. (1) If the absorbancy index (a_s) at a specific wavelength is known, the concentration of a compound can be readily determined by measuring the optical density at that wavelength. With a large a_s, as in nucleotides, very small quantities of the absorbing material (2–4 μg) can be accurately measured. (2) The course of a reaction can be determined by measuring the rate of formation or disappearance of a light-absorbing compound. Thus NADH absorbs strongly at 340 mμ, whereas the oxidized form (NAD$^+$) has no absorption at this wavelength. Therefore reactions involving the production or utilization of NADH (or NADPH) can be assayed by this technique. (3) Compounds can frequently be identified by determining their characteristic absorption spectra in the ultraviolet and visible regions of the spectrum.

Two fundamental laws are associated with spectrophotometry; these are Lambert's and Beer's laws. Lambert's law states that the light absorbed is directly proportional to the *thickness* of the solution being analyzed:

$$A = \log_{10} \frac{I_0}{I} = a_s b$$

where I_0 is the incident light intensity, I is the transmitted light intensity, a_s is the absorbancy index characteristic for the solution, b is the length or thickness of the medium, and A is the absorbancy.

Beer's law states that the amount of light absorbed is directly proportional to the *concentration* of solute in solution:

$$\log_{10} \frac{I_0}{I} = a_s c$$

and the combined Beer-Lambert law is $\log_{10} I_0/I = a_s bc$. If b is held constant by employing a standard cell or cuvette, the Beer-Lambert law reduces to

$$A = \log_{10} \frac{I_0}{I} = a_s c$$

The absorbancy index a_s is defined as A/Cb where C is the concentration of the substance in grams per liter and b the distance in centimeters traveled by the light in solution. The molar absorbancy index a_m is equal to a_s multiplied by the molecular weight of the substance.

All spectrophotometers have the following essential parts:

(1) A source of radiant energy (L)

(2) a monochromator, which is a device for isolating monochromatic light or narrow bands of radiant energy.

The Beckman spectrophotometer, which is a typical instrument, is outlined in our diagram. It consists of either a grating or a prism B,

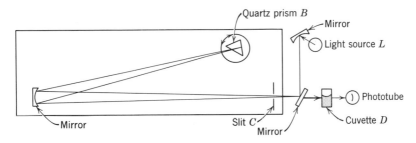

which is used to disperse the radiant energy into a spectrum, together with an exit slit C which selects a narrow portion of the spectrum. The cuvette D is placed in a light-tight unit; the incident light strikes the cuvette, and the emergent light passes into a photocell, which converts the emerging light energy into a signal of measurable electrical energy.

Some important biochemicals with their characteristic molar absorbancies are:

	λ_{max}	$a_M \times 10^{-3}$
NADH	340 mμ	6.22
ATP	260	15.4
NADPH	340	6.22
FAD	445, 366	11.3 (at 445 mμ)
Acetyl-N- acetylcysteamine	232	4.6

For example, based on the $a_{M_{340}}$ of NADH, 0.1 μ mole of NADH in a 3.0 ml volume with a light path of 1 cm has an optical density of 0.207.

Gas Chromatography

Developed largely since 1951, this technique has become the preferred method for rapidly and accurately analyzing any volatile substance. In essence, the volatile material is injected into a column containing a liquid absorbant supported on an inert solid. The basis for the separation of the components of the volatile material is the difference in the partition coefficients of the components as they are carried through the column by an inert gas such as helium. The actual apparatus is quite simple, as may be seen in our sketch on the next page.

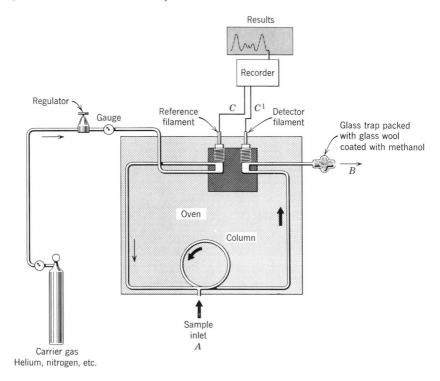

The column is first flushed out with carrier gas to remove previously injected material and to form a stable baseline. The sample is introduced at *A*. The carrier gas transports the injected volatile material into the column, where the components partition into the liquid absorbent and separate; eventually a fraction passes through a suitable detecting device, which sends signals to a recorder, which in turn converts the signals into a useful sequence of peaks. Two detecting devices (of many) will be briefly described to give the student a grasp of the technique.

The *thermal conductivity cell* is a detecting device based on the principle that heat is conducted away from a hot wire by a gas passing over it. Two fine coils of wire with a high temperature coefficient of resistance are placed in two parts of the metal block (C^1 and C). Suitable electrical resistors are inserted in the circuit of C^1 and C to form a Wheatstone bridge circuit. When current is passed through the bridge, the wires C^1 and C are heated. Final equilibrium temperature of the wires depends on the thermal conductivity of the gas passing over the wire coil. If the gas is the same, the wires will have the same temperature and the same resistance, and therefore the bridge is balanced; if an effluent gas now passes through C^1 while only the carrier gas passes through C, the wire temperature will differ; the resistance in turn will be changed, and the bridge becomes unbalanced. The extent of unbalance is measured with a recording potentiometer as indicated.

The second type of detector device is a *hydrogen flame ionization* detector. It has extreme sensitivity, a wide linear response, and is insensitive to water. In theory, when organic material is burned in a hydrogen flame, electrons and ions are produced. The negative ions and electrons move in a high voltage field to an anode and produce a very small current, which is changed to a measurable current by appropriate circuitry. The electrical current is directly proportional to the amount of material burned.

The use of gas chromatography has revolutionized the analysis of fat, fatty acids, flavor components, gaseous mixtures, and any compound which can be converted into a volatile material. Recently great advances have been made in converting quantitatively the nonvolatile amino acids to volatile derivatives, and if this research is successful it will greatly expedite research on protein structure.

Paper Chromatography

Like all simple techniques, this method has revolutionized the separation or detection of reaction products and the determination and identification of compounds. Developed in 1944 by Martin in England, filter paper strips are used to support a stationary water phase while a mobile organic phase moves down the suspended strip of paper in a cylinder, as indicated in the diagram. The substances to be separated are spotted near the top of the hanging sheet. Separation is based on a liquid-liquid partition of the compounds.

The ratio of the distance traveled by the compounds to the distance traveled by the solvent front from the original spot at the top of the paper sheet is called the R_F value of the compound. Under strictly controlled conditions the R_F is an important constant for identification purposes. With a knowledge of how a variety of compounds move in a series of solvents, much can be said about the functional groups of unknown compounds.

The method just described is one-dimensional chromatography. Two-dimensional chromatography is a variant with considerable separatory power, since two different solvents can be employed in sequence to move a single compound.

A large number of variations on paper chromatography have been developed. They include (a) reverse phase chromatography, wherein

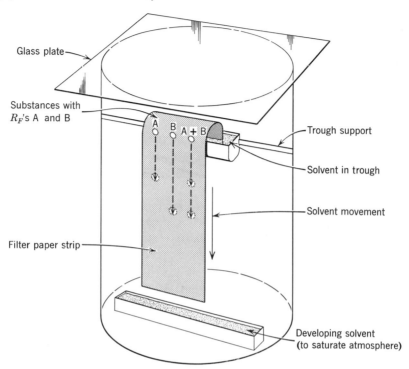

the stationary phase is made nonpolar and the mobile phase is polar; and (b) a combination of paper chromatography and electrophoresis that involves partition chromatography and electrical mobility of ionic species.

A simple experiment for the student consists of chromatographing writing inks on Whatman No. 1 filter paper. Samples of different inks (try Sheaffer's Permanent Jet Black) are placed as small spots along the shorter edge of a piece of Whatman No. 1 filter paper (20 × 25 cm), 2 cm from the edge. After it has dried, the two longer edges of filter paper are stapled together to form a cylinder with the ink spots on one circumference. That end is placed in a jar containing H_2O to a depth

of 1 cm. The water will rapidly rise (in 1 hr) and the different colored components of the inks will migrate in amounts related to their solubility in H_2O and adsorption on cellulose.

Ion Exchange

Electrostatic attraction of oppositely charged ions on a polyelectrolyte surface forms the basis of ion exchange chromatography. Typical systems include the synthetic resin polymers, such as the strongly acidic cation exchanger Dowex-50, a polystyrene sulfonic acid, and the strongly basic anion exchanger Dowex-1, a polystyrene quaternary ammonium salt. Cellulose derivatives such as carboxymethyl cellulose (CMC) and diethylaminoethyl cellulose (DEAE) exchangers have been very successfully used in protein purification.

The basic principle involves an electrostatic interaction with the exchanging ions and the normal charge on the surface of the resin. These reactions are considered to be equilibrium processes and involve diffusion of a given ion to the resin surface and then to the exchange site, the actual exchange, and finally diffusion away from the resin. The rate of movement of a given ionizable compound down the column is a function of its degree of ionization, the concentration of other ions, and the relative affinities of the various ions present in the solution for charged sites on the resin. By adjusting the pH of the eluting solvent and the ionic strength, the electrostatically held ions are eluted differentially to yield the desired separation.

An example of the use of ion exchange resins in the purification of cytochrome c can be cited. Cytochrome c has an isoelectric point of 10.05; that is, at pH 10.05 the number of positive charges will equal the number of negative charges. A column containing a cation exchanger buffered at pH 8.5 is prepared. This column has a full negative charge. Cytochrome c at pH 8.5 has a full positive charge. An impure solution of cytochrome c at pH 8.5 is placed on the column, and water is passed through the column. The contaminating proteins pass freely through the column (the pI of proteins is usually 7.0 or less) but cytochrome c is held firmly by electrostatic attraction to the resin beads. If the eluting solvent pH is now raised to about 10, the cytochrome c will have a net zero charge and will pass rapidly through as a pure component.

Resin columns are extremely useful in the separation and purification of nucleotides, small molecular weight compounds with ionizable groups, amino acids, and peptides. Because of the limited available surface and the lability of proteins, ion resins have not proved too successful in protein purification.

The cellulose derivatives have therefore been developed since they have high absorptive capacities but still hold proteins rather weakly. This means that by mere adjustments of pH and salt concentration, efficient elution of adsorbed proteins can be made. Two very common derivatives already mentioned are CMC, a cationic derivative, and DEAE, an anionic derivative.

In practice the steps we list may be taken.

CM—cellulose:

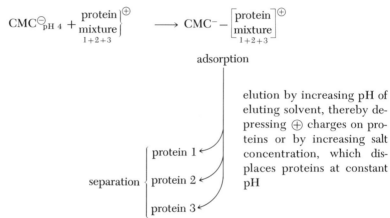

The reverse procedure may be used for DEAE columns, namely placing protein on a DEAE column at pH 8 and eluting by decreasing pH or increasing salt concentration or both.

Purification of Enzymes

If reaction A → B is to be studied in a given tissue, the first step to be taken is the development of a quick, reliable assay for the reaction. An assay system requires a unit of enzyme activity. A unit of enzyme is defined as the amount of enzyme that brings about a specified reaction in a unit of time. The tissue is usually homogenized in buffer at 0–4°C. If mitochondria or particles are to be isolated, an isotonic or hypertonic solution is employed, namely 0.25–0.8M sucrose, with a suitable buffer to control the pH. Under these conditions the general scheme we indicate can be applied for the separation of particulate systems. The term g employed in our diagram is commonly used to specify the gravitational force exerted on the homogenate being centrifuged. It is defined as the gravitational force acting on a 1-g mass at

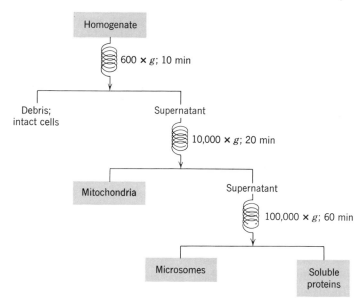

distance r (cm) from the axis of rotation.   It can be readily calculated from the formula

$$F = \frac{S^2 r}{89,500}$$

where F is the relative centrifugal force (g), r is the radial distance in cm from the center or axis of rotation, and S is the speed of rotation of the rotor in rpm.   Thus in the rotor shown, F is $6200 \times g$ at the bottom of the centrifuge tube.

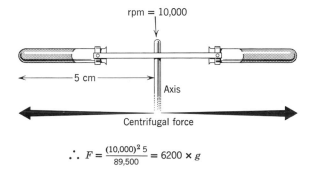

$$\therefore\ F = \frac{(10,000)^2\, 5}{89,500} = 6200 \times g$$

On some occasions acetone powders of tissues can be prepared. These powders are frequently very stable and can be stored for long periods of time with little loss in activity.   In practice, tissue (1 vol) is homogenized in a Waring blender in 5 vol of acetone at 0°C. The smooth slurry is filtered and the cake resuspended in 5 vol of cold acetone and again filtered. This process is repeated until the powder appears thoroughly dehydrated and defatted. One vol of fresh, cold, diethyl ether is then poured over the cake on the Buchner funnel and the cake sucked dry. Traces of acetone and ether are removed in a vacuum desiccator over paraffin strips. These acetone powders are excellent initial sources of enzymes for purification.

A homogenate, a soluble protein extract or an acetone powder extract may now be submitted to a series of standard purification procedures. These involve:

Fractional Precipitation with Ammonium Sulfate. By the addition of a saturated solution of ammonium sulfate, proteins will be salted out and separated by centrifugation. If conditions are kept constant, remarkably good reproducibility can be attained.

Selective Adsorption and Elution on Calcium Phosphate Gels. Proteins are readily adsorbed on these gels and then are differentially eluted by increasing salt concentrations.

Differential Heat Inactivation of Contaminating Proteins. Exposure of protein solutions to increasing temperatures at different pH is a useful technique. Frequently we may select the proper conditions by which the desired protein remains stable and the contaminating proteins are denatured and removed.

Isoelectric Precipitation: Because of the ionic character of proteins, pH adjustment to the point where there is no net charge will result in a minimum solubility with a concomitant precipitation of the protein.

Organic Solvent Precipitation: Either cold acetone or ethanol is frequently used to precipitate proteins differentially from solution by decreasing the dielectric constant of the solution. This results in greater interaction between proteins and a decrease in solubility.

Columns of Cellulose Derivatives. These derivatives, such as CMC or DEAE, are extremely useful, and their applications have already been discussed on pp. 365–366.

These methods are in general the usual approaches to enzyme purification. All steps must be checked for enzyme units, specific activities, yields, and recoveries. Textbooks in this highly technical subject should be consulted for further details.

Criteria of Purity

In order to examine detailed structures of complex proteins, it is mandatory to have proteins that are homogeneous entities. Over a period of years techniques have therefore been developed to analyze protein solutions for homogeneity.

SOLUBILITY CURVE

Pioneered by Northrop and based on the phase rule, this test can be carried out rather easily on a micro scale. It consists of determining the solubility of an increasing amount of protein in a fixed solvent system. The amount in solution is plotted against the total protein added. If only one component (A) is present, a linear response with a sharp break at saturation will occur; if two or more components B, C, etc.) are present, they will behave independently in solution and have their own solubility curves, each reaching a plateau at their own saturation. A typical curve is shown in our sketch.

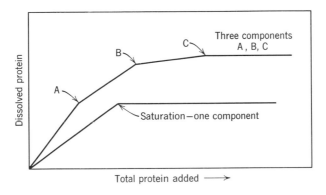

SPECIFIC ACTIVITY/COENZYME RATIO

If a protein has a coenzyme firmly associated with it, and if, by diverse series of precipitations, a constant ratio of specific activity of an enzyme function to the coenzyme concentration is attained, this would be suggestive evidence that a reasonable degree of purification has been achieved.

It might also indicate, however, that the ingenuity of a complex protein system is greater than that of the investigator and that his technique may have achieved zero separation of contaminating proteins!

ELECTROPHORESIS

This powerful method, which was developed by Tiselius in 1937, is based on the principle that in a mixture of proteins each protein with its characteristic surface electrical charge will respond to an applied electrical potential in a different and characteristic manner at a given pH. Proteins are placed in a cell (see Figure A-3-3) composed of glass segments butted together to form leakproof units.

Let us consider a protein solution consisting of three components A, B, and C. Before the electrophoretic field is applied, the solution will be homogeneous from boundary A (ascending) to boundary D (descending). If components A, B, and C carry charges of the same net sign (+ or −) but of different magnitude (number), the components will migrate at different rates, and separation will occur. If the magnitude of electrical charge is in the order A > B > C, the components will separate as indicated in Figure A-3-3. It should be pointed out that the faster-moving component A will be present in pure form in the ascending boundary, as will C in the descending boundary. B will always be mixed with A or with C, however. Concentration gradients will be set up at the boundaries during electrophoretic migration and can be accurately measured by optical systems. A typical concentration gradient curve based on the changes in refraction index is given in Figure A-3-3.

The wide choice of pH and its consequent effect on the electrical charges on a protein molecule gives great versatility to this method and makes possible critical evaluation of the number of components in a protein. In addition the electrophoretic mobility of a given protein can be determined. The pH of solution which gives a zero mobility is defined as the isoelectric point or pI and gives valuable information about the electric charges on a given protein surface.

ULTRACENTRIFUGE

This instrument can measure certain properties of a molecule, such as molecular weight, shape, size, and density, as well as the number of components in a protein solution. The ultracentrifuge subjects a small volume of solution (less than 1 ml contained in a quartz cell) to a carefully controlled centrifugal force and records, by means of optical and photographic systems, the movement of the macromolecules in the centrifugal field.

A specific method, in which the ultracentrifuge operates at about 55,000 rpm, will be described. As indicated in Figure A-3-4, the solute molecules, which are initially uniformly distributed throughout the solution in the cell, are forced toward the bottom of the cell by the centrifugal field. This migration leaves a region at the top of the cell that is devoid of solute and contains only solvent molecules. The migration also leaves a region in the cell where the solute concentration is uniform. A boundary is set up in the cell between solvent and solution in which concentration varies with distance from the axis of rotation.

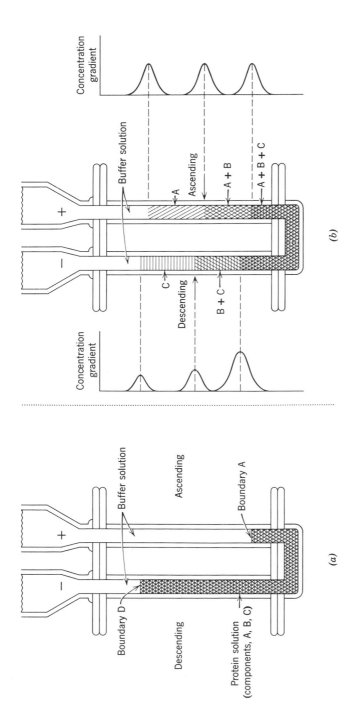

Fig. A-3-3. The U-tube of an electrophoresis cell, showing compensated boundaries and electrophoretic separation of components. (a) and (b) indicate the tube before and after electrophoretic separation, respectively. Courtesy of Beckman Instruments, Inc.

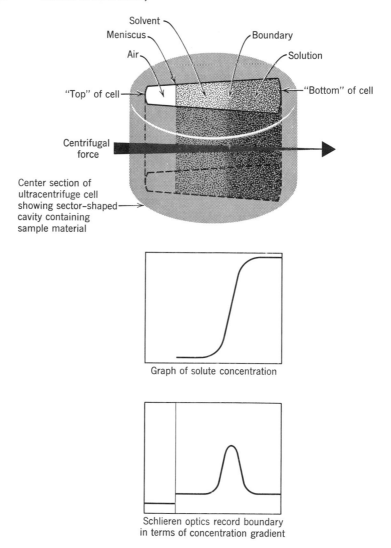

Fig. A-3-4. A typical sedimentation velocity study showing how boundary formed between solvent and solute molecules can be recorded by a method known as Schlieren optics. Courtesy of Beckman Instruments, Inc.

The measurement of the boundary's movement, which represents the movement of the protein molecules, is the basis of the analytic method. By the data obtained, namely, the sedimentation rate, the Svedberg unit (S) can be calculated. A Svedberg unit, named in honor of T.

Svedberg, the Swedish pioneer in the field, is defined as the velocity of the sedimenting molecule per unit of gravitational field or 1×10^{-13} cm/sec/dyne/g. Typical S values are 4.4 for bovine serum albumin, 1.83 for cytochrome c, and 185 for tobacco mosaic virus. With a knowledge of the diffusion coefficient, molecular weights can be readily calculated. The basic equation relates S and molecular weight:

$$\text{mol wt} = \frac{RTS}{D(1 - V\rho)}$$

where R is the gas constant, T the absolute temperature, S the Svedberg unit, D the diffusion constant, V the partial specific vol, and ρ the density of the solution.

To determine the number of components in a solution, a simple centrifugation can be readily made and the number of boundaries based on concentration gradient peaks can be determined. Diffusion coefficient measurements need not be made.

Manometric Techniques

Manometry has been one of the most useful techniques employed in intermediary metabolism. Since many reactions of biochemical interest involve the formation or utilization of a gas (usually CO_2 or O_2) it is not surprising that a sensitive manometer, the Warburg manometer, was devised for measuring them.

The method involves the use of a constant-volume manometer operated in a constant-temperature bath, as indicated in Figure A-3-5. As the reaction proceeds pressure changes are observed as a decrease or increase in the heights of a column (containing a special fluid) attached to the manometer vessel. Since a change of 10 mm in the column height corresponds approximately to 0.015 ml or 15 μl, gas exchanges amounting to approximately 1.0 μ mole can easily be determined (22.4 μl of gas equals 1 μ mole).

In addition to being useful in measuring O_2 or CO_2 exchanges, manometers can also follow reactions involving the formation or utilization of a proton. This is done by carrying out the reaction in the presence of a bicarbonate buffer and an atmosphere of 95 per cent O_2 and 5 per cent CO_2. Thus when a proton is released in a reaction, it combines with bicarbonate anion to produce H_2CO_3, which is in equilibrium with the CO_2 of the atmosphere in the reaction vessel. As a result the pressure increases and this can be accurately measured and converted into microliters or micromoles.

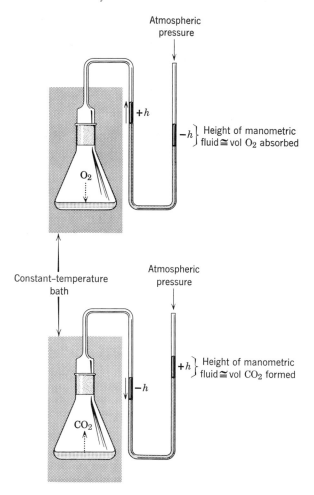

Fig. A-3-5. Diagrammatic representation of Warburg manometers. In one case, O_2 absorption is being measured; in the other case, CO_2 production. The manometric setup is greatly simplified. In actual operation the manometric fluid is maintained in the left limb of the U-tube at a constant level (or at a constant volume) and the pressure change, as measured by an increased height (for CO_2 formation) or a decreased height (for O_2 absorption) in the right limb, is carefully measured. A factor converts height in mm to volume in mm³.

REFERENCES

1. *General reference*—H. H. Willard, L. L. Merritt, Sr. and J. A. Dean, *Instrumental Methods of Analysis*, D. van Nostrand, Co., Princeton, 3rd edition, 1958.

   A useful compilation of instrumental methods commonly used in chemical and biochemical research.

2. Glass electrode—R. G. Bates, *Electrometric pH Determinations*, John Wiley and Sons, New York, 1954.

A modern treatment of the practical and theoretical aspects of pH determinations.

3. Isotopes—G. E. Francis, W. Mulligan, and A. Wormall, *Isotopic Tracers*, The Athlone Press, London, 1954.

A fine discussion of the many aspects of isotopic methodology.

4. C. G. Bell and F. N. Hayes, *Liquid Scintillation Counting*, Pergamon Press, New York, 1958.

The bible, covering techniques and theory in this type of counting.

5. Spectrophotometry, paper chromatography, ion exchange systems, and manometry— W. W. Umbreit, R. H. Burris, and J. F. Stauffer, *Manometric Techniques*, Burgess Publishing Co., Minneapolis, 3rd edition, 1957.

A classic in the field.   All students in biochemistry should become familiar with the contents of this book.

6. Gas chromatography—A. T. James in *Methods of Biochemical Analysis*, edited by David Glick, Interscience Publishers, New York, 1960, Vol. 8, Chapter 1.

An excellent article written by one of the pioneers in this field.

7. Purification of enzymes; criteria of purity—*Methods in Enzymology*, edited by S. P. Colowick and N. O. Kaplan, Academic Press, New York, 1955 to date; several volumes.

A multivolume work which is the bible for the practicing biochemist.   Students should become acquainted with these volumes.

Index

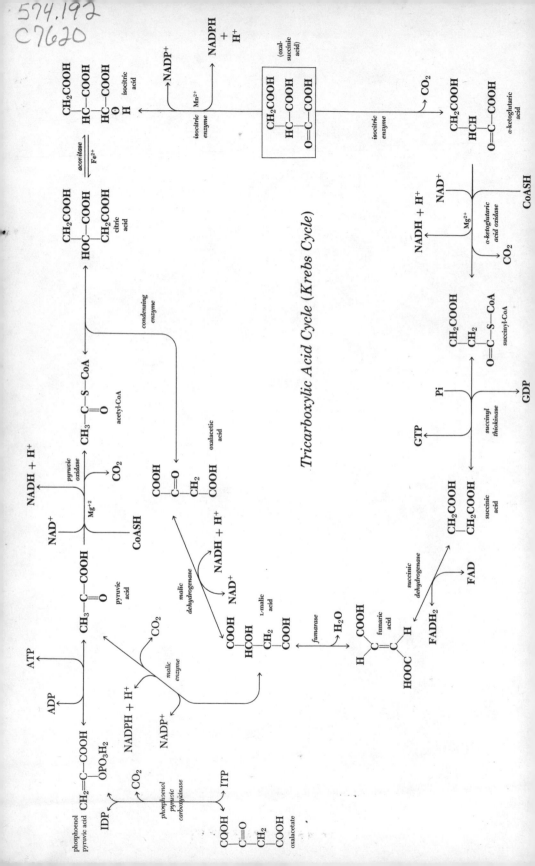

Tricarboxylic Acid Cycle (Krebs Cycle)